MW00835489

<u>Legal Notice</u>

For information on bulk purchases and licensing agreements, please email

support@SATPrepGet800.com

ISBN-13: 978-1-951619-01-5

This is the Solution Guide to the book "Abstract Algebra for Beginners."

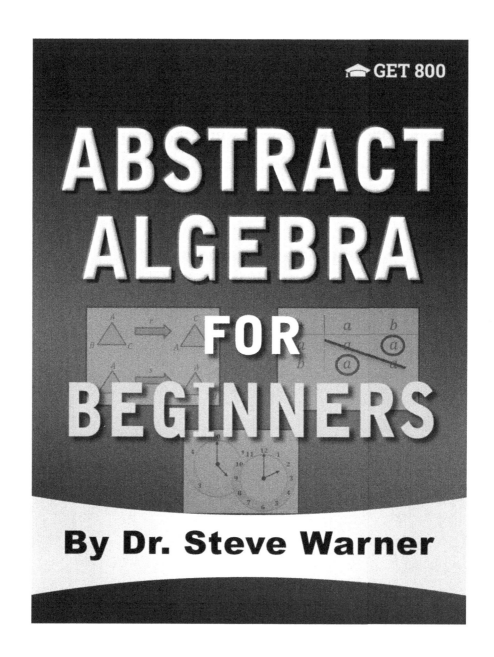

Also Available from Dr. Steve Warner

CONNECT WITH DR. STEVE WARNER

www.facebook.com/SATPrepGet800

www.youtube.com/TheSATMathPrep

www.twitter.com/SATPrepGet800

www.linkedin.com/in/DrSteveWarner

www.pinterest.com/SATPrepGet800

Also Available from Dr. Steve Warner

CONNECT WITH DR. STEVE WARNER

www.facebook.com/SATPrepGet800

www.youtube.com/TheSATMathPrep

www.twitter.com/SATPrepGet800

www.linkedin.com/in/DrSteveWarner

www.pinterest.com/SATPrepGet800

Abstract Algebra
for Beginners

Solution Guide

Dr. Steve Warner

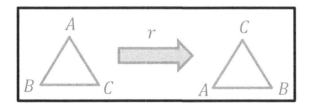
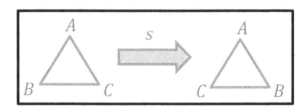

Table of Contents

Problem Set 1

LEVEL 1

1. Determine whether each of the following statements is true or false:

   (i) $x \in \{x\}$

   (ii) $\alpha \in \{\alpha, \beta, \gamma\}$

   (iii) $-5 \in \{5\}$

   (iv) $0 \in \mathbb{Z}$

   (v) $-27 \in \mathbb{N}$

   (vi) $\frac{11}{29} \in \mathbb{Q}$

   (vii) $\emptyset \subseteq \{a, b, c\}$

   (viii) $\{\Delta\} \subseteq \{\delta, \Delta\}$

   (ix) $\{x, y, z\} \subseteq \{x, y, z\}$

   (x) $\{1, 4, \{7, 9\}\} \subseteq \{1, 4, 7, 9\}$

Solutions:

(i) $\{x\}$ has exactly 1 element, namely x. So, $x \in \{x\}$ is **true**.

(ii) $\{\alpha, \beta, \gamma\}$ has exactly 3 elements, namely α, β, and γ. In particular, $\alpha \in \{\alpha, \beta, \gamma\}$ is **true**.

(iii) $\{5\}$ has exactly 1 element, namely 5. So, $-5 \notin \{5\}$. Therefore, $-5 \in \{5\}$ is **false**.

(iv) $\mathbb{Z} = \{\ldots, -4, -3, -2, -1, 0, 1, 2, 3, 4, \ldots\}$. In particular, $0 \in \mathbb{Z}$ is **true**.

(v) $\mathbb{N} = \{0, 1, 2, 3, \ldots\}$. Therefore, $-27 \in \mathbb{N}$ is **false**.

(vi) Since $11, 29 \in \mathbb{Z}$ and $29 \neq 0$, $\frac{11}{29} \in \mathbb{Q}$ is **true**.

(vii) The empty set is a subset of every set. So, $\emptyset \subseteq \{a, b, c\}$ is **true**.

(viii) The only element of $\{\Delta\}$ is Δ. Since Δ is also an element of $\{\delta, \Delta\}$, $\{\Delta\} \subseteq \{\delta, \Delta\}$ is **true**.

(ix) Every set is a subset of itself. So, $\{x, y, z\} \subseteq \{x, y, z\}$ is **true**.

(x) $\{7, 9\} \in \{1, 4, \{7, 9\}\}$, but $\{7, 9\} \notin \{1, 4, 7, 9\}$. So, $\{1, 4, \{7, 9\}\} \subseteq \{1, 4, 7, 9\}$ is **false**.

2. Determine the cardinality of each of the following sets:

   (i) $\{\text{cat}, \text{dog}, \text{zebra}\}$

   (ii) $\{0, 2, 5, 11, 17\}$

   (iii) $\{1, 2, \ldots, 52\}$

   (iv) $\left\{\frac{1}{2}, \frac{1}{3}, \ldots, \frac{1}{11}\right\}$

Solutions:

    (i) $|\{\text{cat, dog, zebra}\}| = \mathbf{3}$.

    (ii) $\{0, 2, 5, 11, 17\} = \mathbf{5}$.

    (iii) $|\{1, 2, \dots, 52\}| = \mathbf{52}$.

    (iv) $\left|\left\{\frac{1}{2}, \frac{1}{3}, \dots, \frac{1}{11}\right\}\right| = \mathbf{10}$.

3. List the elements of $\{k, x, t\} \times \{5, 6\}$.

Solution: $(k, 5), (k, 6), (x, 5), (x, 6), (t, 5), (t, 6)$

4. Let $A = \{0\}$. Evaluate (i) A^2; (ii) A^3; (iii) $\mathcal{P}(A)$.

Solutions:

    (i) $\{0\}^2 = \{0\} \times \{0\} = \{(0, 0)\}$.

    (ii) $\{0\}^3 = \{0\} \times \{0\} \times \{0\} = \{(0, 0, 0)\}$.

    (iii) $\mathcal{P}(\{0\}) = \{\emptyset, \{0\}\}$

5. Let $A = \{a, b, \Delta, \delta\}$ and $B = \{b, c, \delta, \gamma\}$. Determine each of the following:

       (i) $A \cup B$

       (ii) $A \cap B$

       (iii) $A \setminus B$

       (iv) $B \setminus A$

       (v) $A \,\Delta\, B$

Solutions:

    (i) $A \cup B = \{a, b, c, \Delta, \delta, \gamma\}$.

    (ii) $A \cap B = \{b, \delta\}$.

    (iii) $A \setminus B = \{a, \Delta\}$

    (iv) $B \setminus A = \{c, \gamma\}$

    (v) $A \,\Delta\, B = \{a, \Delta\} \cup \{c, \gamma\} = \{a, c, \Delta, \gamma\}$

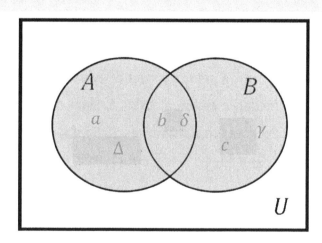

6. Draw Venn diagrams for $(A \setminus B) \setminus C$ and $A \setminus (B \setminus C)$. Are these two sets equal for all sets A, B, and C? If so, prove it. If not, provide a counterexample.

Solution:

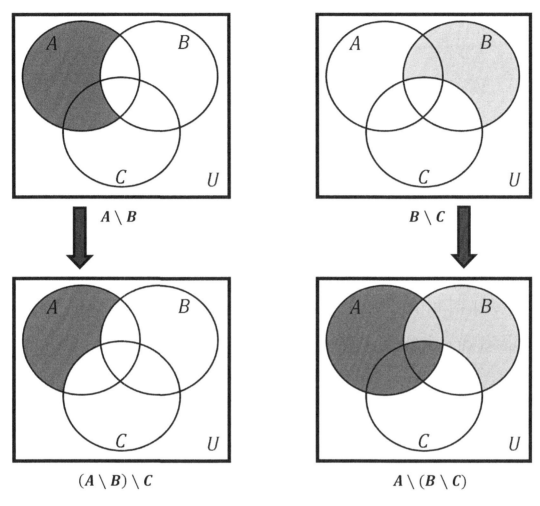

$A \setminus B$

$B \setminus C$

$(A \setminus B) \setminus C$

$A \setminus (B \setminus C)$

From the Venn diagrams, it looks like $(A \setminus B) \setminus C \subseteq A \setminus (B \setminus C)$, but $(A \setminus B) \setminus C \neq A \setminus (B \setminus C)$.

Let's come up with a counterexample. Let $A = \{1, 2\}$, $B = \{1, 3\}$, and $C = \{1, 4\}$. Then we have $(A \setminus B) \setminus C = \{2\} \setminus \{1, 4\} = \{2\}$ and $A \setminus (B \setminus C) = \{1, 2\} \setminus \{3\} = \{1, 2\}$.

We see that $(A \setminus B) \setminus C \neq A \setminus (B \setminus C)$.

Note: Although it was not asked in the question, let's prove that $(A \setminus B) \setminus C \subseteq A \setminus (B \setminus C)$. Let $x \in (A \setminus B) \setminus C$. Then $x \in A \setminus B$ and $x \notin C$. Since $x \in A \setminus B$, $x \in A$ and $x \notin B$. In particular, $x \in A$. Since $x \notin B$, $x \notin B \setminus C$ (because if $x \in B \setminus C$, then $x \in B$). So, we have $x \in A$ and $x \notin B \setminus C$. Therefore, $x \in A \setminus (B \setminus C)$. Since $x \in (A \setminus B) \setminus C$ was arbitrary, $(A \setminus B) \setminus C \subseteq A \setminus (B \setminus C)$. $\square$

7. Compute the power set of each of the following sets:

    (i) $\emptyset$

    (ii) $\{b\}$

    (iii) $\{\Delta, \Gamma\}$

    (iv) $\{\emptyset, \{\emptyset\}\}$

    (v) $\{\{\emptyset\}\}$

Solutions:

    (i) $\mathcal{P}(\emptyset) = \{\emptyset\}$

    (ii) $\mathcal{P}(\{b\}) = \{\emptyset, \{b\}\}$

    (iii) $\mathcal{P}(\{\Delta, \Gamma\}) = \{\emptyset, \{\Delta\}, \{\Gamma\}, \{\Delta, \Gamma\}\}$

    (iv) $\mathcal{P}(\{\emptyset, \{\emptyset\}\}) = \{\emptyset, \{\emptyset\}, \{\{\emptyset\}\}, \{\emptyset, \{\emptyset\}\}\}$

    (v) $\mathcal{P}(\{\{\emptyset\}\}) = \{\emptyset, \{\{\emptyset\}\}\}$

8. Determine whether each of the following statements is true or false:

    (i) $1 \in \emptyset$

    (ii) $\emptyset \in \emptyset$

    (iii) $\emptyset \in \{\emptyset, \{\emptyset\}\}$

    (iv) $\{\emptyset\} \in \emptyset$

    (v) $\{\emptyset\} \in \{\emptyset\}$

    (vi) $5 \in \{3k \mid k = 1, 2, 3, 4\}$

    (vii) $13 \in 3\mathbb{Z} + 1$

    (viii) $\emptyset \subseteq \emptyset$

    (ix) $\emptyset \subseteq \{\emptyset\}$

    (x) $\{\emptyset\} \subseteq \emptyset$

    (xi) $\{\emptyset\} \subseteq \{\emptyset\}$

Solutions:

    (i)   The empty set has no elements. So, $x \in \emptyset$ is false for any x. In particular, $1 \in \emptyset$ is **false**.

    (ii) The empty set has no elements. So, $x \in \emptyset$ is false for any x. In particular, $\emptyset \in \emptyset$ is **false**.

    (iii) The set $\{\emptyset, \{\emptyset\}\}$ has exactly 2 elements, namely $\emptyset$ and $\{\emptyset\}$. In particular, $\emptyset \in \{\emptyset, \{\emptyset\}\}$ is **true**.

    (iv) The empty set has no elements. So, $x \in \emptyset$ is false for any x. In particular, $\{\emptyset\} \in \emptyset$ is **false**.

(v)   The set $\{\emptyset\}$ has 1 element, namely $\emptyset$. Since $\{\emptyset\} \neq \emptyset$, $\{\emptyset\} \in \{\emptyset\}$ is **false**.

(vi) $\{3k \mid k = 1, 2, 3, 4\} = \{3, 6, 9, 12\}$. So, $5 \notin \{3k \mid k = 1, 2, 3, 4\}$. Therefore, it follows that $5 \in \{3k \mid k = 1, 2, 3, 4\}$ is **false**.

(vii) $3\mathbb{Z} + 1 = \{\ldots, -5, -2, 1, 4, 7, 10, 13, 16 \ldots\}$. In particular, $13 \in 3\mathbb{Z} + 1$ is **true**.

(viii) The empty set is a subset of every set. So, $\emptyset \subseteq X$ is true for any X. In particular, $\emptyset \subseteq \emptyset$ is **true**. (This can also be done by using the fact that every set is a subset of itself.)

(ix) Again, (as in (viii)), $\emptyset \subseteq X$ is true for any X. In particular, $\emptyset \subseteq \{\emptyset\}$ is **true**.

(x)   The only subset of $\emptyset$ is $\emptyset$. So, $\{\emptyset\} \subseteq \emptyset$ is **false**.

(xi) Every set is a subset of itself. So, $\{\emptyset\} \subseteq \{\emptyset\}$ is **true**.

9. Determine the cardinality of each of the following sets:

    (i) $\{x, x, y, z, z, z\}$

    (ii) $\{\{0, 1\}, \{2, 3, 4\}\}$

    (iii) $\{8, 9, 10, \ldots, 4226, 4227\}$

Solutions:

(i) $\{x, x, y, z, z, z\} = \{x, y, z\}$. Therefore, $|\{x, x, y, z, z, z\}| = |\{x, y, z\}| = \mathbf{3}$.

(ii) $\{\{0, 1\}, \{2, 3, 4\}\}$ consists of the 2 elements $\{0, 1\}$ and $\{2, 3, 4\}$. So, $|\{\{0, 1\}, \{2, 3, 4\}\}| = \mathbf{2}$.

(iii) $|\{8, 9, 10, \ldots, 4226, 4227\}| = 4227 - 8 + 1 = \mathbf{4220}$.

Note: For number (iii), we used the fence-post formula (see Notes 3 and 4 after Example 1.7).

10. Compute $\{a, b\}^4$.

Solution: $\{a, b\}^4 = \{a, b\} \times \{a, b\} \times \{a, b\} \times \{a, b\} = \{(a, a, a, a), (a, a, a, b), (a, a, b, a), (a, a, b, b),$
$(a, b, a, a), (a, b, a, b), (a, b, b, a), (a, b, b, b), (b, a, a, a), (b, a, a, b), (b, a, b, a), (b, a, b, b),$
$(b, b, a, a), (b, b, a, b), (b, b, b, a), (b, b, b, b)\}$,

11. Let $A = \{\emptyset, \{\emptyset, \{\emptyset\}\}\}$ and $B = \{\emptyset, \{\emptyset\}\}$. Compute each of the following:

    (i) $A \cup B$

    (ii) $A \cap B$

    (iii) $A \setminus B$

    (iv) $B \setminus A$

    (v) $A \mathbin{\Delta} B$

Solutions:

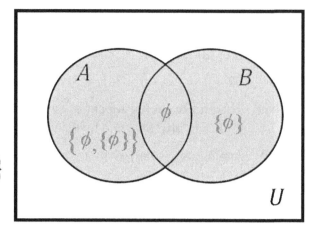

(i) $A \cup B = \{\emptyset, \{\emptyset\}, \{\emptyset, \{\emptyset\}\}\}$.

(ii) $A \cap B = \{\emptyset\}$.

(iii) $A \setminus B = \{\{\emptyset, \{\emptyset\}\}\}$

(iv) $B \setminus A = \{\{\emptyset\}\}$

(v) $A \, \Delta \, B = \{\{\emptyset, \{\emptyset\}\}\} \cup \{\{\emptyset\}\} = \{\{\emptyset\}, \{\emptyset, \{\emptyset\}\}\}$

12. Prove the following:

    (i)   The operation of forming unions is commutative.

    (ii)   The operation of forming intersections is commutative.

    (iii) The operation of forming intersections is associative.

Proofs:

(i) Let A and B be sets. Then $x \in A \cup B$ if and only if $x \in A$ or $x \in B$ if and only if $x \in B$ or $x \in A$ if and only if $x \in B \cup A$. Since x was arbitrary, we have shown $\forall x(x \in A \cup B \leftrightarrow x \in B \cup A)$. Therefore, $A \cup B = B \cup A$. So, the operation of forming unions is commutative. $\qquad \square$

(ii) Let A and B be sets. Then $x \in A \cap B$ if and only if $x \in A$ and $x \in B$ if and only if $x \in B$ and $x \in A$ if and only if $x \in B \cap A$. Since x was arbitrary, we have $\forall x(x \in A \cap B \leftrightarrow x \in B \cap A)$. Therefore, $A \cap B = B \cap A$. So, the operation of forming intersections is commutative. $\qquad \square$

(iii) Let A, B, and C be sets. Then $x \in (A \cap B) \cap C$ if and only if $x \in A \cap B$ and $x \in C$ if and only if $x \in A$, $x \in B$ and $x \in C$ if and only if $x \in A$ and $x \in B \cap C$ if and only if $x \in A \cap (B \cap C)$. Since x was arbitrary, we have shown $\forall x\big(x \in (A \cap B) \cap C \leftrightarrow x \in A \cap (B \cap C)\big)$.

Therefore, we have shown that $(A \cap B) \cap C = A \cap (B \cap C)$. So, the operation of forming intersections is associative. $\qquad \square$

LEVEL 3

13. Determine the cardinality of each of the following sets:

    (i) $\{\{\{0, 1\}\}\}$

    (ii) $\{\{x, y\}, x, \{x\}, \{x, \{x, y, z\}\}\}$

    (iii) $\{a, \{a\}, \{a, a\}, \{a, a, a, a\}, \{a, a, \{a\}\}, \{a, \{a\}, \{a\}\}\}$

Solutions:

(i) The only element of $\{\{\{0, 1\}\}\}$ is $\{\{0, 1\}\}$. So, $\big|\{\{\{0, 1\}\}\}\big| = \mathbf{1}$.

12

(ii) The elements of $\big\{\{x,y\},x,\{x\},\{x,\{x,y,z\}\}\big\}$ are $\{x,y\}$, x, $\{x\}$, and $\{x,\{x,y,z\}\}$. So, we see that $\Big|\big\{\{x,y\},x,\{x\},\{x,\{x,y,z\}\}\big\}\Big| = \mathbf{4}.$

(iii) We have:
$$\Big\{a,\{a\},\{a,a\},\{a,a,a,a\},\{a,a,\{a\}\},\{a,\{a\},\{a\}\}\Big\}$$
$$= \Big\{a,\{a\},\{a\},\{a\},\{a,\{a\}\},\{a,\{a\}\}\Big\}$$
$$= \Big\{a,\{a\},\{a,\{a\}\}\Big\}.$$

So, $\Big|\big\{a,\{a\},\{a,a\},\{a,a,a,a\},\{a,a,\{a\}\},\{a,\{a\},\{a\}\}\big\}\Big| = \Big|\big\{a,\{a\},\{a,\{a\}\}\big\}\Big| = \mathbf{3}.$

14. Prove that $4\mathbb{Z} \subseteq 2\mathbb{Z}$.

Proof: Let $t \in 4\mathbb{Z}$. Then there is $k \in \mathbb{Z}$ such that $t = 4k = (2 \cdot 2)k = 2(2k)$. Since 2 and k are integers, so is $2k$. Therefore, $t \in 2\mathbb{Z}$. Since $t \in 4\mathbb{Z}$ was arbitrary, $\forall t(t \in 4\mathbb{Z} \to t \in 2\mathbb{Z})$. Therefore, we have shown $4\mathbb{Z} \subseteq 2\mathbb{Z}$. □

15. How many subsets does $\{a,b,c,d\}$ have? Draw a tree diagram for the subsets of $\{a,b,c,d\}$.

Solution: $|\{a,b,c,d\}| = 4$. Therefore, $\{a,b,c,d\}$ has $2^4 = \mathbf{16}$ subsets. We can also say that the size of the power set of $\{a,b,c,d\}$ is 16, that is, $|\mathcal{P}(\{a,b,c,d\})| = 16$. Here is a tree diagram.

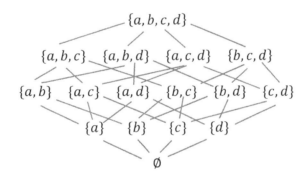

16. Let A, B, C, D, and E be sets such that $A \subseteq B$, $B \subseteq C$, $C \subseteq D$, and $D \subseteq E$. Prove that $A \subseteq E$.

Proof: Suppose that A, B, C, D, and E are sets such that $A \subseteq B$, $B \subseteq C$, $C \subseteq D$, and $D \subseteq E$. Since $A \subseteq B$ and $B \subseteq C$, by Theorem 1.14, we have $A \subseteq C$. Since $A \subseteq C$ and $C \subseteq D$, again by Theorem 1.14, we have $A \subseteq D$. Finally, since $A \subseteq D$ and $D \subseteq E$, once again by Theorem 1.14, we have $A \subseteq E$. □

17. Let A, B, C, and D be sets with $A \subseteq B$ and $C \subseteq D$. Prove that $A \times C \subseteq B \times D$.

Proof: Let A, B, C, and D be sets with $A \subseteq B$ and $C \subseteq D$ and let $(x,y) \in A \times C$. Then $x \in A$ and $y \in C$. Since $x \in A$ and $A \subseteq B$, $x \in B$. Since $y \in C$ and $C \subseteq D$, $y \in D$. Therefore, $(x,y) \in B \times D$. Since $(x,y) \in A \times C$ was arbitrary, $A \times C \subseteq B \times D$. □

18. Prove or provide a counterexample:

(i) Every pairwise disjoint set of sets is disjoint.

(ii) Every disjoint set of sets is pairwise disjoint.

Solutions:

(i) This is **false**. Let $A = \{1\}$ and let $\boldsymbol{X} = \{A\}$. $\boldsymbol{X}$ is pairwise disjoint, but $\cap \boldsymbol{X} = A = \{1\} \neq \emptyset$.

However, the following slightly modified statement is **true**: "Every pairwise disjoint set of sets consisting of at least two sets is disjoint."

Let $\boldsymbol{X}$ be a pairwise disjoint set of sets with at least two sets, say $A, B \in \boldsymbol{X}$. Suppose towards contradiction that $x \in \cap \boldsymbol{X}$. Then $x \in A$ and $x \in B$. So, $x \in A \cap B$. But $A \cap B = \emptyset$ because $\boldsymbol{X}$ is pairwise disjoint. This contradiction shows that the statement $x \in \cap \boldsymbol{X}$ is false. Therefore, $\boldsymbol{X}$ is disjoint. □

(ii) This is **false**. Let $A = \{0,1\}$, $B = \{1,2\}$, $C = \{0,2\}$, and $\boldsymbol{X} = \{A, B, C\}$. Then $\boldsymbol{X}$ is disjoint because $\cap \boldsymbol{X} = A \cap B \cap C = \{0,1\} \cap \{1,2\} \cap \{0,2\} = \{1\} \cap \{0,2\} = \emptyset$. However, $\boldsymbol{X}$ is **not** pairwise disjoint because $A \cap B = \{0,1\} \cap \{1,2\} = \{1\} \neq \emptyset$.

19. Let A and B be sets. Prove that $A \cap B \subseteq A$.

Proof: Suppose that A and B are sets and let $x \in A \cap B$. Then $x \in A$ and $x \in B$. In particular, $x \in A$. Since x was an arbitrary element of A, we have shown that every element of $A \cap B$ is an element of A. That is, $\forall x(x \in A \cap B \rightarrow x \in A)$ is true. Therefore, $A \cap B \subseteq A$. □

LEVEL 4

20. A relation R is **reflexive** if $\forall x(xRx)$ and **symmetric** if $\forall x \forall y(xRy \rightarrow yRx)$. For example, the relation "=" is reflexive and symmetric because $\forall x(x = x)$ and $\forall x \forall y(x = y \rightarrow y = x)$. Show that $\subseteq$ is reflexive, but $\in$ is not. Then decide if each of $\subseteq$ and $\in$ is symmetric.

Solutions: ($\subseteq$ **is reflexive**) Let A be a set. By Theorem 1.9, A is a subset of itself. So, $A \subseteq A$ is true. Since A was arbitrary, $\forall x(A \subseteq A)$ is true. Therefore, $\subseteq$ is reflexive. □

($\in$ is **not** reflexive) Since the empty set has no elements, $\emptyset \notin \emptyset$. This **counterexample** shows that $\in$ is not reflexive.

($\subseteq$ is **not** symmetric) $\{1\} \subseteq \{1, 2\}$, but $\{1, 2\} \not\subseteq \{1\}$. This **counterexample** shows that $\subseteq$ is not symmetric.

($\in$ is **not** symmetric) $\emptyset \in \{\emptyset\}$, but $\{\emptyset\} \notin \emptyset$. This **counterexample** shows that $\in$ is not symmetric.

Note: A **conjecture** is an educated guess. In math, conjectures are made all the time based upon evidence from examples (but examples alone cannot be used to prove a conjecture). A logical argument is usually needed to prove a conjecture, whereas a single **counterexample** is used to disprove a conjecture. For example, $\emptyset \notin \emptyset$ is a counterexample to the conjecture "$\in$ is reflexive."

21. Determine whether each of the following statements is true or false:

    (i) $0 \in \{0, \{1\}\}$

    (ii) $\{b\} \in \{a, b\}$

    (iii) $\{1\} \in \{\{1\}, x, 2, y\}$

    (iv) $\emptyset \in \{\{\emptyset\}\}$

    (v) $\{\{\emptyset\}\} \in \emptyset$

Solutions:

    (i)   The set $\{0, \{1\}\}$ has exactly 2 elements, namely 0 and $\{1\}$. So, $0 \in \{0, \{1\}\}$ is **true**.

    (ii)   The set $\{a, b\}$ has exactly 2 elements, namely a and b. So, $\{b\} \in \{a, b\}$ is **false**.

    (iii) The set $\{\{1\}, x, 2, y\}$ has exactly 4 elements, namely $\{1\}$, x, 2 , and y. So, $\{1\} \in \{\{1\}, x, 2, y\}$ is **true**.

    (iv) The set $\{\{\emptyset\}\}$ has exactly 1 element, namely $\{\emptyset\}$. Since $\emptyset$ is not equal to $\{\emptyset\}$, $\emptyset \in \{\{\emptyset\}\}$ is **false**.

    (v)   The empty set has no elements. So, $x \in \emptyset$ is false for any x. In particular, $\{\{\emptyset\}\} \in \emptyset$ is **false**.

22. We say that a set A is **transitive** if $\forall x (x \in A \rightarrow x \subseteq A)$. Determine if each of the following sets is transitive:

    (i) $\emptyset$

    (ii) $\{\emptyset\}$

    (iii) $\{\{\emptyset\}\}$

    (iv) $\{\emptyset, \{\emptyset\}\}$

    (v) $\{\emptyset, \{\emptyset\}, \{\{\emptyset\}\}\}$

    (vi) $\{\{\emptyset\}, \{\emptyset, \{\emptyset\}\}\}$

Solutions:

    (i)   Since $\emptyset$ has no elements, $\emptyset$ **is transitive**. (The statement "$x \in \emptyset \rightarrow x \subseteq \emptyset$" is true simply because "$x \in \emptyset$" is always false. In other words, the statement is vacuously true.)

    (ii)   The only element of $\{\emptyset\}$ is $\emptyset$, and $\emptyset \subseteq \{\emptyset\}$ is true. So, $\{\emptyset\}$ **is transitive**.

    (iii) $\{\emptyset\} \in \{\{\emptyset\}\}$ and $\emptyset \in \{\emptyset\}$, but $\emptyset \notin \{\{\emptyset\}\}$. So, $\{\{\emptyset\}\}$ **is not transitive**.

    (iv) $\{\emptyset, \{\emptyset\}\}$ has 2 elements, namely $\emptyset$ and $\{\emptyset\}$. Both sets are subsets of $\{\emptyset, \{\emptyset\}\}$. It follows that $\{\emptyset, \{\emptyset\}\}$ **is transitive**.

    (v) $\{\emptyset, \{\emptyset\}, \{\{\emptyset\}\}\}$ has 3 elements, namely $\emptyset$, $\{\emptyset\}$, and $\{\{\emptyset\}\}$. All three of these sets are subsets of $\{\emptyset, \{\emptyset\}, \{\{\emptyset\}\}\}$. It follows that $\{\emptyset, \{\emptyset\}, \{\{\emptyset\}\}\}$ **is transitive**.

(vi) $\{\emptyset\} \in \Big\{\{\emptyset\}, \{\emptyset, \{\emptyset\}\}\Big\}$ and $\emptyset \in \{\emptyset\}$, but $\emptyset \notin \Big\{\{\emptyset\}, \{\emptyset, \{\emptyset\}\}\Big\}$. So, $\Big\{\{\emptyset\}, \{\emptyset, \{\emptyset\}\}\Big\}$ **is not transitive**.

23. Let A, B, C, and D be sets. Determine if each of the following statements is true or false. If true, provide a proof. If false, provide a counterexample.

    (i) $(A \times B) \cap (C \times D) = (A \cap C) \times (B \cap D)$

    (ii) $(A \times B) \cup (C \times D) = (A \cup C) \times (B \cup D)$

Solutions:

    (i)   This is **true**.

        Proof: $(x, y) \in (A \times B) \cap (C \times D)$ if and only if $(x, y) \in A \times B$ and $(x, y) \in C \times D$ if and only if $x \in A$, $y \in B$, $x \in C$, and $y \in D$ if and only if $x \in A \cap C$ and $y \in B \cap D$ if and only if $(x, y) \in (A \cap C) \times (B \cap D)$. Therefore, $(A \times B) \cap (C \times D) = (A \cap C) \times (B \cap D)$.   □

    (ii)   This is **false**. If $A = \{0\}, B = \{1\}, C = \{2\}, D = \{3\}$, then $A \times B = \{(0, 1)\}$, $C \times D = \{(2, 3)\}$, and so, $(A \times B) \cup (C \times D) = \{(0, 1), (2, 3)\}$. Also, $A \cup C = \{0, 2\}$, $B \cup D = \{1, 3\}$, and so, $(A \cup C) \times (B \cup D) = \{(0, 1), (0, 3), (2, 1), (2, 3)\}$. Since $(2, 1) \in (A \cup C) \times (B \cup D)$, but $(2, 1) \notin (A \times B) \cup (C \times D)$, we see that $(A \times B) \cup (C \times D) \neq (A \cup C) \times (B \cup D)$.

24. Prove that $B \subseteq A$ if and only if $A \cap B = B$.

Proof: Suppose that $B \subseteq A$. By part (ii) of Problem 12 and Problem 19, $A \cap B = B \cap A \subseteq B$. Let $x \in B$. Since $B \subseteq A$, $x \in A$. Therefore, $x \in A$ and $x \in B$. So, $x \in A \cap B$. Since x was an arbitrary element of B, we have shown that every element of B is an element of $A \cap B$. That is, $\forall x(x \in B \rightarrow x \in A \cap B)$. Therefore, $B \subseteq A \cap B$. Since $A \cap B \subseteq B$ and $B \subseteq A \cap B$, it follows that $A \cap B = B$.

Now, suppose that $A \cap B = B$ and let $x \in B$. Then $x \in A \cap B$. So, $x \in A$ and $x \in B$. In particular, $x \in A$. Since x was an arbitrary element of B, we have shown that every element of B is an element of A. That is, $\forall x(x \in B \rightarrow x \in A)$. Therefore, $B \subseteq A$.   □

25. Let A, B, and C be sets. Prove each of the following:

    (i) $A \cap (B \cup C) = (A \cap B) \cup (A \cap C)$.

    (ii) $A \cup (B \cap C) = (A \cup B) \cap (A \cup C)$.

    (iii) $C \setminus (A \cup B) = (C \setminus A) \cap (C \setminus B)$.

    (iv) $C \setminus (A \cap B) = (C \setminus A) \cup (C \setminus B)$.

Proofs:

    (i) $x \in A \cap (B \cup C) \Leftrightarrow x \in A$ and $x \in B \cup C \Leftrightarrow x \in A$ and either $x \in B$ or $x \in C \Leftrightarrow x \in A$ and $x \in B$ or $x \in A$ and $x \in C \Leftrightarrow x \in A \cap B$ or $x \in A \cap C \Leftrightarrow x \in (A \cap B) \cup (A \cap C)$.   □

    (ii) $x \in A \cup (B \cap C) \Leftrightarrow x \in A$ or $x \in B \cap C \Leftrightarrow$ either $x \in A$ or we have both $x \in B$ and $x \in C \Leftrightarrow$ we have both $x \in A$ or $x \in B$ and $x \in A$ or $x \in C \Leftrightarrow x \in A \cup B$ and $x \in A \cup C \Leftrightarrow x \in (A \cup B) \cap (A \cup C)$.   □

16

(iii) $x \in C \setminus (A \cup B) \Leftrightarrow x \in C$ and $x \notin A \cup B \Leftrightarrow x \in C$ and $x \notin A$ and $x \notin B \Leftrightarrow x \in C$ and $x \notin A$ and $x \in C$ and $x \notin B \Leftrightarrow x \in C \setminus A$ and $x \in C \setminus B \Leftrightarrow x \in (C \setminus A) \cap (C \setminus B)$. $\qquad \square$

(iv) $x \in C \setminus (A \cap B) \Leftrightarrow x \in C$ and $x \notin A \cap B \Leftrightarrow x \in C$ and $x \notin A$ or $x \notin B \Leftrightarrow x \in C$ and $x \notin A$ or $x \in C$ and $x \notin B \Leftrightarrow x \in C \setminus A$ or $x \in C \setminus B \Leftrightarrow x \in (C \setminus A) \cup (C \setminus B)$. $\qquad \square$

Notes: Let's let p, q, and r be the statements $x \in A$, $x \in B$, and $x \in C$, respectively.

(1) In (i) above, the statement "$x \in A$ and either $x \in B$ or $x \in C$" can be written $p \wedge (q \vee r)$. It can easily be shown that this is equivalent to $(p \wedge q) \vee (p \wedge r)$. In words, this is the statement "$x \in A$ and $x \in B$ or $x \in A$ and $x \in C$." Here it needs to be understood that the word "and" takes precedence over the word "or."

Similarly, we can use the logical equivalence $p \vee (q \wedge r) \equiv (p \vee q) \wedge (p \vee r)$ to help understand the proof of (ii).

(2) The equivalences $p \wedge (q \vee r) \equiv (p \wedge q) \vee (p \wedge r)$ and $p \vee (q \wedge r) \equiv (p \vee q) \wedge (p \vee r)$ are known as the **distributive laws**.

The rules $A \cap (B \cup C) = (A \cap B) \cup (A \cap C)$ and $A \cup (B \cap C) = (A \cup B) \cap (A \cup C)$ are also known as the **distributive laws**.

(3) To clarify (iii) and (iv), note that $\neg(p \vee q) \equiv \neg p \wedge \neg q$ and $\neg(p \wedge q) \equiv \neg p \vee \neg q$ (these equivalences can be easily checked). These two equivalences are known as **De Morgan's laws**. For (iii), we can use the logical equivalence $\neg(p \vee q) \equiv \neg p \wedge \neg q$ with p the statement $x \in A$ and q the statement $x \in B$ to get

$$x \notin A \cup B \equiv \neg x \in A \cup B \equiv \neg(x \in A \vee x \in B) \equiv \neg(p \vee q) \equiv \neg p \wedge \neg q \text{ (by De Morgan's law)}$$
$$\equiv \neg x \in A \wedge \neg x \in B \equiv x \notin A \wedge x \notin B.$$

So, the statement "$x \in C$ and $x \notin A \cup B$" is equivalent to $x \in C \wedge x \notin A \wedge x \notin B$.

Similarly, we can use the logical equivalence $\neg(p \wedge q) \equiv \neg p \vee \neg q$ to see that the statement "$x \in C$ and $x \notin A \cap B$" is equivalent to "$x \in C$ and $x \notin A$ or $x \notin B$."

(4) The rules $C \setminus (A \cup B) = (C \setminus A) \cap (C \setminus B)$ and $C \setminus (A \cap B) = (C \setminus A) \cup (C \setminus B)$ are also known as **De Morgan's laws**.

LEVEL 5

26. Let A and B be sets with $A \subseteq B$. Prove that $\mathcal{P}(A) \subseteq \mathcal{P}(B)$.

Proof: Let A and B be sets with $A \subseteq B$ and let $X \in \mathcal{P}(A)$. Then $X \subseteq A$ Since $X \subseteq A$ and $A \subseteq B$, by Theorem 1.14, $X \subseteq B$. So, $X \in \mathcal{P}(B)$. Since $X \in \mathcal{P}(A)$ was arbitrary, $\forall X(X \in \mathcal{P}(A) \rightarrow X \in \mathcal{P}(B))$. Therefore, $\mathcal{P}(A) \subseteq \mathcal{P}(B)$. $\qquad \square$

27. Prove that if A is a transitive set, then $\mathcal{P}(A)$ is also a transitive set (see Problem 22 above for the definition of a transitive set).

Proof: Let A be a transitive set, let $x \in \mathcal{P}(A)$, and let $y \in x$. Since $x \in \mathcal{P}(A)$, $x \subseteq A$. Since $y \in x$ and $x \subseteq A$, $y \in A$. Since A is transitive and $y \in A$, $y \subseteq A$. So, $y \in \mathcal{P}(A)$. Since $y \in x$ was arbitrary, $\forall y(y \in x \rightarrow y \in \mathcal{P}(A))$. Therefore, $x \subseteq \mathcal{P}(A)$. Since x was arbitrary, $\forall x(x \in \mathcal{P}(A) \rightarrow x \subseteq \mathcal{P}(A))$. Thus, $\mathcal{P}(A)$ is transitive. $\qquad\qquad\square$

28. Let $A = \{a, b, c, d\}$, $B = \{X \mid X \subseteq A \wedge d \notin X\}$, and $C = \{X \mid X \subseteq A \wedge d \in X\}$. Show that there is a natural one-to-one correspondence between the elements of B and the elements of C. Then generalize this result to a set with $n + 1$ elements for $n > 0$.

Solution: We define the one-to-one correspondence as follows: If $Y \in B$, then Y is a subset of A that does not contain d. Let Y_d be the set that contains the same elements as Y, but with d thrown in. Then the correspondence $Y \rightarrow Y_d$ is a one-to-one correspondence. We can see this correspondence in the table below.

Elements of B	Elements of C
$\emptyset$	$\{d\}$
$\{a\}$	$\{a, d\}$
$\{b\}$	$\{b, d\}$
$\{c\}$	$\{c, d\}$
$\{a, b\}$	$\{a, b, d\}$
$\{a, c\}$	$\{a, c, d\}$
$\{b, c\}$	$\{b, c, d\}$
$\{a, b, c\}$	$\{a, b, c, d\}$

For the general result, we start with a set A with $n + 1$ elements, and we let d be some element from A. Define B and C the same way as before: $B = \{X \mid X \subseteq A \wedge d \notin X\}$, and $C = \{X \mid X \subseteq A \wedge d \in X\}$. Also, as before, if $Y \in B$, then Y is a subset of A that does not contain d. Let Y_d be the set that contains the same elements as Y, but with d thrown in. Then the correspondence $Y \rightarrow Y_d$ is a one-to-one correspondence.

Notes: (1) B consists of the subsets of A that do not contain the element d, while C consists of the subsets of A that do contain d.

(2) Observe that in the case where $A = \{a, b, c, d\}$, B and C each have $8 = 2^3$ elements. Also, there is no overlap between B and C (they have no elements in common). So, we have a total of $8 + 8 = 16$ elements. Since there are exactly $2^4 = 16$ subsets of A, we see that we have listed every subset of A.

(3) We could also do the computation in Note 2 as follows: $2^3 + 2^3 = 2 \cdot 2^3 = 2^1 \cdot 2^3 = 2^{1+3} = 2^4$. It's nice to see the computation this way because it mimics the computation we will do in the more general case. In case your algebra skills are not that strong, here is an explanation of each step:

18

Adding the same thing to itself is equivalent to multiplying that thing by 2. For example, 1 apple plus 1 apple is 2 apples. Similarly, $1x + 1x = 2x$. This could be written more briefly as $x + x = 2x$. Replacing x by 2^3 gives us $2^3 + 2^3 = 2 \cdot 2^3$ (the first equality in the computation above).

Next, by definition, $x^1 = x$. So, $2^1 = 2$. Therefore, we can rewrite $2 \cdot 2^3$ as $2^1 \cdot 2^3$.

Now, 2^3 means to multiply 2 by itself 3 times. So, $2^3 = 2 \cdot 2 \cdot 2$. Thus, $2^1 \cdot 2^3 = 2 \cdot 2 \cdot 2 \cdot 2 = 2^4$. This leads to the rule of exponents which says that if you multiply two expressions with the same base, you can add the exponents. So, $2^1 \cdot 2^3 = 2^{1+3} = 2^4$.

(4) In the more general case, B and C each have 2^n elements. The reason for this is that A has $n + 1$ elements. When we remove the element d from A, the resulting set has n elements, and therefore, 2^n subsets. B consists of precisely the subsets of this new set (A with d removed), and so, B has exactly 2^n elements. The one-to-one correspondence $Y \to Y_d$ shows that C has the same number of elements as B. Therefore, C also has 2^n elements.

(5) In the general case, there is still no overlap between B and C. It follows that the total number of elements when we combine B and C is $2^n + 2^n = 2 \cdot 2^n = 2^1 \cdot 2^n = 2^{1+n} = 2^{n+1}$. See Note 3 above for an explanation as to how all this algebra works.

(6) By a **one-to-one correspondence** between the elements of B and the elements of C, we mean a pairing where we match each element of B with exactly one element of C so that each element of C is matched with exactly one element of B. The table given in the solution above provides a nice example of such a pairing.

(7) In the case where $A = \{a, b, c, d\}$, B consists of all the subsets of $\{a, b, c\}$. In other words, $B = \{X \mid X \subseteq \{a, b, c\}\} = \mathcal{P}(\{a, b, c\})$.

A description of C is a bit more complicated. It consists of the subsets of $\{a, b, c\}$ with d thrown into them. We could write this as $C = \{X \cup \{d\} \mid X \subseteq \{a, b, c\}\}$.

(5) In the general case, we can write $K = A \setminus \{d\}$ (this is the set consisting of all the elements of A, except d). We then have $B = \{X \mid X \subseteq K\} = \mathcal{P}(K)$ and $C = \{X \cup \{d\} \mid X \subseteq K\} = \mathcal{P}(A) \setminus \mathcal{P}(K)$.

29. Let X be a nonempty set of sets. Prove the following:

    (i)   For all $A \in X$, $A \subseteq \bigcup X$.

    (ii)   For all $A \in X$, $\bigcap X \subseteq A$.

Proofs:

    (i)   Let X be a nonempty set of sets, let $A \in X$, and let $x \in A$. Then there is $B \in X$ such that $x \in B$ (namely A). So, $x \in \bigcup X$. Since x was an arbitrary element of A, we have shown that $A \subseteq \bigcup X$. Since A was an arbitrary element of X, we have shown that for all $A \in X$, we have $A \subseteq \bigcup X$.   □

(ii)   Let X be a nonempty set of sets, let $A \in X$, and let $x \in \bigcap X$. Then for every $B \in X$, we have $x \in B$. In particular, $x \in A$ (because $A \in X$). Since x was an arbitrary element of $\bigcap X$, we have shown that $\bigcap X \subseteq A$. Since A was an arbitrary element of X, we have shown that for all $A \in X$, we have $\bigcap X \subseteq A$. $\square$

30. Let A be a set and let X be a nonempty set of sets. Prove each of the following:

(i) $A \cap \bigcup X = \bigcup \{A \cap B \mid B \in X\}$

(ii) $A \cup \bigcap X = \bigcap \{A \cup B \mid B \in X\}$

(iii) $A \setminus \bigcup X = \bigcap \{A \setminus B \mid B \in X\}$

(iv) $A \setminus \bigcap X = \bigcup \{A \setminus B \mid B \in X\}$.

Proofs:

(i) $x \in A \cap \bigcup X \Leftrightarrow x \in A$ and $x \in \bigcup X \Leftrightarrow x \in A$ and there is a $B \in X$ with $x \in B \Leftrightarrow x \in A \cap B$ for some $B \in X \Leftrightarrow x \in \bigcup \{A \cap B \mid B \in X\}$. $\square$

(ii) $x \in A \cup \bigcap X \Leftrightarrow x \in A$ or $x \in \bigcap X \Leftrightarrow x \in A$ or $x \in B$ for every $B \in X \Leftrightarrow x \in A \cup B$ for every $B \in X \Leftrightarrow x \in \bigcap \{A \cup B \mid B \in X\}$. $\square$

(iii) $x \in A \setminus \bigcup X \Leftrightarrow x \in A$ and $x \notin \bigcup X \Leftrightarrow x \in A$ and $x \notin B$ for every $B \in X \Leftrightarrow x \in A \setminus B$ for every $B \in X \Leftrightarrow x \in \bigcap \{A \setminus B \mid B \in X\}$. $\square$

(iv) $x \in A \setminus \bigcap X \Leftrightarrow x \in A$ and $x \notin \bigcap X \Leftrightarrow x \in A$ and $x \notin B$ for some $B \in X \Leftrightarrow x \in A \setminus B$ for some $B \in X \Leftrightarrow x \in \bigcup \{A \setminus B \mid B \in X\}$. $\square$

Note: The rules in (i) and (ii) are known as the **generalized distributive laws** and the rules in (iii) and (iv) are known as the **generalized De Morgan's laws.**

Problem Set 2

LEVEL 1

1. For each of the following multiplication tables defined on the set $S = \{a, b\}$, determine if each of the following is true or false:

    (i) $\star$ defines a binary operation on S.

    (ii) $\star$ is commutative in S.

    (iii) a is an identity with respect to $\star$.

    (iv) b is an identity with respect to $\star$.

I

$\star$	a	b
a	a	a
b	a	a

II

$\star$	a	b
a	a	b
b	c	a

III

$\star$	a	b
a	a	b
b	b	a

IV

$\star$	a	b
a	a	a
b	b	b

Solutions:

(i)   For tables I, III, and IV, $\star$ **does** define a binary operation because only a and b appear inside each of these tables. For table II, $\star$ does **not** define a binary operation because an element different from a and b appears in the table (assuming that $c \neq a$ and $c \neq b$).

(ii)   For commutativity, since there are just two elements a and b, we need only check if a and b commute ($a \star b = b \star a$). This is very easy to see just by looking at the tables. We simply check if the entries on opposite sides of the main diagonal are the same.

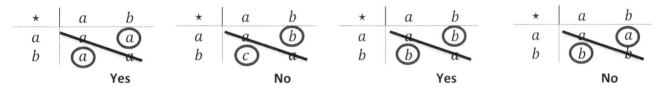

We see that for tables I and III, $\star$ **is** commutative for S, whereas for tables II and IV, $\star$ **is not** commutative for S.

(iii) To see if a is an identity with respect to $\star$, we need to check if $a \star a = a$, $a \star b = b$, and $b \star a = b$. This is also very easy to see just by looking at the tables. We simply check if the row corresponding to a is the same as the "input row," and if the column corresponding to a is the same as the "input column."

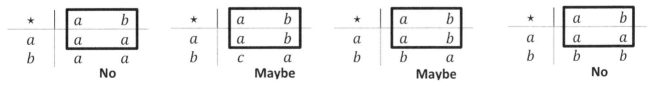

We see that for tables I and IV, the row corresponding to a is **not** the same as the "input row." So, for I and IV, a is **not** an identity with respect to $\star$.

We still need to check the columns for tables II and III

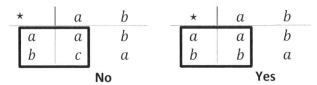

No   Yes

We see that for table II, the column corresponding to a is **not** the same as the "input column." So, for II, a is **not** an identity with respect to $\star$.

For table III, a **is** an identity with respect to $\star$.

(iv) To see if b is an identity with respect to $\star$, we need to check if $a \star b = a$, $b \star a = a$, and $b \star b = b$. Again, this is very easy to see just by looking at the tables. In this case, we see that for each table, the row corresponding to b is **not** the same as the "input row."

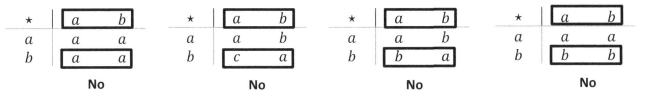

No   No   No   No

So, b is **not** an identity with respect to $\star$ in all four cases.

Notes: (1) Table I defines a semigroup $(S,\star)$. To see that $\star$ is associative in S, just observe that all the outputs are the same. Therefore, there cannot be a counterexample to associativity. For example, $(a \star b) \star b = a \star b = a$ and $a \star (b \star b) = a \star a = a$.

(2) Table I does **not** define a monoid. Parts (iii) and (iv) showed us that there is no identity with respect to $\star$.

(3) Table III defines a commutative group $(S,\star)$ with identity a. a and b are each their own inverses because $a \star a = a$ and $b \star b = a$ (remember that a is the identity). With your current knowledge, associativity can be checked by brute force. There are eight equations that need to be verified. For example, $(a \star a) \star b = a \star b = b$ and $a \star (a \star b) = a \star b = b$. So, $(a \star a) \star b = a \star (a \star b)$. See the solution to Problem 2 below for details.

(4) Table IV defines a semigroup $(S,\star)$ known as the **left zero semigroup**. The name of this semigroup comes from the fact that $a \star a = a$ and $a \star b = a$, so that a is behaving just like 0 behaves when multiplying on the left (0 times anything equals 0). Notice that $b \star a = b \neq a$, so that a does **not** behave like 0 when multiplying on the right. Similar computations show that b also behaves like 0 from the left. The dedicated reader may want to check associativity by brute force, as described in Note 3.

(5) Table IV does **not** define a monoid. Parts (iii) and (iv) showed us that there is no identity with respect to $\star$.

2. Show that there are exactly two monoids on the set $S = \{e, a\}$, where e is the identity. Which of these monoids are groups? Which of these monoids are commutative?

Solution: Let's let e be the identity. Since $e \star x = x \star e = x$ for all x in the monoid, we can easily fill out the first row and the first column of the table.

$\star$	e	a
e	e	a
a	a	$\boxed{\cdot}$

The entry labeled with $\boxed{\cdot}$ must be either e or a because we need $\star$ to be a binary operation on S.

Case 1: If we let $\boxed{\cdot}$ be a, we get the following table.

$\star$	e	a
e	e	a
a	a	a

Associativity holds because any computation of the form $(x \star y) \star z$ or $x \star (y \star z)$ will result in a if any of x, y, or z is a. So, all that is left to check is that $(e \star e) \star e = e \star (e \star e)$. But each side of that equation is equal to e.

So, with this multiplication table, $(S, \star)$ **is** a monoid.

This monoid is **not** a group because a has no inverse. Indeed, $a \star e = a \neq e$ and $a \star a = a \neq e$.

This monoid **is** commutative because $a \star e = a$ and $e \star a = a$.

Case 2: If we let $\boxed{\cdot}$ be e, we get the following table.

$\star$	e	a
e	e	a
a	a	e

Let's check that associativity holds. There are eight instances to check.

$$
\begin{aligned}
(e \star e) \star e &= e \star e = e & e \star (e \star e) &= e \star e = e \\
(e \star e) \star a &= e \star a = a & e \star (e \star a) &= e \star a = a \\
(e \star a) \star e &= a \star e = a & e \star (a \star e) &= e \star a = a \\
(a \star e) \star e &= a \star e = a & a \star (e \star e) &= a \star e = a \\
(e \star a) \star a &= a \star a = e & e \star (a \star a) &= e \star e = e \\
(a \star e) \star a &= a \star a = e & a \star (e \star a) &= a \star a = e \\
(a \star a) \star e &= e \star e = e & a \star (a \star e) &= a \star a = e \\
(a \star a) \star a &= e \star a = a & a \star (a \star a) &= e \star a = a
\end{aligned}
$$

So, with this multiplication table, $(S, \star)$ **is** a monoid.

Since $e \star e = e$, e is its own inverse. Since $a \star a = e$, a is also its own inverse. Therefore, each element of this monoid is invertible. It follows that this monoid **is** a group.

This monoid **is** commutative because $a \star e = a$ and $e \star a = a$.

3. The addition and multiplication tables below are defined on the set $S = \{0, 1\}$. Show that $(S, +, \cdot)$ does **not** define a ring.

+	0	1
0	0	1
1	1	0

$\cdot$	0	1
0	1	0
1	0	1

Solution 1: We have $0(1 + 1) = 0 \cdot 0 = 1$ and $0 \cdot 1 + 0 \cdot 1 = 0 + 0 = 0$. So, $0(1 + 1) \neq 0 \cdot 1 + 0 \cdot 1$. Therefore, multiplication is **not** distributive over addition in S, and so, $(S, +, \cdot)$ does not define a ring.

Notes: (1) Both multiplication tables given are the same, except that we interchanged the roles of 0 and 1 (in technical terms, $(S, +)$ and $(S, \cdot)$ are **isomorphic**).

Both tables represent the unique table for a group with 2 elements. See Problem 2 for details.

(2) Since $(S, +)$ is a commutative group and $(S, \cdot)$ is a monoid (in fact, it's a commutative group), we know that the only possible way $(S, +, \cdot)$ can fail to be a ring is for distributivity to fail.

Solution 2: By Theorem 2.14, if $(S, +, \cdot)$ were a ring, we would have $0 \cdot 0 = 0$. So, $(S, +, \cdot)$ does not define a ring.

4. Let $S = \{0, 1\}$ and define addition $(+)$ and multiplication $(\cdot)$ so that $(S, +, \cdot)$ is a ring. Assume that 0 is the additive identity in S and 1 is the multiplicative identity in S. Draw the tables for addition and multiplication and verify that with these tables, $(S, +, \cdot)$ is a ring. Is $(S, +, \cdot)$ a field?

Solution: Since $(S, +)$ is a commutative group, by the solution to Problem 2, the addition table must be the following.

+	0	1
0	0	1
1	1	0

Since $(S, \cdot)$ is a monoid and 1 is the multiplicative identity, again by the solution to Problem 2, the multiplication table must be one of the following.

$\cdot$	0	1
0	1	0
1	0	1

$\cdot$	0	1
0	0	0
1	0	1

However, we showed in Problem 3 that if we use the table on the left, then $(S, +, \cdot)$ will **not** define a ring.

So, the addition and multiplication tables must be as follows:

+	0	1
0	0	1
1	1	0

$\cdot$	0	1
0	0	0
1	0	1

Since we already know that $(S, +)$ is a commutative group and $(S, \cdot)$ is a monoid, all we need to verify is that distributivity holds. Since $\cdot$ is commutative for S (by the solution to Problem 2), it suffices to verify left distributivity. We will do this by brute force. There are eight instances to check.

$$0(0 + 0) = 0 \cdot 0 = 0 \qquad\qquad 0 \cdot 0 + 0 \cdot 0 = 0 + 0 = 0$$
$$0(0 + 1) = 0 \cdot 1 = 0 \qquad\qquad 0 \cdot 0 + 0 \cdot 1 = 0 + 0 = 0$$
$$0(1 + 0) = 0 \cdot 1 = 0 \qquad\qquad 0 \cdot 1 + 0 \cdot 0 = 0 + 0 = 0$$
$$0(1 + 1) = 0 \cdot 0 = 0 \qquad\qquad 0 \cdot 1 + 0 \cdot 1 = 0 + 0 = 0$$
$$1(0 + 0) = 1 \cdot 0 = 0 \qquad\qquad 1 \cdot 0 + 1 \cdot 0 = 0 + 0 = 0$$
$$1(0 + 1) = 1 \cdot 1 = 1 \qquad\qquad 1 \cdot 0 + 1 \cdot 1 = 0 + 1 = 1$$
$$1(1 + 0) = 1 \cdot 1 = 1 \qquad\qquad 1 \cdot 1 + 1 \cdot 0 = 1 + 0 = 1$$
$$1(1 + 1) = 1 \cdot 0 = 0 \qquad\qquad 1 \cdot 1 + 1 \cdot 1 = 1 + 1 = 0$$

So, we see that left distributivity holds, and therefore $(S, +, \cdot)$ is a ring.

It is easy to see that multiplication is commutative in S. Also, 1 is invertible with $1^{-1} = 1$. It follows that $(S, +, \cdot)$ is a field.

5. The addition and multiplication tables below are defined on the set $S = \{0, 1, 2\}$. Show that $(S, +, \cdot)$ does **not** define a field.

+	0	1	2
0	0	1	2
1	1	2	0
2	2	0	1

$\cdot$	0	1	2
0	0	0	0
1	0	1	2
2	0	2	2

Solution: We have $2 \cdot 0 = 0$, $2 \cdot 1 = 2$, and $2 \cdot 2 = 2$. So, 2 has no multiplicative inverse, and therefore, $(S, +, \cdot)$ does **not** define a field.

Note: It's not difficult to check that $(S, +)$ is a group with identity 0 and $(S, \cdot)$ is a monoid with identity 1. However, $(S, +, \cdot)$ is not a ring, as distributivity fails. Here is a counterexample:

$$2(1 + 1) = 2 \cdot 2 = 2 \qquad\qquad 2 \cdot 1 + 2 \cdot 1 = 2 + 2 = 1$$

We could have used this computation to verify that $(S, +, \cdot)$ is not a field.

6. Give an example of an integral domain that is **not** a field.

Solution: $(\mathbb{Z}, +, \cdot)$ is a ring with no zero divisors. Therefore, it is an integral domain. Since 2 has no multiplicative inverse in $\mathbb{Z}$, $(\mathbb{Z}, +, \cdot)$ is not a field.

7. Let $(R, +, \cdot)$ be a ring. Prove each of the following:

    (i)   If $a, b \in R$ with $a + b = b$, then $a = 0$.

    (ii)   If $a, b \in R$, b^{-1} exists, and $ab = b$, then $a = 1$.

    (iii)   If $a, b \in R$, a^{-1} exists, and $ab = 1$, then $b = \frac{1}{a}$.

    (iv)   If $(R, +, \cdot)$ is a field, $a, b \in R$ and $ab = 0$, then $a = 0$ or $b = 0$ (in other words, every field is an integral domain). Is this still true if we replace "field" by "ring?"

    (v)   If $a \in R$, then $-a = -1a$

    (vi) $(-1)(-1) = 1$.

Proofs:

   (i)   Let $a, b \in R$ with $a + b = b$. Then we have

$$a = a + 0 = a + \big(b + (-b)\big) = (a + b) + (-b) = b + (-b) = 0. \qquad \square$$

   (ii)   Let $a, b \in R$ and $ab = b$. Then we have

$$a = a \cdot 1 = a(bb^{-1}) = (ab)b^{-1} = bb^{-1} = 1. \qquad \square$$

   (iii)   Let $a, b \in R$ and $ab = 1$. Then $b = 1b = (a^{-1}a)b = a^{-1}(ab) = a^{-1} \cdot 1 = a^{-1} = \frac{1}{a}$. $\qquad \square$

   (iv)   Let $a, b \in R$ and $ab = 0$. Assume that $a \neq 0$. Then $b = 1b = (a^{-1}a)b = a^{-1}(ab) = a^{-1} \cdot 0$. By Theorem 2.14, $a^{-1} \cdot 0 = 0$. So, $b = 0$. $\qquad \square$

    This is **not** still true if we replace "field" by "ring." $(C_4, +, \cdot)$ is a counterexample (clock arithmetic with a 4-hour clock). Here are the addition and multiplication tables:

+	0	1	2	3
0	0	1	2	3
1	1	2	3	0
2	2	3	0	1
3	3	0	1	2

$\cdot$	0	1	2	3
0	0	0	0	0
1	0	1	2	3
2	0	2	0	2
3	0	3	2	1

    Observe that in this ring, $2 \cdot 2 = 0$.

   (v)   Let $a \in R$. Then $-1a + a = -1a + 1a = (-1 + 1)a = 0 \cdot a = 0$ (by Theorem 2.14). So, $-1a$ is the additive inverse of a. Thus, $-1a = -a$. $\qquad \square$

   (vi) $(-1)(-1) + (-1) = (-1)(-1) + (-1) \cdot 1 = (-1)(-1 + 1) = (-1)(0) = 0$ (by Theorem 2.14). So, $(-1)(-1)$ is the additive inverse of -1. Therefore, $(-1)(-1) = -(-1)$. $\qquad \square$

8. Let $(F, +, \cdot)$ be a field with $\mathbb{N} \subseteq F$. Prove that $\mathbb{Q} \subseteq F$.

Proof: Let $n \in \mathbb{Z}$. If $n \in \mathbb{N}$, then $n \in F$ because $\mathbb{N} \subseteq F$. If $n \notin \mathbb{N}$, then $-n \in \mathbb{N}$. So, $-n \in F$. Since F is a field, we have $n = -(-n) \in F$. For each $n \in \mathbb{Z}^*$, $\frac{1}{n} = n^{-1} \in F$ because $n \in F$ and the multiplicative inverse property holds in F. Now, let $\frac{m}{n} \in \mathbb{Q}$. Then $m \in \mathbb{Z}$ and $n \in \mathbb{Z}^*$. Since $\mathbb{Z} \subseteq F$, $m \in F$. Since $n \in \mathbb{Z}^*$, we have $\frac{1}{n} \in F$. Therefore, $\frac{m}{n} = \frac{m \cdot 1}{1 \cdot n} = \frac{m}{1} \cdot \frac{1}{n} = m\left(\frac{1}{n}\right) \in F$ because F is closed under multiplication. Since $\frac{m}{n}$ was an arbitrary element of $\mathbb{Q}$, we see that $\mathbb{Q} \subseteq F$. $\qquad\square$

9. Let $\mathbb{F}$ be a field. Prove that F^n is a vector space over F.

Proof: We first prove that $(F^n, +)$ is a commutative group.

(Closure) Let $(a_1, a_2, \ldots, a_n), (b_1, b_2, \ldots, b_n) \in F^n$. Then $a_1, a_2, \ldots, a_n, b_1, b_2, \ldots, b_n \in F$. By definition, $(a_1, a_2, \ldots, a_n) + (b_1, b_2, \ldots, b_n) = (a_1 + b_1, a_2 + b_2, \ldots, a_n + b_n)$. Since F is closed under addition, $a_1 + b_1, a_2 + b_2, \ldots, a_n + b_n \in F$. Therefore, $(a_1, a_2, \ldots, a_n) + (b_1, b_2, \ldots, b_n) \in F^n$.

(Associativity) Let $(a_1, a_2, \ldots, a_n), (b_1, b_2, \ldots, b_n), (c_1, c_2, \ldots, c_n) \in F^n$. Since addition is associative in F, we have

$$[(a_1, a_2, \ldots, a_n) + (b_1, b_2, \ldots, b_n)] + (c_1, c_2, \ldots, c_n) = (a_1 + b_1, a_2 + b_2, \ldots, a_n + b_n) + (c_1, c_2, \ldots, c_n)$$
$$= ((a_1 + b_1) + c_1, (a_2 + b_2) + c_2, \ldots, (a_n + b_n) + c_n)$$
$$= (a_1 + (b_1 + c_1), a_2 + (b_2 + c_2), \ldots, a_n + (b_n + c_n))$$
$$= (a_1, a_2, \ldots, a_n) + (b_1 + c_1, b_2 + c_2, \ldots, b_n + c_n)$$
$$= (a_1, a_2, \ldots, a_n) + [(b_1, b_2, \ldots, b_n) + (c_1, c_2, \ldots, c_n)].$$

(Commutativity) Let $(a_1, a_2, \ldots, a_n), (b_1, b_2, \ldots, b_n) \in F^n$. Since addition is commutative in F, we have

$$(a_1, a_2, \ldots, a_n) + (b_1, b_2, \ldots, b_n) = (a_1 + b_1, a_2 + b_2, \ldots, a_n + b_n) = (b_1 + a_1, b_2 + a_2, \ldots, b_n + a_n)$$
$$= (b_1, b_2, \ldots, b_n) + (a_1, a_2, \ldots, a_n).$$

(Identity) We show that $(0, 0, \ldots, 0)$ is an additive identity for F^n. Let $(a_1, a_2, \ldots, a_n) \in F^n$. Since 0 is an additive identity for F, we have

$$(0, 0, \ldots, 0) + (a_1, a_2, \ldots, a_n) = (0 + a_1, 0 + a_2, \ldots, 0 + a_n) = (a_1, a_2, \ldots, a_n).$$
$$(a_1, a_2, \ldots, a_n) + (0, 0, \ldots, 0) = (a_1 + 0, a_2 + 0, \ldots, a_n + 0) = (a_1, a_2, \ldots, a_n).$$

(Inverse) Let $(a_1, a_2, \ldots, a_n) \in F^n$. Then $a_1, a_2, \ldots, a_n \in F$. Since F has the additive inverse property, $-a_1, -a_2, \ldots, -a_n \in F$. So, $(-a_1, -a_2, \ldots, -a_n) \in F^n$ and

$$(a_1, a_2, \ldots, a_n) + (-a_1, -a_2, \ldots, -a_n) = (a_1 - a_1, a_2 - a_2, \ldots, a_n - a_n) = (0, 0, \ldots, 0).$$
$$(-a_1, -a_2, \ldots, -a_n) + (a_1, a_2, \ldots, a_n) = (-a_1 + a_1, -a_2 + a_2, \ldots, -a_n + a_n) = (0, 0, \ldots, 0).$$

Now, let's prove that F^n has the remaining vector space properties.

(Closure under scalar multiplication) Let $k \in F$ and let $(a_1, a_2, \ldots, a_n) \in F^n$. Then $a_1, a_2, \ldots, a_n \in F$. By definition, $k(a_1, a_2, \ldots, a_n) = (ka_1, ka_2, \ldots, ka_n)$. Since F is closed under multiplication, $ka_1, ka_2, \ldots, ka_n \in F$. Therefore, $k(a_1, a_2, \ldots, a_n) \in F^n$.

(Scalar multiplication identity) Let 1 be the multiplicative identity of F and let $(a_1, a_2, \ldots, a_n) \in F^n$. Then $1(a_1, a_2, \ldots, a_n) = (1a_1, 1a_2, \ldots, 1a_n) = (a_1, a_2, \ldots, a_n)$.

(Associativity of scalar multiplication) Let $j, k \in F$ and $(a_1, a_2, \ldots, a_n) \in F^n$. Then since multiplication is associative in F, we have

$$(jk)(a_1, a_2, \ldots, a_n) = \left((jk)a_1, (jk)a_2, \ldots, (jk)a_n\right) = (j(ka_1), j(ka_2), \ldots, j(ka_n))$$
$$= j(ka_1, ka_2, \ldots, ka_n) = j\left(k(a_1, a_2, \ldots, a_n)\right).$$

(Distributivity of 1 scalar over 2 vectors) Let $k \in F$ and $(a_1, a_2, \ldots, a_n), (b_1, b_2, \ldots, b_n) \in F^n$. Since multiplication is distributive over addition in F, we have

$$k\left((a_1, a_2, \ldots, a_n) + (b_1, b_2, \ldots, b_n)\right) = k\left((a_1 + b_1, a_2 + b_2, \ldots, a_n + b_n)\right)$$
$$= \left(k(a_1 + b_1), k(a_2 + b_2), \ldots, k(a_n + b_n)\right) = \left((ka_1 + kb_1), (ka_2 + kb_2), \ldots, (ka_n + kb_n)\right)$$
$$= (ka_1, ka_2, \ldots, ka_n) + (kb_1, kb_2, \ldots, kb_n) = k(a_1, a_2, \ldots, a_n) + k(b_1, b_2, \ldots, b_n).$$

(Distributivity of 2 scalars over 1 vector) Let $j, k \in F$ and $(a_1, a_2, \ldots, a_n) \in F^n$. Since multiplication is distributive over addition in F, we have

$$(j + k)(a_1, a_2, \ldots, a_n) = \left((j + k)a_1, (j + k)a_2, \ldots, (j + k)a_n\right)$$
$$= (ja_1 + ka_1, ja_2 + ka_2, \ldots, ja_n + ka_n) = (ja_1, ja_2, \ldots, ja_n) + (ka_1, ka_2, \ldots, ka_n)$$
$$= j(a_1, a_2, \ldots, a_n) + k(a_1, a_2, \ldots, a_n).$$

10. Let V be a vector space over $\mathbb{F}$. Prove each of the following:

    (i)   For every $v \in V$, $-(-v) = v$.

    (ii)   For every $v \in V$, $0v = 0$.

    (iii) For every $k \in \mathbb{F}$, $k \cdot 0 = 0$.

    (iv) For every $v \in V$, $-1v = -v$.

Proofs:

    (i)   Since $-v$ is the additive inverse of v, we have $v + (-v) = -v + v = 0$. But this equation also says that v is the additive inverse of $-v$. So, $-(-v) = v$.   □

    (ii)   Let $v \in V$. Then $0v = (0 + 0)v = 0v + 0v$. So, we have

$$0 = -0v + 0v = -0v + (0v + 0v) = (-0v + 0v) + 0v = 0 + 0v = 0v. \quad □$$

    (iii) Let $k \in \mathbb{F}$. Then $k \cdot 0 = k(0 + 0) = k \cdot 0 + k \cdot 0$. So, we have

$$0 = -k \cdot 0 + k \cdot 0 = -k \cdot 0 + (k \cdot 0 + k \cdot 0) = (-k \cdot 0 + k \cdot 0) + k \cdot 0 = 0 + k \cdot 0 = k \cdot 0. \quad □$$

    (iv) Let $v \in V$. Then we have $v + (-1v) = 1v + (-1v) = \left(1 + (-1)\right)v = 0v = 0$ by (ii) and we have $-1v + v = -1v + 1v = (-1 + 1)v = 0v = 0$ again by (ii). So, $-1v = -v$.   □

11. Assume that a group $(G, \star)$ of order 4 exists with $G = \{e, a, b, c\}$, where e is the identity, $a^2 = b$ and $b^2 = e$. Construct the table for the operation of such a group.

Solution: Since $e \star x = x \star e = x$ for all x in the group, we can easily fill out the first row and the first column of the table.

$\star$	e	a	b	c
e	e	a	b	c
a	a			
b	b			
c	c			

We now add in $a \star a = a^2 = b$ and $b \star b = b^2 = e$.

$\star$	e	a	b	c
e	e	a	b	c
a	a	b	$\boxdot$	
b	b		e	
c	c			

Now, the entry labeled with $\boxdot$ cannot be a or b because a and b appear in that row. It also cannot be e because e appears in that column. Therefore, the entry labeled with $\boxdot$ must be c. It follows that the entry to the right of $\boxdot$ must be e, and the entry at the bottom of the column must be a.

$\star$	e	a	b	c
e	e	a	b	c
a	a	b	c	e
b	b	$\odot$	e	
c	c		a	

Now, the entry labeled with $\odot$ cannot be b or e because b and e appear in that row. It also cannot be a because a appears in that column. Therefore, the entry labeled with $\odot$ must be c. The rest of the table is then determined.

$\star$	e	a	b	c
e	e	a	b	c
a	a	b	c	e
b	b	c	e	a
c	c	e	a	b

Note: Observe that in the table we produced, $b = a \star a = a^2$ and $c = b \star a = a^2 \star a = a^3$. So, another way to draw the table is as follows:

$\star$	e	a	a^2	a^3
e	e	a	a^2	a^3
a	a	a^2	a^3	e
a^2	a^2	a^3	e	a
a^3	a^3	e	a	a^2

This group is the **cyclic group of order 4**.

12. Let A be a nonempty set. Prove that $(\mathcal{P}(A),\ \cap)$ is a commutative monoid that is not a group.

Proof: Let $X, Y \in \mathcal{P}(A)$, then $X \subseteq A$ nd $Y \subseteq A$. If $x \in X \cap Y$, then $x \in X$ and $x \in Y$. In particular, $x \in X$. Since $X \subseteq A$, $x \in A$. So, $\forall x (x \in X \cap Y \to x \in A)$. It follows that $X \cap Y \subseteq A$, and therefore, $X \cap Y \in \mathcal{P}(A)$. This shows that $\cap$ is a binary operation on $\mathcal{P}(A)$. By parts (ii) and (iii) of Problem 12 from Problem Set 1, $\cap$ is commutative and associative in $\mathcal{P}(A)$. Also, A is an identity for $(\mathcal{P}(A),\ \cap)$ because if $X \in \mathcal{P}(A)$, then $X \cap A = X$ and $A \cap X = X$. It follows that $(\mathcal{P}(A),\ \cap)$ is a commutative monoid. To see that $(\mathcal{P}(A),\ \cap)$ is **not** a group, note that $\emptyset$ has no inverse in $\mathcal{P}(A)$. Indeed, if $B \in \mathcal{P}(A)$, then by Theorem 1.10, $\emptyset \subseteq B$. So, by Problem 24 in Problem Set 1, $B \cap \emptyset = \emptyset \neq A$. $\qquad\square$

13. Let $(R, +,\ \cdot)$ be a ring and define addition and multiplication on $R \times R$ componentwise. That is, for $a, b, c, d \in R$, we define addition and multiplication by $(a, b) + (c, d) = (a + c, b + d)$ and $(a, b)(c, d) = (ac, bd)$. Prove that $(R \times R, +,\ \cdot)$ is a ring. If $(R, +,\ \cdot)$ is a domain, does it follow that $(R \times R, +,\ \cdot)$ must be a domain?

Proof: Let $(a, b), (c, d) \in R \times R$. Then $a, b, c, d \in R$. Since R is closed under addition and multiplication, $a + c, b + d, ac, bd \in R$. So, $(a + c, b + d), (ac, bd) \in R \times R$. So, $R \times R$ is closed under addition and multiplication.

Let $(a, b), (c, d), (e, f) \in R \times R$. Since addition and multiplication are associative in R, we have

$$(a, b) + \big((c, d) + (e, f)\big) = (a, b) + (c + e, d + f) = \big(a + (c + e), b + (d + f)\big)$$
$$= \big((a + c) + e, (b + d) + f\big) = (a + c, b + d) + (e, f) = \big((a, b) + (c, d)\big) + (e, f).$$
$$(a, b) \cdot \big((c, d) \cdot (e, f)\big) = (a, b) \cdot (ce, df) = \big(a(ce), b(df)\big)$$
$$= \big((ac)e, (bd)f\big) = (ac, bd) \cdot (e, f) = \big((a, b) \cdot (c, d)\big) \cdot (e, f).$$

So, addition and multiplication are associative in $R \times R$.

For all $(a, b) \in R \times R$, we have

$$(0, 0) + (a, b) = (0 + a, 0 + b) = (a, b) \text{ and } (a, b) + (0, 0) = (a + 0, b + 0) = (a, b).$$
$$(1, 1) \cdot (a, b) = (1a, 1b) = (a, b) \text{ and } (a, b) \cdot (1, 1) = (a \cdot 1, b \cdot 1) = (a, b).$$

So, $(0, 0)$ is an additive identity and $(1, 1)$ is a multiplicative identity.

For all $(a, b) \in R \times R$, we have

$$(a, b) + (-a, -b) = (a - a, b - b) = (0, 0) \text{ and } (-a, -b) + (a, b) = (-a + a, -b + b) = (0, 0).$$

So, $(-a,-b)$ is an additive inverse of (a,b).

Let $(a,b),(c,d) \in R \times R$. Since addition is commutative in R, we have

$$(a,b) + (c,d) = (a+c, b+d) = (c+a, d+b) = (c,d) + (a,b).$$

So, addition is commutative in $R \times R$.

Therefore, $(R \times R, +, \cdot)$ is a ring.

Let $(a,b),(c,d),(e,f) \in R \times R$. Since multiplication is distributive over addition in R, we have

$$(a,b)\big((c,d) + (e,f)\big) = (a,b)(c+e, d+f) = \big(a(c+e), b(d+f)\big)$$
$$= (ac+ae, bd+bf) = (ac, bd) + (ae, bf) = (a,b)(c,d) + (a,b)(e,f).$$

So, multiplication is distributive over addition in $R \times R$.

If $R \neq \{0\}$, then $(R \times R, +, \cdot)$ will **not** be a domain. To see this, let $a \in R$ with $a \neq 0$. Then we have $(a,0),(0,a) \in R \times R$ and $(a,0) \cdot (0,a) = (a \cdot 0, 0 \cdot a) = (0,0)$. Since $(a,0),(0,a) \neq (0,0)$, we see that $(a,0)$ and $(0,a)$ are zero divisors. $\square$

14. Let $(F, +, \cdot)$ be a field. Prove that $(F, \cdot)$ is a commutative monoid.

Proof: Let $(F, +, \cdot)$ be a field. Then $\cdot$ is a binary operation on F and $(F^*, \cdot)$ is a commutative group.

Let $x, y \in F$. If $x, y \in F^*$, then $xy = yx$. If $x = 0$, then $xy = 0y = 0$ and $yx = y \cdot 0 = 0$ by Theorem 2.14. If $y = 0$, then $xy = x \cdot 0 = 0$ and $yx = 0x = 0$ by Theorem 2.14. In all cases, we have $xy = yx$.

Next, let $x, y, z \in F$. If $x, y, z \in F^*$, then $(xy)z = x(yz)$. If $x = 0$, then $(xy)z = (0y)z = 0z = 0$ and $x(yz) = 0(yz) = 0$. If $y = 0$, then $(xy)z = (x \cdot 0)z = 0z = 0$ and $x(yz) = x(0z) = x \cdot 0 = 0$. If $z = 0$, we have $(xy)z = (xy) \cdot 0 = 0$ and $x(yz) = x(y \cdot 0) = x \cdot 0 = 0$. In all cases, we have $(xy)z = x(yz)$.

Let $x \in F$. If $x \in F^*$, then $1x = x \cdot 1 = x$. If $x = 0$, then by Theorem 2.14, $1x = 1 \cdot 0 = 0$ and $x \cdot 1 = 0 \cdot 1 = 0$. In all cases, we have $1x = x \cdot 1 = x$.

Therefore, $(F, \cdot)$ is a commutative monoid. $\square$

LEVEL 4

15. Let $(G, \star)$ be a group with $a, b \in G$, and let a^{-1} and b^{-1} be the inverses of a and b, respectively. Prove

   (i) $(a \star b)^{-1} = b^{-1} \star a^{-1}$.

   (ii) the inverse of a^{-1} is a.

Proof of (i): Let $a, b \in G$. Then we have

$$(a \star b) \star (b^{-1} \star a^{-1}) = a \star \big(b \star (b^{-1} \star a^{-1})\big) = a \star \big((b \star b^{-1}) \star a^{-1}\big) = a \star (e \star a^{-1}) = a \star a^{-1} = e$$

So, $(a \star b)^{-1} = (b^{-1} \star a^{-1})$. $\qquad\square$

Notes: (1) For the first and second equalities we used the associativity of $\star$ in G.

(2) For the third equality, we used the inverse property of $\star$ in G.

(3) For the fourth equality, we used the identity property of $\star$ in G.

(4) For the last equality, we again used the inverse property of $\star$ in G.

(5) Since multiplying $a \star b$ by $b^{-1} \star a^{-1}$ results in the identity element e, it follows that $b^{-1} \star a^{-1}$ is the inverse of $a \star b$.

(6) By Note 4 following Theorem 2.9, we get $(b^{-1} \star a^{-1}) \star (a \star b) = e$ for free.

Proof of (ii): Let $a \in G$. Since a^{-1} is the inverse of a, we have $a \star a^{-1} = a^{-1} \star a = e$. But this sequence of equations also says that a is the inverse of a^{-1}. $\qquad\square$

16. Let $(G, \star)$ be a group such that $a^2 = e$ for all $a \in G$. Prove that $(G, \star)$ is commutative.

Proof: Let $a, b \in G$. Then $(a \star a) \star (b \star b) = a^2 \star b^2 = e \star e = e = (ab)^2 = (a \star b) \star (a \star b)$. So, we have $(a \star a) \star (b \star b) = (a \star b) \star (a \star b)$.

We multiply on the left by a^{-1} and on the right by b^{-1} to get

$$a^{-1} \star (a \star a \star b \star b) \star b^{-1} = a^{-1} \star (a \star b \star a \star b) \star b^{-1}$$
$$(a^{-1} \star a) \star a \star b \star (b \star b^{-1}) = (a^{-1} \star a) \star b \star a \star (b \star b^{-1})$$
$$(e \star a) \star (b \star e) = (e \star b) \star (a \star e)$$
$$a \star b = b \star a$$
$\qquad\square$

Note: To make the proof less tedious, we have omitted some of the parentheses starting in the fourth line. The associativity of $\star$ allows us to do this. In general, there are two possible meanings for the expression $x \star y \star z$. It could mean $(x \star y) \star z$ or it could mean $x \star (y \star z)$. Since both meanings produce the same result (by associativity), we can simply write $x \star y \star z$ without worrying about the notation being unclear.

We have done this several times in the proof above. For example, we wrote $a \star a \star b \star b$ in the fourth line. This could have multiple meanings, but all those meanings lead to the same result.

17. Let $\mathbb{Z}[x]_n = \{a_n x^n + a_{n-1} x^{n-1} + \cdots + a_1 x + a_0 \mid a_0, a_1, \ldots, a_n \in \mathbb{Z}\}$. In other words, $\mathbb{Z}[x]_n$ consists of all polynomials of degree at most n with integer coefficients. Prove that $(\mathbb{Z}[x]_n, +)$ is a commutative group for $n = 0, 1,$ and 2, where addition is defined in the "usual way." What if we replace "polynomials of degree at most n" by polynomials of degree exactly n." Do we still get a commutative group?

Proof: $\mathbb{Z}[x]_0 = \{a_0 \mid a_0 \in \mathbb{Z}\} = \mathbb{Z}$, and we already know that $(\mathbb{Z}, +)$ is a group.

$\mathbb{Z}[x]_1 = \{a_1 x + a_0 \mid a_0, a_1 \in \mathbb{Z}\}$. Let $a_1 x + a_0, b_1 x + b_0 \in \mathbb{Z}[x]_1$. We have

$$(a_1 x + a_0) + (b_1 x + b_0) = (a_1 + b_1)x + (a_0 + b_0).$$

Since $\mathbb{Z}$ is closed under addition, $a_1 + b_1, a_0 + b_0 \in \mathbb{Z}$. Therefore, $\mathbb{Z}[x]_1$ is closed under addition.

Simple computations show that addition is associative in $\mathbb{Z}[x]_1$, $0 = 0x + 0$ is an additive identity in $\mathbb{Z}[x]_1$, and the additive inverse of $a_1 x + a_0$ is $-a_1 x - a_0$. One more simple computation can be used to verify that addition is commutative in $\mathbb{Z}[x]_1$. So, $(\mathbb{Z}[x]_1, +)$ is a commutative group.

$\mathbb{Z}[x]_2 = \{a_2 x^2 + a_1 x + a_0 \mid a_0, a_1, a_2 \in \mathbb{Z}\}$. Let $a_2 x^2 + a_1 x + a_0, b_2 x^2 + b_1 x + b_0 \in \mathbb{Z}[x]_2$. We have

$$(a_2 x^2 + a_1 x + a_0) + (b_2 x^2 + b_1 x + b_0) = (a_2 + b_2)x^2 + (a_1 + b_1)x + (a_0 + b_0).$$

Since $\mathbb{Z}$ is closed under addition, $a_2 + b_2, a_1 + b_1, a_0 + b_0 \in \mathbb{Z}$. Therefore, $\mathbb{Z}[x]_2$ is closed under addition.

Simple computations show that addition is associative in $\mathbb{Z}[x]_2$, $0 = 0x^2 + 0x + 0$ is an additive identity in $\mathbb{Z}[x]_2$, and the additive inverse of $a_2 x^2 + a_1 x + a_0$ is $-a_2 x^2 - a_1 x - a_0$. One more simple computation can be used to verify that addition is commutative in $\mathbb{Z}[x]_2$. So, $(\mathbb{Z}[x]_2, +)$ is a commutative group.

If we replace "polynomials of degree at most n" by "polynomials of degree exactly n," we do not get a group. Closure is no longer satisfied. For example, $x + 1$ and $-x$ have degree 1, whereas the sum $(x + 1) + (-x) = 1$ has degree 0. □

LEVEL 5

18. Prove that there are exactly two groups of order 4, up to renaming the elements.

Solution: Let $G = \{e, a, b, c\}$. We will run through the possible cases.

Case 1: Suppose that $a^2 = e$.

Since $e \star x = x \star e = x$ for all x in the group, we can easily fill out the first row, the first column, and one more entry of the table.

$\star$	e	a	b	c
e	e	a	b	c
a	a	e	$\boxdot$	
b	b	$\boxdot$		
c	c			

Each of the entries labeled with $\boxdot$ cannot be a, e, or b (Why?), and so they must be c. So, we get the following:

$\star$	e	a	b	c
e	e	a	b	c
a	a	e	c	b
b	b	c		
c	c	b		

33

Now, if $b^2 = e$, the rest of the table is determined:

$\star$	e	a	b	c
e	e	a	b	c
a	a	e	c	b
b	b	c	e	a
c	c	b	a	e

This table gives a group $(G,\star)$ called the **Klein four group**.

If $b^2 = a$, the rest of the table is also determined:

$\star$	e	a	b	c
e	e	a	b	c
a	a	e	c	b
b	b	c	a	e
c	c	b	e	a

This table gives a group $(G,\star)$ called the **Cyclic group of order 4**.

Observe that we cannot have $b^2 = b$ or $b^2 = c$ because b and c already appear in the row (and column) corresponding to b.

$\star$	e	a	b	c
e	e	a	b	c
a	a	e	c	b
b	b	c	~~b,c~~	
c	c	b		

Case 2: Suppose that $a^2 \neq e$.

If $b^2 = e$ or $c^2 = e$, then by renaming elements, we get the same groups in Case 1. So, we may assume that $a^2 \neq e$, $b^2 \neq e$, and $c^2 \neq e$.

So, a, a^2, and a^3 are distinct elements. If $a^3 \neq e$, then $a^4 = e$, and so, $(a^2)^2 = e$. But a^2 must be equal to either b or c. So, $b^2 = e$ or $c^2 = e$, contrary to our assumption.

It follows that $a^3 = e$. So, $a \star a^2 = e$. Therefore, a and a^2 are inverses of each other. If $a^2 = b$, then c must be its own inverse. So, $c^2 = c \star c = e$, contrary to our assumption. Similarly, if $a^2 = c$, then b must be its own inverse. So, $b^2 = b \star b = e$, contrary to our assumption.

It follows that there are exactly 2 groups of order 4, up to renaming the elements. These 2 groups are the **Klein four group** and the **Cyclic group of order 4**. $\square$

19. Prove that $(\mathbb{Q}, +, \cdot)$ is a field.

Proof: We first prove that $(\mathbb{Q}, +)$ is a commutative group.

(Closure) Let $x, y \in \mathbb{Q}$. Then there exist $a, c \in \mathbb{Z}$ and $b, d \in \mathbb{Z}^*$ such that $x = \frac{a}{b}$ and $y = \frac{c}{d}$. We have $x + y = \frac{a}{b} + \frac{c}{d} = \frac{ad+bc}{bd}$. Since $\mathbb{Z}$ is closed under multiplication, $ad \in \mathbb{Z}$ and $bc \in \mathbb{Z}$. Since $\mathbb{Z}$ is closed under addition, $ad + bc \in \mathbb{Z}$. Since $\mathbb{Z}^*$ is closed under multiplication, $bd \in \mathbb{Z}^*$. Therefore, $x + y \in \mathbb{Q}$.

(Associativity) Let $x, y, z \in \mathbb{Q}$. Then there exist $a, c, e \in \mathbb{Z}$ and $b, d, f \in \mathbb{Z}^*$ such that $x = \frac{a}{b}$, $y = \frac{c}{d}$, and $z = \frac{e}{f}$. Since multiplication and addition are associative in $\mathbb{Z}$, multiplication is (both left and right) distributive over addition in $\mathbb{Z}$ (see the Note below), and multiplication is associative in $\mathbb{Z}^*$, we have

$$(x + y) + z = \left(\frac{a}{b} + \frac{c}{d}\right) + \frac{e}{f} = \frac{ad + bc}{bd} + \frac{e}{f} = \frac{(ad + bc)f + (bd)e}{(bd)f} = \frac{((ad)f + (bc)f) + (bd)e}{(bd)f}$$

$$= \frac{a(df) + (b(cf) + b(de))}{b(df)} = \frac{a(df) + b(cf + de)}{b(df)} = \frac{a}{b} + \frac{cf + de}{df} = \frac{a}{b} + \left(\frac{c}{d} + \frac{e}{f}\right) = x + (y + z).$$

(Identity) Let $\overline{0} = \frac{0}{1}$. We show that $\overline{0}$ is an identity for $(\mathbb{Q}, +)$. Let $x \in \mathbb{Q}$. Then there exist $a \in \mathbb{Z}$ and $b \in \mathbb{Z}^*$ such that $x = \frac{a}{b}$. Since 0 is an identity for $\mathbb{Z}$, and $0 \cdot x = x \cdot 0 = 0$ for all $x \in \mathbb{Z}$, we have

$$x + \overline{0} = \frac{a}{b} + \frac{0}{1} = \frac{a \cdot 1 + b \cdot 0}{b \cdot 1} = \frac{a + 0}{b} = \frac{a}{b} = x \text{ and } \overline{0} + x = \frac{0}{1} + \frac{a}{b} = \frac{0b + 1a}{1b} = \frac{0 + a}{b} = \frac{a}{b} = x.$$

(Inverse) Let $x \in \mathbb{Q}$. Then there exist $a \in \mathbb{Z}$ and $b \in \mathbb{Z}^*$ such that $x = \frac{a}{b}$. Let $y = \frac{-1a}{b}$. Since $\mathbb{Z}$ is closed under multiplication, $-1a \in \mathbb{Z}$. So, $y \in \mathbb{Q}$. Since multiplication is associative and commutative in $\mathbb{Z}$ and $(-1)n = -n$ for all $n \in \mathbb{Z}$, we have

$$x + y = \frac{a}{b} + \frac{-1a}{b} = \frac{ab + b(-1a)}{b \cdot b} = \frac{ab + (-1a)b}{b^2} = \frac{ab + (-1)(ab)}{b^2} = \frac{ab - ab}{b^2} = \frac{0}{b^2} = \overline{0}$$

$$y + x = \frac{-1a}{b} + \frac{a}{b} = \frac{(-1a)b + ba}{b \cdot b} = \frac{-1(ab) + ab}{b^2} = \frac{-ab + ab}{b^2} = \frac{0}{b^2} = \overline{0}$$

So, y is the additive inverse of x.

(Commutativity) Let $x, y \in \mathbb{Q}$. Then there exist $a, c \in \mathbb{Z}$ and $b, d \in \mathbb{Z}^*$ such that $x = \frac{a}{b}$ and $y = \frac{c}{d}$. Since multiplication and addition are commutative in $\mathbb{Z}$, and multiplication is commutative in $\mathbb{Z}^*$, we have

$$x + y = \frac{a}{b} + \frac{c}{d} = \frac{ad + bc}{bd} = \frac{bc + ad}{db} = \frac{cb + da}{db} = \frac{c}{d} + \frac{a}{b} = y + x.$$

So, $(\mathbb{Q}, +)$ is a commutative group.

We next prove that $(\mathbb{Q} \setminus \{0\}, \cdot)$ is a commutative group.

(Closure) Let $x, y \in \mathbb{Q}^*$. Then there exist $a, b, c, d \in \mathbb{Z}^*$ such that $x = \frac{a}{b}$ and $y = \frac{c}{d}$. We have $xy = \frac{a}{b} \cdot \frac{c}{d} = \frac{ac}{bd}$. Since $\mathbb{Z}^*$ is closed under multiplication, $ac, bd \in \mathbb{Z}^*$. Therefore, $xy \in \mathbb{Q}^*$.

(Associativity) Let $x, y, z \in \mathbb{Q}^*$. Then there exist $a, b, c, d, e, f \in \mathbb{Z}^*$ such that $x = \frac{a}{b}$, $y = \frac{c}{d}$, and $z = \frac{e}{f}$. Since multiplication is associative in $\mathbb{Z}^*$, we have

$$(xy)z = \left(\frac{a}{b} \cdot \frac{c}{d}\right)\frac{e}{f} = \left(\frac{ac}{bd}\right)\frac{e}{f} = \frac{(ac)e}{(bd)f} = \frac{a(ce)}{b(df)} = \frac{a}{b}\left(\frac{ce}{df}\right) = \frac{a}{b}\left(\frac{c}{d} \cdot \frac{e}{f}\right) = x(yz).$$

(Identity) Let $\overline{1} = \frac{1}{1}$. We show that $\overline{1}$ is an identity for $(\mathbb{Q}^*, \cdot)$. Let $x \in \mathbb{Q}^*$. Then there exist $a, b \in \mathbb{Z}^*$ such that $x = \frac{a}{b}$. Since 1 is an identity for $\mathbb{Z}^*$, we have

$$x \cdot \overline{1} = \frac{a}{b} \cdot \frac{1}{1} = \frac{a \cdot 1}{b \cdot 1} = \frac{a}{b} = x \text{ and } \overline{1}x = \frac{1}{1} \cdot \frac{a}{b} = \frac{1a}{1b} = \frac{a}{b} = x.$$

(Inverse) Let $x \in \mathbb{Q}^*$. Then there exist $a, b \in \mathbb{Z}^*$ such that $x = \frac{a}{b}$. Let $y = \frac{b}{a}$. Then $y \in \mathbb{Q}^*$ (note that $a \neq 0$). Since multiplication is commutative in $\mathbb{Z}^*$, we have

$$xy = \frac{a}{b} \cdot \frac{b}{a} = \frac{ab}{ba} = \frac{ab}{ab} = \frac{1}{1} = \overline{1}.$$

So, y is the multiplicative inverse of x.

(Commutativity) Let $x, y \in \mathbb{Q}^*$. Then there exist $a, b, c, d \in \mathbb{Z}^*$ such that $x = \frac{a}{b}$ and $y = \frac{c}{d}$. Since multiplication is commutative in $\mathbb{Z}^*$, we have

$$xy = \frac{a}{b} \cdot \frac{c}{d} = \frac{ac}{bd} = \frac{ca}{db} = \frac{c}{d} \cdot \frac{a}{b} = yx.$$

So, $(\mathbb{Q}^*, \cdot)$ is a commutative group.

Now we prove that multiplication is distributive over addition in $\mathbb{Q}$.

(Distributivity) Let $x, y, z \in \mathbb{Q}$. Then there exist $a, c, e \in \mathbb{Z}$ and $b, d, f \in \mathbb{Z}^*$ such that $x = \frac{a}{b}$, $y = \frac{c}{d}$, and $z = \frac{e}{f}$. Let's start with left distributivity.

$$x(y + z) = \frac{a}{b}\left(\frac{c}{d} + \frac{e}{f}\right) = \frac{a}{b}\left(\frac{cf + de}{df}\right) = \frac{a(cf + de)}{b(df)}$$

$$xy + xz = \frac{a}{b} \cdot \frac{c}{d} + \frac{a}{b} \cdot \frac{e}{f} = \frac{ac}{bd} + \frac{ae}{bf} = \frac{(ac)(bf) + (bd)(ae)}{(bd)(bf)}$$

We need to verify that $\frac{(ac)(bf)+(bd)(ae)}{(bd)(bf)} = \frac{a(cf+de)}{b(df)}$.

Since $\mathbb{Z}$ is a ring, $(ac)(bf) + (bd)(ae) = bacf + bade = ba(cf + de)$ (see Note 1 below).

Since multiplication is associative and commutative in $\mathbb{Z}^*$, we have

$$(bd)(bf) = b\big(d(bf)\big) = b\big((db)f\big) = b\big((bd)f\big) = b\big(b(df)\big).$$

So, $\frac{(ac)(bf)+(bd)(ae)}{(bd)(bf)} = \frac{ba(cf+de)}{b(b(df))} = \frac{a(cf+de)}{b(df)}$.

For right distributivity, we can use left distributivity together with the commutativity of multiplication in $\mathbb{Q}$.

$$(y + z)x = x(y + z) = xy + xz = yx + zx \qquad \square$$

Notes: (1) We skipped many steps when verifying $(ac)(bf) + (bd)(ae) = ba(cf + de)$. The dedicated reader may want to verify this equality carefully, making sure to use only the fact that $\mathbb{Z}$ is a ring, and making a note of which ring property is being used at each step.

(2) In the very last step of the proof, we cancelled one b in the numerator of the fraction with b in the denominator of the fraction. In general, if $j \in \mathbb{Z}$ and $m, k \in \mathbb{Z}^*$, then $\frac{mj}{mk} = \frac{j}{k}$. To verify that this is true, simply observe that since $\mathbb{Z}$ is a ring, we have $(mj)k = m(jk) = m(kj) = (mk)j$.

(3) There is another issue here. It's not obvious that the definitions of addition and multiplication are even well-defined (see Lesson 3 for details).

First, suppose that $\frac{a}{b} = \frac{a'}{b'}$ and $\frac{c}{d} = \frac{c'}{d'}$. We need to check that $\frac{a}{b} + \frac{c}{d} = \frac{a'}{b'} + \frac{c'}{d'}$, or equivalently, $\frac{ad+bc}{bd} = \frac{a'd'+b'c'}{b'd'}$.

Since $\frac{a}{b} = \frac{a'}{b'}$, we have $ab' = ba'$. Since $\frac{c}{d} = \frac{c'}{d'}$, we have $cd' = dc'$. Now, since $ab' = ba'$, $cd' = dc'$, multiplication is commutative and associative in $\mathbb{Z}$, and multiplication is distributive over addition in $\mathbb{Z}$, we have

$$(ad + bc)(b'd') = adb'd' + bcb'd' = ab'dd' + cd'bb' = ba'dd' + dc'bb'$$
$$= bda'd' + bdb'c' = (bd)(a'd' + b'c').$$

Therefore, $\frac{ad+bc}{bd} = \frac{a'd'+b'c'}{b'd'}$, as desired.

We also need to check that $\frac{a}{b} \cdot \frac{c}{d} = \frac{a'}{b'} \cdot \frac{c'}{d'}$, or equivalently, $\frac{ac}{bd} = \frac{a'c'}{b'd'}$.

Since $\frac{a}{b} = \frac{a'}{b'}$, we have $ab' = ba'$. Since $\frac{c}{d} = \frac{c'}{d'}$, we have $cd' = dc'$. Now, since $ab' = ba'$, $cd' = dc'$, and multiplication is commutative and associative in $\mathbb{Z}$, we have

$$(ac)(b'd') = (ab')(cd') = (ba')(dc') = (bd)(a'c')$$

Therefore, $\frac{ac}{bd} = \frac{a'c'}{b'd'}$, as desired. $\qquad \square$

20. Prove that $(\mathbb{C}, +, \cdot)$ is a field. You may use the fact that $(\mathbb{R}, +, \cdot)$ is a field.

Proof: We first prove that $(\mathbb{C}, +)$ is a commutative group.

(Closure) Let $z, w \in \mathbb{C}$. Then there are $a, b, c, d \in \mathbb{R}$ such that $z = a + bi$ and $w = c + di$. By definition, $z + w = (a + bi) + (c + di) = (a + c) + (b + d)i$. Since $\mathbb{R}$ is closed under addition, $a + b \in \mathbb{R}$ and $c + d \in \mathbb{R}$. Therefore, $z + w \in \mathbb{C}$.

(Associativity) Let $z, w, v \in \mathbb{C}$. Then there are $a, b, c, d, e, f \in \mathbb{R}$ such that $z = a + bi, w = c + di$, and $v = e + fi$. Since addition is associative in $\mathbb{R}$, we have

$$(z + w) + v = \big((a + bi) + (c + di)\big) + (e + fi) = \big((a + c) + (b + d)i\big) + (e + fi)$$
$$= \big((a + c) + e\big) + \big((b + d) + f\big)i = \big(a + (c + e)\big) + \big(b + (d + f)\big)i$$
$$= (a + bi) + \big((c + e) + (d + f)i\big) = (a + bi) + \big((c + di) + (e + fi)\big) = z + (w + v).$$

(Commutativity) Let $z, w \in \mathbb{C}$. Then there are $a, b, c, d \in \mathbb{R}$ such that $z = a + bi$ and $w = c + di$. Since addition is commutative in $\mathbb{R}$, we have

$$z + w = (a + bi) + (c + di) = (a + c) + (b + d)i = (c + a) + (d + b)i$$
$$= (c + di) + (a + bi) = w + z.$$

(Identity) Let $\overline{0} = 0 + 0i$. We show that $\overline{0}$ is an additive identity for $\mathbb{C}$. Since $0 \in \mathbb{R}$, $\overline{0} \in \mathbb{C}$. Let $z \in \mathbb{C}$. Then there are $a, b \in \mathbb{R}$ such that $z = a + bi$. Since 0 is an additive identity in $\mathbb{R}$, we have

$$\overline{0} + z = (0 + 0i) + (a + bi) = (0 + a) + (0 + b)i = a + bi.$$
$$z + \overline{0} = (a + bi) + (0 + 0i) = (a + 0) + (b + 0)i = a + bi.$$

(Inverse) Let $z \in \mathbb{C}$. Then there are $a, b \in \mathbb{R}$ such that $z = a + bi$. Let $w = -a + (-b)i$. Then

$$z + w = (a + bi) + (-a + (-b)i) = \big(a + (-a)\big) + \big(b + (-b)\big)i = 0 + 0i = \overline{0}.$$
$$w + z = (-a + (-b)i) + (a + bi) = (-a + a) + (-b + b)i = 0 + 0i = \overline{0}.$$

We next prove that $(\mathbb{C}^*, \ \cdot)$ is a commutative group.

(Closure) Let $z, w \in \mathbb{C}^*$. Then there are $a, b, c, d \in \mathbb{R}$ such that $z = a + bi$ and $w = c + di$. By definition, $zw = (a + bi)(c + di) = (ac - bd) + (ad + bc)i$. Since $\mathbb{R}$ is closed under multiplication, we have $ac, bd, ad, bc \in \mathbb{R}$. Also, $-bd$ is the additive inverse of bd in $\mathbb{R}$. Since $\mathbb{R}$ is closed under addition, we have $ac - bd = ac + (-bd) \in \mathbb{R}$ and $ad + bc \in \mathbb{R}$. Therefore, $zw \in \mathbb{C}$.

We still need to show that $zw \neq 0$. If $zw = 0$, then $ac - bd = 0$ and $ad + bc = 0$. So, $ac = bd$ and $ad = -bc$. Multiplying each side of the last equation by c gives us $acd = -bc^2$. Replacing ac with bd on the left gives $bd^2 = -bc^2$, or equivalently, $bd^2 + bc^2 = 0$. So, $b(d^2 + c^2) = 0$. If $d^2 + c^2 = 0$, then $c = 0$ and $d = 0$, and so, $w = 0$. If $b = 0$, then $ac = 0$, and so, $a = 0$ or $c = 0$. If $a = 0$, then $z = 0$. If $c = 0$ and $a \neq 0$, then since $ad = -bc = 0$, we have $d = 0$. So, $w = 0$. So, we see that $zw = 0$ implies $z = 0$ or $w = 0$. By contrapositive, since $z, w \in \mathbb{C}^*$, we must have $zw \neq 0$, and so, $zw \in \mathbb{C}^*$.

(Associativity) Let $z, w, v \in \mathbb{C}^*$. Then there are $a, b, c, d, e, f \in \mathbb{R}$ such that $z = a + bi, w = c + di$, and $v = e + fi$. Since addition and multiplication are associative in $\mathbb{R}$, addition is commutative in $\mathbb{R}$, and multiplication is distributive over addition in $\mathbb{R}$, we have

$$(zw)v = \big((a+bi)(c+di)\big)(e+fi) = \big((ac-bd) + (ad+bc)i\big)(e+fi)$$
$$= [(ac-bd)e - (ad+bc)f] + [(ac-bd)f + (ad+bc)e]i$$
$$= (ace - bde - adf - bcf) + (acf - bdf + ade + bce)i$$
$$= (ace - adf - bcf - bde) + (acf + ade + bce - bdf)i$$
$$= [a(ce-df) - b(cf+de)] + [a(cf+de) + b(ce-df)]i$$
$$= (a+bi)\big((ce-df) + (cf+de)i\big) = (a+bi)\big((c+di)(e+fi)\big) = z(wv).$$

(Commutativity) Let $z, w \in \mathbb{C}^*$. Then there are $a, b, c, d \in \mathbb{R}$ such that $z = a + bi$ and $w = c + di$. Since addition and multiplication are commutative in $\mathbb{R}$, we have

$$zw = (a+bi)(c+di) = (ac - bd) + (ad + bc)i$$
$$= (ca - db) + (cb + da)i = (c+di)(a+bi) = wz$$

(Identity) Let $\overline{1} = 1 + 0i$. We show that $\overline{1}$ is a multiplicative identity for $\mathbb{C}^*$. Since $0, 1 \in \mathbb{R}$, $\overline{1} \in \mathbb{C}^*$. Let $z \in \mathbb{C}^*$. Then there are $a, b \in \mathbb{R}$ such that $z = a + bi$. Since 0 is an additive identity in $\mathbb{R}$, 1 is a multiplicative identity in $\mathbb{R}$, and $0 \cdot x = x \cdot 0 = 0$ for all $x \in \mathbb{R}$, we have

$$\overline{1}z = (1+0i)(a+bi) = (1a - 0b) + (1b + 0a)i = 1a + 1bi = a + bi.$$

$$z \cdot \overline{1} = (a+bi)(1+0i) = (a \cdot 1 - b \cdot 0) + (a \cdot 0 + b \cdot 1)i = a \cdot 1 + b \cdot 1i = a + bi.$$

(Inverse) Let $z \in \mathbb{C}^*$. Then there are $a, b \in \mathbb{R}$ such that $z = a + bi$. Let $w = \frac{a}{a^2+b^2} + \frac{-b}{a^2+b^2}i$. Then we have

$$zw = (a+bi)\left(\frac{a}{a^2+b^2} + \frac{-b}{a^2+b^2}i\right)$$
$$= \left(a \cdot \frac{a}{a^2+b^2} - b \cdot \frac{-b}{a^2+b^2}\right) + \left(a \cdot \frac{-b}{a^2+b^2} + b \cdot \frac{a}{a^2+b^2}\right)i$$
$$= \frac{a^2+b^2}{a^2+b^2} + \frac{-ab+ba}{a^2+b^2}i = 1 + 0i = \overline{1}.$$
$$wz = \left(\frac{a}{a^2+b^2} + \frac{-b}{a^2+b^2}i\right)(a+bi)$$
$$= \left(\frac{a}{a^2+b^2} \cdot a - \frac{-b}{a^2+b^2} \cdot b\right) + \left(\frac{a}{a^2+b^2} \cdot b + \frac{-b}{a^2+b^2} \cdot a\right)i$$
$$= \frac{a^2+b^2}{a^2+b^2} + \frac{ab-ba}{a^2+b^2}i = 1 + 0i = \overline{1}.$$

We now prove distributivity.

(Left Distributivity) Let $z, w, v \in \mathbb{C}$. Then there are $a, b, c, d, e, f \in \mathbb{R}$ such that $z = a + bi, w = c + di$, and $v = e + fi$. Since multiplication is left distributive over addition in $\mathbb{R}$, and addition is associative and commutative in $\mathbb{R}$, we have

$$z(w + v) = (a + bi)[(c + di) + (e + fi)] = (a + bi)[(c + e) + (d + f)i]$$
$$= [a(c + e) - b(d + f)] + [a(d + f) + b(c + e)]i$$
$$= (ac + ae - bd - bf) + (ad + af + bc + be)i$$
$$= [(ac - bd) + (ad + bc)i] + [(ae - bf) + (af + be)i]$$
$$(a + bi)(c + di) + (a + bi)(e + fi) = zw + zv.$$

(Right Distributivity) Let $z, w, v \in \mathbb{C}$. There are $a, b, c, d, e, f \in \mathbb{R}$ such that $z = a + bi$, $w = c + di$, and $v = e + fi$. Since multiplication is right distributive over addition in $\mathbb{R}$, and addition is associative and commutative in $\mathbb{R}$, we have

$$(w + v)z = [(c + di) + (e + fi)](a + bi) = [(c + e) + (d + f)i](a + bi)$$
$$= [(c + e)a - (d + f)b] + [(c + e)b + (d + f)a]i$$
$$= (ca + ea - db - fb) + (cb + eb + da + fa)i$$
$$= [(ca - db) + (cb + da)i] + [(ea - fb) + (eb + fa)i]$$
$$(c + di)(a + bi) + (e + fi)(a + bi) = wz + vz.$$

Therefore, $(\mathbb{C}, +, \cdot)$ is field. $\qquad\qquad\qquad\qquad\qquad\qquad\qquad\qquad\qquad\qquad\qquad\qquad\square$

21. Let $S = \{a, b\}$, where $a \neq b$. How many binary operations are there on S? How many semigroups are there of the form $(S, \star)$, up to renaming the elements?

Solution: The number of binary operations is $2^4 = \mathbf{16}$. Let's draw all possible multiplication tables for $(S, \star)$, where $\star \colon S \times S \to S$ is a binary operation.

Of the 16 binary operations, 8 give rise to semigroups. However, 3 of these are essentially the same as 3 of the others. The 5 circled multiplication tables represent the 5 semigroups of order 2. The 3 tables in rectangles that are crossed out also represent semigroups. However, if you interchange the roles of a and b you'll see that they are the same as 3 of the others with the names changed (arrows are present to indicate the tables that are essentially the same as these). The other 8 tables represent operations that are not associative (the reader should find a counterexample to associativity for each of these). I leave it to the reader to verify that the 5 circled multiplication tables represent semigroups.

Note: A **magma** is a pair $(M, \star)$, where M is a set and $\star$ is a binary operation on M (and no other conditions). In the solution above we showed that there are 16 magmas of the form $(\{a, b\}, \star)$, and of these, 8 are semigroups. However, there are only 5 semigroups up to renaming the elements. Of the 16 magmas, there are only 10 up to renaming the elements. See if you can find the duplicates.

22. Let $R[x] = \{a_k x^k + a_{k-1} x^{k-1} + \cdots + a_1 x + a_0 \mid k \in \mathbb{N} \wedge a_0, a_1, \ldots, a_k \in R\}$, where R is a ring. Prove that $R[x]$ is both a left R-module and a right R-module.

Proof: Addition in $(\mathbb{Z}[x], +, \cdot)$ is defined by

$$a_k x^k + a_{k-1} x^{k-1} + \cdots + a_1 x + a_0) + (b_k x^k + b_{k-1} x^{k-1} + \cdots + b_1 x + b_0)$$
$$= (a_k + b_k) x^k + (a_{k-1} + b_{k-1}) x^{k-1} + \cdots + (a_1 + b_1) x + (a_0 + b_0).$$

Since $\mathbb{Z}$ is closed under addition, $a_k + b_k, a_{k-1} + b_{k-1}, \ldots, a_1 + b_1, a_0 + b_0 \in \mathbb{Z}$. Therefore, $\mathbb{Z}[x]$ is closed under addition.

Simple computations show that addition is associative in $\mathbb{Z}[x]$, $0 = 0x^k + 0x^{k-1} + \cdots + 0x + 0$ is an additive identity in $\mathbb{Z}[x]$, and the additive inverse of $a_k x^k + a_{k-1} x^{k-1} + \cdots + a_1 x + a_0$ is $-a_k x^k - a_{k-1} x^{k-1} - \cdots - a_1 x - a_0$. One more simple computation can be used to verify that addition is commutative.

To turn $R[x]$ into a left R-module, we define scalar multiplication as follows:

If $c \in R$ and $a_k x^k + a_{k-1} x^{k-1} + \cdots + a_1 x + a_0 \in R[x]$, then

$$c \cdot (a_k x^k + a_{k-1} x^{k-1} + \cdots + a_1 x + a_0) = (ca_k) x^k + (ca_{k-1}) x^{k-1} + \cdots + (ca_1) x + (ca_0).$$

We now prove the remaining left R-module properties:

(Closure under scalar multiplication) Let $c \in R$ and let $a_k x^k + a_{k-1} x^{k-1} + \cdots + a_1 x + a_0 \in R[x]$. Then $a_k, a_{k-1}, \ldots, a_1, a_0 \in R$. Since R is a ring, R is closed under multiplication. Therefore, we have $ca_k, ca_{k-1}, \ldots ca_1, ca_0 \in R$. So, $(ca_k) x^k + (ca_{k-1}) x^{k-1} + \cdots + (ca_1) x + (ca_0) \in R[x]$. Therefore, $c \cdot (a_k x^k + a_{k-1} x^{k-1} + \cdots + a_1 x + a_0) \in R[x]$.

(Scalar multiplication identity) Let $a_k x^k + a_{k-1} x^{k-1} + \cdots + a_1 x + a_0 \in R[x]$ and let 1 be the multiplicative identity in R. Then

$$1 \cdot (a_k x^k + a_{k-1} x^{k-1} + \cdots + a_1 x + a_0) = (1a_k) x^k + (1a_{k-1}) x^{k-1} + \cdots + (1a_1) x + (1a_0)$$
$$= a_k x^k + a_{k-1} x^{k-1} + \cdots + a_1 x + a_0.$$

(Associativity of scalar multiplication) Let $c, d \in R$ and $a_k x^k + a_{k-1} x^{k-1} + \cdots + a_1 x + a_0 \in R[x]$. Then since multiplication is associative in R, we have

$$(cd)(a_k x^k + a_{k-1} x^{k-1} + \cdots + a_1 x + a_0)$$
$$= \big((cd)a_k\big)x^k + \big((cd)a_{k-1}\big)x^{k-1} + \cdots + \big((cd)a_1\big)x + (cd)a_0$$
$$= (c(da_k)x^k + \big(c(da_{k-1})\big)x^{k-1} + \cdots + \big(c(da_1)\big)x + c(da_0)$$
$$= c\Big((da_k)x^k + (da_{k-1})x^{k-1} + \cdots + (da_1)x + da_0\Big)$$
$$= c\Big(d(a_k x^k + a_{k-1} x^{k-1} + \cdots + a_1 x + a_0 a_1, a_2, \ldots, a_n)\Big).$$

(Distributivity of 1 scalar over 2 vectors) Let $c \in R$, $a_k x^k + a_{k-1} x^{k-1} + \cdots + a_1 x + a_0 \in R[x]$, and $b_k x^k + b_{k-1} x^{k-1} + \cdots + b_1 x + b_0 \in R[x]$. Since multiplication is left distributive over addition in R, we have

$$c\Big((a_k x^k + a_{k-1} x^{k-1} + \cdots + a_1 x + a_0) + (b_k x^k + b_{k-1} x^{k-1} + \cdots + b_1 x + b_0)\Big)$$
$$= c\Big((a_k + b_k)x^k + (a_{k-1} + b_{k-1})x^{k-1} + \cdots + (a_1 + b_1)x + (a_0 + b_0)\Big)$$
$$= [c(a_k + b_k)]x^k + [c(a_{k-1} + b_{k-1})]x^{k-1} + \cdots + [c(a_1 + b_1)]x + c(a_0 + b_0)$$
$$= (ca_k + cb_k)x^k + (ca_{k-1} + cb_{k-1})x^{k-1} + \cdots + (ca_1 + cb_1)x + (ca_0 + cb_0)$$
$$= \Big((ca_k)x^k + + \cdots + (ca_1)x + (ca_0)\Big) + \Big((cb_k)x^k + \cdots + (cb_1)x + (cb_0)\Big)$$
$$= c \cdot (a_k x^k + a_{k-1} x^{k-1} + \cdots + a_1 x + a_0) + c \cdot (b_k x^k + b_{k-1} x^{k-1} + \cdots + b_1 x + b_0).$$

(Distributivity of 2 scalars over 1 vector) Let $c, d \in R$ and $a_k x^k + a_{k-1} x^{k-1} + \cdots + a_1 x + a_0 \in R[x]$. Since multiplication is distributive over addition in R, we have

$$(c + d)(a_k x^k + a_{k-1} x^{k-1} + \cdots + a_1 x + a_0)$$
$$= [(c + d)a_k]x^k + [(c + d)a_{k-1}]x^{k-1} + \cdots + [(c + d)a_1]x + (c + d)a_0$$
$$= (ca_k + da_k)x^k + (ca_{k-1} + da_{k-1})x^{k-1} + \cdots + (ca_1 + da_1)x + (ca_0 + da_0)$$
$$= \Big((ca_k)x^k + \cdots + (ca_1)x + (ca_0)\Big) + \Big((da_k)x^k + \cdots + (da_1)x + (da_0)\Big)$$
$$= c(a_k x^k + a_{k-1} x^{k-1} + \cdots + a_1 x + a_0) + d(a_k x^k + a_{k-1} x^{k-1} + \cdots + a_1 x + a_0).$$

Similarly, to turn $R[x]$ into a right R-module, we define scalar multiplication as follows: if $c \in R$ and $a_k x^k + a_{k-1} x^{k-1} + \cdots + a_1 x + a_0 \in R[x]$, then

$$(a_k x^k + a_{k-1} x^{k-1} + \cdots + a_1 x + a_0) \cdot c = (a_k c)x^k + (a_{k-1} c)x^{k-1} + \cdots + (a_1 c)x + (a_0 c).$$

The verifications of the right R-module properties are nearly identical to the computations made above. Just replace all multiplications on the left with multiplications on the right. □

LEVEL 1

1. Let $C = (-\infty, 2]$ and $D = (-1, 3]$. Compute each of the following:

    (i) $C \cup D$

    (ii) $C \cap D$

    (iii) $C \setminus D$

    (iv) $D \setminus C$

    (v) $C \Delta D$

Solutions:

(i) $C \cup D = (-\infty, 3]$

(ii) $C \cap D = (-1, 2]$

(iii) $C \setminus D = (-\infty, -1]$

(iv) $D \setminus C = (2, 3]$

(v) $C \Delta D = (-\infty, -1] \cup (2, 3]$

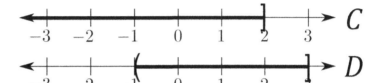

2. Find all partitions of the three-element set $\{a, b, c\}$ and the four-element set $\{a, b, c, d\}$.

Solution: The partitions of $\{a, b, c\}$ are $\{\{a\}, \{b\}, \{c\}\}$, $\{\{a\}, \{b, c\}\}$, $\{\{b\}, \{a, c\}\}$, $\{\{c\}, \{a, b\}\}$, and $\{\{a, b, c\}\}$.

The partitions of $\{a, b, c, d\}$ are $\{\{a\}, \{b\}, \{c\}, \{d\}\}$, $\{\{a\}, \{b\}, \{c, d\}\}$, $\{\{a\}, \{c\}, \{b, d\}\}$, $\{\{a\}, \{d\}, \{b, c\}\}$, $\{\{b\}, \{c\}, \{a, d\}\}$, $\{\{b\}, \{d\}, \{a, c\}\}$, $\{\{c\}, \{d\}, \{a, b\}\}$, $\{\{a, b\}, \{c, d\}\}$, $\{\{a, c\}, \{b, d\}\}$, $\{\{a, d\}, \{b, c\}\}$, $\{\{a, b, c\}, \{d\}\}$, $\{\{a, b, d\}, \{c\}\}$, $\{\{a, c, d\}, \{b\}\}$, $\{\{b, c, d\}, \{a\}\}$, and $\{\{a, b, c, d\}\}$.

3. Let $A = \{1, 2, 3, 4\}$ and let $R = \{(1, 1), (1, 3), (2, 2), (2, 4), (3, 1), (3, 3), (4, 2), (4, 4)\}$. Note that R is an equivalence relation on A. Find the equivalence classes of R.

Solution: The equivalence classes of R are $\{1, 3\}$ and $\{2, 4\}$.

LEVEL 2

4. Find the domain, range, and field of each of the following relations:

    (i) $R = \{(a, b), (c, d), (e, f), (f, a)\}$

    (ii) $S = \{(2k, 2t + 1) \mid k, t \in \mathbb{Z}\}$

Solutions:

(i) $\text{dom } R = \{a, c, e, f\}$; $\text{ran } R = \{a, b, d, f\}$; $\text{field } R = \{a, b, c, d, e, f\}$

(ii) $\text{dom } S = 2\mathbb{Z} = \mathbb{E}$; $\text{ran } S = \{2t + 1 \mid t \in \mathbb{Z}\} = \mathbb{O}$; $\text{field } S = \mathbb{Z}$

5. Prove that for each $n \in \mathbb{Z}^+$, $\equiv_n$ (see part 4 of Example 3.12) is an equivalence relation on $\mathbb{Z}$.

Proof: Let $a \in \mathbb{Z}$. Then $a - a = 0 = n \cdot 0$. So, $n \mid a - a$. Therefore, $a \equiv_n a$, and so, $\equiv_n$ is reflexive. Let $a, b \in \mathbb{Z}$ and suppose that $a \equiv_n b$. Then $n \mid b - a$. So, there is $k \in \mathbb{Z}$ such that $b - a = nk$. Thus, $a - b = -(b - a) = -nk = n(-k)$. Since $k \in \mathbb{Z}$, $-k \in \mathbb{Z}$. So, $n \mid a - b$, and therefore, $b \equiv_n a$. So, $\equiv_n$ is symmetric. Let $a, b, c \in \mathbb{Z}$ with $a \equiv_n b$ and $b \equiv_n c$. Then $n \mid b - a$ and $n \mid c - b$. So, there are $j, k \in \mathbb{Z}$ such that $b - a = nj$ and $c - b = nk$. So, $c - a = (c - b) + (b - a) = nk + nj = n(k + j)$. Since $\mathbb{Z}$ is closed under addition, $k + j \in \mathbb{Z}$. Therefore, $n \mid c - a$. So, $a \equiv_n c$. Thus, $\equiv_n$ is transitive. Since $\equiv_n$ is reflexive, symmetric, and transitive, $\equiv_n$ is an equivalence relation on $\mathbb{Z}$. $\square$

LEVEL 3

6. Prove that there do not exist sets A and B such that the relation $<$ on $\mathbb{R}$ is equal to $A \times B$.

Proof: Suppose toward contradiction that $<= A \times B$ for some sets A and B. Since $1 < 2$ and $2 < 3$, we have $(1, 2), (2, 3) \in A \times B$. Since $(2, 3) \in A \times B$, $2 \in A$. Since $(1, 2) \in A \times B$, $2 \in B$. Therefore, $(2, 2) \in A \times B$. Since $<= A \times B$, $2 < 2$, contradicting that $<$ is antireflexive. Therefore, there do not exist sets A and B such that $<$ is equal to $A \times B$. $\square$

7. Let X be a set of equivalence relations on a nonempty set A. Prove that $\bigcap X$ is an equivalence relation on A.

Proof: Let X be a set of equivalence relations on a nonempty set A. Let $x \in A$ and let $R \in X$. Since R is reflexive, $(x, x) \in R$. Since $R \in X$ was arbitrary, $\forall R \in X\big((x, x) \in R\big)$. So, $(x, x) \in \bigcap X$. Since $x \in A$ was arbitrary, $\bigcap X$ is reflexive.

Let $(x, y) \in \bigcap X$ and let $R \in X$. Then $(x, y) \in R$. Since R is an equivalence relation, R is symmetric. Therefore, $(y, x) \in R$. Since $R \in X$ was arbitrary, $\forall R \in X\big((y, x) \in R\big)$. So, $(y, x) \in \bigcap X$. Since $(x, y) \in \bigcap X$ was arbitrary, $\bigcap X$ is symmetric.

Let $(x, y), (y, z) \in \bigcap X$ and let $R \in X$. Then $(x, y), (y, z) \in R$. Since R is an equivalence relation, R is transitive. Therefore, $(x, z) \in R$. Since $R \in X$ was arbitrary, $\forall R \in X\big((x, z) \in R\big)$. So, $(x, z) \in \bigcap X$. Since $(x, y), (y, z) \in \bigcap X$ was arbitrary, $\bigcap X$ is transitive.

Since $\bigcap X$ is reflexive, symmetric, and transitive, $\bigcap X$ is an equivalence relation. $\square$

LEVEL 4

8. Let $R = \{(x, y) \in \mathbb{R} \times \mathbb{R} \mid x - y \in \mathbb{Z}\}$. Prove that R is an equivalence relation on $\mathbb{R}$ and describe the equivalence classes of R.

Proof: If $x \in \mathbb{R}$, then $x - x = 0 \in \mathbb{Z}$. So, xRx, and therefore, R is reflexive. If xRy, then $x - y \in \mathbb{Z}$. It follows that $y - x = -(x - y) \in \mathbb{Z}$. So, yRx, and therefore, R is symmetric. If xRy and yRz, then $x - y \in \mathbb{Z}$ and $y - z \in \mathbb{Z}$. It follows that $x - z = (x - y) + (y - z) \in \mathbb{Z}$ (because the sum of two integers is an integer). So, xRy, and therefore, R is transitive. Since R is reflexive, symmetric, and transitive, R is an equivalence relation.

For each $r \in \mathbb{R}$ with $0 \leq r < 1$, the set $X_r = \{r + n \mid n \in \mathbb{Z}\}$ is an equivalence class of R. To see this, first note that if $n, m \in \mathbb{Z}$, then $(r + n) - (r + m) = n - m \in \mathbb{Z}$. So, any two elements of X_r are equivalent. Also, if x is equivalent to $r + n$, then there is an integer m so that $(r + n) - x = m$. It follows that $x = r + (n - m)$, and so, $x \in X_r$.

Now, if $x \in \mathbb{R}$, then let n be an integer with $n \leq x < n + 1$. Then $0 \leq x - n < 1$. Let $r = x - n$. We have $x - r = x - (x - n) = n$, and so, $x \in X_r$.

Finally, if $0 \leq r < 1$ and $0 \leq s < 1$ with $r \leq s$ and rRs, then we have $s - r \geq 0$ and $s - r < 1$. Therefore, $s - r = 0$, and so, $s = r$. $\square$

9. Let R be a relation on a set A. Determine if each of the following statements is true or false. If true, provide a proof. If false, provide a counterexample.

    (i)   If R is symmetric and transitive on A, then R is reflexive on A.

    (ii)   If R is antisymmetric on A, then R is not symmetric on A.

Solutions:

    (i)   This is **false**. Let $A = \{0, 1\}$ and $R = \{(0, 0)\}$. Then R is symmetric and transitive, but not reflexive (because $(1, 1) \notin R$).

    (ii)   This is **false**. $\emptyset$ is both symmetric and antisymmetric on any set A.

10. Define a sum and product on $\mathbb{Z}_n$ as follows: For $x, y \in \mathbb{Z}_n$, let $[x]_n + [y]_n = [x + y]_n$ and let $[x]_n \cdot [y]_n = [xy]_n$. Prove that $(\mathbb{Z}_n, +, \cdot)$ is a commutative ring.

Proof: It was already proved that addition and multiplication are well-defined at the end of Lesson 3. We first prove that $(\mathbb{Z}_n, +)$ is a commutative group.

(Closure) Let $[x]_n, [y]_n \in \mathbb{Z}_n$. Then $[x]_n + [y]_n = [x + y]_n \in \mathbb{Z}_n$.

(Associativity) Let $[x]_n, [y]_n, [z]_n \in \mathbb{Z}_n$. Since addition is associative in $\mathbb{Z}$, we have

$$([x]_n + [y]_n) + [z]_n = [x + y]_n + [z]_n = [(x + y) + z]_n = [x + (y + z)]_n$$
$$= [x]_n + [y + z]_n = [x]_n + ([y]_n + [z]_n).$$

(Commutativity) Let $[x]_n, [y]_n \in \mathbb{Z}_n$. Since addition is commutative in $\mathbb{Z}$, we have

$$[x]_n + [y]_n = [x + y]_n = [y + x]_n = [y]_n + [x]_n.$$

(Identity) We show that $[0]_n$ is the additive identity. Let $[x]_n \in \mathbb{Z}_n$. Since 0 is an additive identity in $\mathbb{Z}$, we have: $[0]_n + [x]_n = [0 + x]_n = [x]_n$ and $[x]_n + [0]_n = [x + 0]_n = [x]_n$.

(Inverse) Let $[x]_n \in \mathbb{Z}_n$. We show that $[-x]_n$ is the additive inverse of $[x]_n$. Since $-x$ is the additive inverse of x in $\mathbb{Z}$, we have

$$[x]_n + [-x]_n = [x + (-x)]_n = [0]_n.$$
$$[-x]_n + [x]_n = [-x + x]_n = [0]_n.$$

We next prove that $(\mathbb{Z}_n, \cdot)$ is a commutative monoid.

(Closure) Let $[x]_n, [y]_n \in \mathbb{Z}_n$. Then $[x]_n \cdot [y]_n = [xy]_n \in \mathbb{Z}_n$.

(Associativity) Let $[x]_n, [y]_n, [z]_n \in \mathbb{Z}_n$. Since multiplication is associative in $\mathbb{Z}$, we have

$$([x]_n \cdot [y]_n) \cdot [z]_n = [xy]_n \cdot [z]_n = [(xy)z]_n = [x(yz)]_n = [x]_n \cdot [yz]_n = [x]_n \cdot ([y]_n \cdot [z]_n).$$

(Commutativity) Let $[x]_n, [y]_n \in \mathbb{Z}_n$. Since multiplication is commutative in $\mathbb{Z}$, we have

$$[x]_n \cdot [y]_n = [xy]_n = [yx]_n = [y]_n \cdot [x]_n.$$

(Identity) We show that $[1]_n$ is the multiplicative identity. Let $[x]_n \in \mathbb{Z}_n$. Since 1 is a multiplicative identity in $\mathbb{Z}$, we have

$$[1]_n \cdot [x]_n = [1x]_n = [x]_n \quad \text{and} \quad [x]_n \cdot [1]_n = [x \cdot 1]_n = [x]_n.$$

We now prove distributivity. Since $(\mathbb{Z}_n, \cdot)$ is commutative, it suffices to prove left distributivity.

(Left Distributivity) Let $[x]_n, [y]_n, [z]_n \in \mathbb{Z}_n$. Since multiplication is distributive over addition in $\mathbb{Z}$, we have

$$[x]_n([y]_n + [z]_n) = [x]_n \cdot [y + z]_n = [x(y + z)]_n = [xy + xz]_n$$
$$= [xy]_n + [xz]_n = [x]_n \cdot [y]_n + [x]_n \cdot [z]_n.$$

$\square$

LEVEL 5

11. For $a, b \in \mathbb{N}$, we will say that a divides b, written $a|b$, if there is a natural number k such that $b = ak$. Notice that | is a binary relation on $\mathbb{N}$. Prove that $(\mathbb{N}, |)$ is a partially ordered set, but it is not a linearly ordered set.

Proof: If $a \in \mathbb{N}$ then $a = a \cdot 1$, so that $a|a$. Therefore, | is reflexive. If $a|b$ and $b|a$, then there are natural numbers j and k such that $b = ja$ and $a = kb$. If $a = 0$, then $b = j \cdot 0 = 0$, and so, $a = b$. Suppose $a \neq 0$. We have $a = k(ja) = (kj)a$. Thus, $(kj - 1)a = (kj)a - 1a = 0$. So, $kj - 1 = 0$, and therefore, $kj = 1$. So, $k = j = 1$. Thus, $b = ja = 1a = a$. Therefore, | is antisymmetric. If $a|b$ and $b|c$, then there are natural numbers j and k such that $b = ja$ and $c = kb$. Then $c = kb = k(ja) = (kj)a$. Since the product of two natural numbers is a natural number, $kj \in \mathbb{N}$. So, $a|c$. Therefore, | is transitive. Since | is reflexive, antisymmetric, and transitive on $\mathbb{N}$, $(\mathbb{N}, |)$ is a partially ordered set. Since 2 and 3 do not divide each other, $(\mathbb{N}, |)$ is **not** linearly ordered. $\square$

12. Let P be a partition of a set S. Prove that there is an equivalence relation $\sim$ on S for which the elements of P are the equivalence classes of $\sim$. Conversely, if $\sim$ is an equivalence relation on a set S, prove that the equivalence classes of $\sim$ form a partition of S.

Proof: Let P be a partition of S, and define the relation $\sim$ by $x \sim y$ if and only if there is $X \in P$ with $x, y \in X$.

Let $x \in S$. Since P is a partition of S, $S = \bigcup P$. So, there is $X \in P$ with $x \in X$. It follows that $x \sim x$. Therefore, $\sim$ is reflexive.

If $x \sim y$, then there is $X \in P$ with $x, y \in X$. So, $y, x \in X$ (obviously!). Thus, $y \sim x$, and therefore, $\sim$ is symmetric.

If $x \sim y$ and $y \sim z$, then there are $X, Y \in P$ with $x, y \in X$ and $y, z \in Y$. Since $y \in X$ and $y \in Y$, we have $y \in X \cap Y$. Since P is a partition and $X \cap Y \neq \emptyset$, we must have $X = Y$. So, $z \in X$. Thus, $x, z \in X$, and therefore, $x \sim z$. So, $\sim$ is transitive.

Since $\sim$ is reflexive, symmetric, and transitive on S, $\sim$ is an equivalence relation on S.

We still need to show that $P = \{[x] \mid x \in S\}$. Let $X \in P$ and let $x \in X$. We show that $X = [x]$. Let $y \in X$. Since $x, y \in X$, $x \sim y$. So $y \in [x]$. Thus, $X \subseteq [x]$. Now, let $y \in [x]$. Then $x \sim y$. So, there is $Y \in P$ such that $x, y \in Y$. Since $x \in X$ and $x \in Y$, $x \in X \cap Y$. Since P is a partition and $X \cap Y \neq \emptyset$, we must have $X = Y$. So, $y \in X$. Thus, $[x] \subseteq X$. Since $X \subseteq [x]$ and $[x] \subseteq X$, we have $X = [x]$. Since $X \in P$ was arbitrary, we have shown $P \subseteq \{[x] \mid x \in S\}$.

Now, let $X \in \{[x] \mid x \in S\}$. Then there is $x \in S$ such that $X = [x]$. Since P is a partition of S, $S = \bigcup P$. So, there is $Y \in P$ with $x \in Y$. We will show that $X = Y$. Let $y \in X$. Then $x \sim y$. So, there is $Z \in P$ with $x, y \in Z$. Since $x \in Y$ and $x \in Z$, $x \in Y \cap Z$. Since P is a partition and $Y \cap Z \neq \emptyset$, we must have $Y = Z$. So, $y \in Y$. Since $y \in X$ was arbitrary, $X \subseteq Y$. Now, let $y \in Y$. Then $x \sim y$. So, $y \in [x] = X$. Since $y \in Y$ was arbitrary, $Y \subseteq X$. Since $X \subseteq Y$ and $Y \subseteq X$, we have $X = Y$. Therefore, $X \in P$. Since $X \in \{[x] \mid x \in S\}$ was arbitrary, we have $\{[x] \mid x \in S\} \subseteq P$.

Since $P \subseteq \{[x] \mid x \in S\}$ and $\{[x] \mid x \in S\} \subseteq P$, we have $P = \{[x] \mid x \in S\}$, as desired.

Now, let $\sim$ be an equivalence relation on S. We first show that $\bigcup\{[x] \mid x \in S\} = S$.

Let $y \in \bigcup\{[x] \mid x \in S\}$. Then there is $x \in S$ with $y \in [x]$. By definition of $[x]$, $y \in S$. Therefore, $\bigcup\{[x] \mid x \in S\} \subseteq S$. Now, let $y \in S$. Since $\sim$ is an equivalence relation, $y \sim y$. So, $y \in [y]$. Thus, $y \in \bigcup\{[x] \mid x \in S\}$. So, we have $S \subseteq \bigcup\{[x] \mid x \in S\}$. Since $\bigcup\{[x] \mid x \in S\} \subseteq S$ and $S \subseteq \bigcup\{[x] \mid x \in S\}$, $\bigcup\{[x] \mid x \in S\} = S$.

We next show that if $x, y \in S$, then $[x] \cap [y] = \emptyset$ or $[x] = [y]$.

Suppose $[x] \cap [y] \neq \emptyset$ and let $z \in [x] \cap [y]$. Then $x \sim z$ and $y \sim z$. Since $\sim$ is symmetric, $z \sim y$. Since $\sim$ is transitive, $x \sim y$. Let $w \in [x]$. Then $x \sim w$. By symmetry, $y \sim x$. By transitivity, $y \sim w$. So, $w \in [y]$. Since $w \in [x]$ was arbitrary, $[x] \subseteq [y]$. By a symmetric argument, $[y] \subseteq [x]$.

47

Since $[x] \subseteq [y]$ and $[y] \subseteq [x]$, we have $[x] = [y]$.

Since $\bigcup\{[x] \mid x \in S\} = S$ and every pair of equivalence classes are either disjoint or equal, the set of equivalence classes partitions S. $\qquad \square$

Problem Set 4

LEVEL 1

1. Determine if each of the following relations are functions. For each such function, determine if it is injective. State the domain and range of each function.

    (i) $R = \{(a, b), (b, b), (c, d), (e, a)\}$

    (ii) $S = \{(a, a), (a, b), (b, a)\}$

    (iii) $T = \{(a, b) \mid a, b \in \mathbb{R} \wedge b < 0 \wedge a^2 + b^2 = 9\}$

Solutions:

(i) R is a function. It is **not** injective. dom $R = \{a, b, c, e\}$ and ran $R = \{a, b, d\}$.

(ii) S **is not** a function.

(iii) T is a function. It is **not** injective. dom $T = (-3, 3)$ and ran $T = [-3, 0)$.

2. Define $f : \mathbb{Z} \to \mathbb{Z}$ by $f(n) = n^2$. Let $A = \{0, 1, 2, 3, 4\}$, $B = \mathbb{N}$, and $C = \{-2n \mid n \in \mathbb{N}\}$. Evaluate each of the following:

    (i) $f[A]$

    (ii) $f^{-1}[A]$

    (iii) $f^{-1}[B]$

    (iv) $f[B \cup C]$

Solutions:

(i) $f[A] = \{0, 1, 4, 9, 16\}$.

(ii) $f^{-1}[A] = \{-2, -1, 0, 1, 2\}$.

(iii) $f^{-1}[B] = \mathbb{Z}$.

(iv) $f[B \cup C] = \{n^2 \mid n \in \mathbb{N}\}$.

3. Let A, B, and C be sets. Prove the following:

    (i) $\preccurlyeq$ is transitive.

    (ii) $\prec$ is transitive.

    (iii) If $A \preccurlyeq B$ and $B \prec C$, then $A \prec C$.

    (iv)   If $A \prec B$ and $B \preccurlyeq C$, then $A \prec C$.

Proofs:

(i)   Suppose that $A \preccurlyeq B$ and $B \preccurlyeq C$. Then there are functions $f : A \hookrightarrow B$ and $g : B \hookrightarrow C$. By Theorem 4.6, $g \circ f : A \hookrightarrow C$. So, $A \preccurlyeq C$. Therefore, $\preccurlyeq$ is transitive. $\qquad\square$

(ii) Suppose that $A \prec B$ and $B \prec C$. Then $A \preccurlyeq B$ and $B \preccurlyeq C$. By (i), $A \preccurlyeq C$. Assume toward contradiction that $A \sim C$. Since $\sim$ is symmetric, $C \sim A$. In particular, $C \preccurlyeq A$. Since $C \preccurlyeq A$ and $A \preccurlyeq B$, by (i), $C \preccurlyeq B$. Since $B \preccurlyeq C$ and $C \preccurlyeq B$, by the Cantor-Schroeder-Bernstein Theorem, $B \sim C$, contradicting $B \prec C$. It follows that $A \nsim C$, and thus, $A \prec C$. □

(iii) Suppose that $A \preccurlyeq B$ and $B \prec C$. Then $B \preccurlyeq C$. By (i), $A \preccurlyeq C$. Assume toward contradiction that $A \sim C$. The rest of the argument is the same as (ii). □

(iv) Suppose that $A \prec B$ and $B \preccurlyeq C$. Then $A \preccurlyeq B$. By (i), $A \preccurlyeq C$. Assume toward contradiction that $A \sim C$. Since $\sim$ is symmetric, $C \sim A$. In particular, $C \preccurlyeq A$. Since $B \preccurlyeq C$ and $C \preccurlyeq A$, by (i), $B \preccurlyeq A$. Since $A \preccurlyeq B$ and $B \preccurlyeq A$, by the Cantor-Schroeder-Bernstein Theorem, $A \sim B$, contradicting $A \prec B$. It follows that $A \nsim C$, and thus, $A \prec C$. □

4. Write the elements of S_4 in cycle notation.

Solution: The elements of S_4 are $(1), (12), (13), (14), (23), (24), (34), (123), (124), (134), (234),$ $(132), (142), (143), (243), (1234), (1342), (1423), (1432), (1243), (1324), (12)(34), (13)(24),$ and $(14)(23)$.

Note: There are many ways to write the same permutation in cycle notation. For example, (12) is the same permutation as (21). Both permutations send 1 to 2, 2 to 1, and the other numbers to themselves. As a more extreme example, (123) is the same permutation as $(13)(12)$. The latter way of writing the permutation is a bit less "natural" because the number 1 is repeated twice. It turns out that every permutation can be written as a product of cycles in a way that each number appears no more than once. In the solution above, I have written each permutation in the most "natural" way.

5. Draw a group multiplication table for S_3.

Solution:

$(S_3, \circ)$	(1)	(12)	(13)	(23)	(123)	(132)
(1)	(1)	(12)	(13)	(23)	(123)	(132)
(12)	(12)	(1)	(132)	(123)	(23)	(13)
(13)	(13)	(123)	(1)	(132)	(12)	(23)
(23)	(23)	(132)	(123)	(1)	(13)	(12)
(123)	(123)	(13)	(23)	(12)	(132)	(1)
(132)	(132)	(23)	(12)	(13)	(1)	(123)

LEVEL 2

6. Find sets A and B and a function f such that $f[A \cap B] \neq f[A] \cap f[B]$.

Solution: Define $f: \{a, b\} \to \{0\}$ by $\{(a, 0), (b, 0)\}$. Let $A = \{a\}$ and $B = \{b\}$. Then $A \cap B = \emptyset$. Therefore, $f[A \cap B] = \emptyset$ and $f[A] \cap f[B] = \{0\} \cap \{0\} = \{0\}$.

7. Let $f: A \to B$ and let $V \subseteq B$. Prove that $f[f^{-1}[V]] \subseteq V$.

Proof: Let $y \in f[f^{-1}[V]]$. Then there is $x \in f^{-1}[V]$ with $y = f(x)$. Since $x \in f^{-1}[V]$, we have $y = f(x) \in V$. Since $y \in f[f^{-1}[V]]$ was arbitrary, $f[f^{-1}[V]] \subseteq V$. $\qquad\square$

8. Define $\mathcal{P}_k(\mathbb{N})$ for each $k \in \mathbb{N}$ by $\mathcal{P}_0(\mathbb{N}) = \mathbb{N}$ and $\mathcal{P}_{k+1}(\mathbb{N}) = \mathcal{P}(\mathcal{P}_k(\mathbb{N}))$ for $k > 0$. Find a set B such that for all $k \in \mathbb{N}$, $\mathcal{P}_k(\mathbb{N}) \prec B$.

Solution: Let $B = \bigcup\{\mathcal{P}_n(\mathbb{N}) \mid n \in \mathbb{N}\}$. Let $k \in \mathbb{N}$. Since $\mathcal{P}_k(\mathbb{N}) \subseteq B$, by Note 1 following Example 4.20, $\mathcal{P}_k(\mathbb{N}) \preccurlyeq B$. Since k was arbitrary, we have $\mathcal{P}_k(\mathbb{N}) \preccurlyeq B$ for all $k \in \mathbb{N}$. Again, let $k \in \mathbb{N}$. We have $\mathcal{P}_k(\mathbb{N}) \prec \mathcal{P}_{k+1}(\mathbb{N})$ and $\mathcal{P}_{k+1}(\mathbb{N}) \preccurlyeq B$. By Problem 3 (part (iv)), $\mathcal{P}_k(\mathbb{N}) \prec B$. Since $k \in \mathbb{N}$ was arbitrary, we have shown that for all $k \in \mathbb{N}$, $\mathcal{P}_k(\mathbb{N}) \prec B$.

9. Prove that if $A \sim B$ and $C \sim D$, then $A \times C \sim B \times D$.

Proof: Suppose that $A \sim B$ and $C \sim D$. Then there exist bijections $h: A \to B$ and $k: C \to D$. Define $f: A \times C \to B \times D$ by $f(a, c) = (h(a), k(c))$.

Suppose $(a, c), (a', c') \in A \times C$ with $f((a, c)) = f((a', c'))$. Then $(h(a), k(c)) = (h(a'), k(c'))$. So, $h(a) = h(a')$ and $k(c) = k(c')$. Since h is an injection, $a = a'$. Since k is an injection, $c = c'$. Since $a = a'$ and $c = c'$, $(a, c) = (a', c')$. Since $(a, c), (a', c') \in A \times C$ were arbitrary, f is an injection.

Now, let $(b, d) \in B \times D$. Since h and k are bijections, h^{-1} and k^{-1} exist. Let $a = h^{-1}(b)$, $c = k^{-1}(d)$. Then $f(a, c) = (h(a), k(c)) = (h(h^{-1}(b)), k(k^{-1}(d))) = (b, d)$. Since $(b, d) \in B \times D$ was arbitrary, f is a surjection.

Since f is both an injection and a surjection, $A \times C \sim B \times D$. $\qquad\square$

LEVEL 3

10. For $f, g \in {}^{\mathbb{R}}\mathbb{R}$, define $f \preccurlyeq g$ if and only if for all $x \in \mathbb{R}$, $f(x) \leq g(x)$. Is $({}^{\mathbb{R}}\mathbb{R}, \preccurlyeq)$ a poset? Is it a linearly ordered set? What if we replace $\preccurlyeq$ by $\preccurlyeq^*$, where $f \preccurlyeq^* g$ if and only if there is an $x \in \mathbb{R}$ such that $f(x) \leq g(x)$?

Solution: If $f \in {}^{\mathbb{R}}\mathbb{R}$, then for all $x \in \mathbb{R}$, $f(x) = f(x)$. So, $f \preccurlyeq f$, and therefore, $\preccurlyeq$ is reflexive.

Let $f, g \in {}^{\mathbb{R}}\mathbb{R}$ with $f \preccurlyeq g$ and $g \preccurlyeq f$. Then for all $x \in \mathbb{R}$, $f(x) \leq g(x)$ and $g(x) \leq f(x)$. So, $f = g$, and therefore, $\preccurlyeq$ is antisymmetric.

Let $f, g, h \in {}^{\mathbb{R}}\mathbb{R}$ with $f \preccurlyeq g$ and $g \preccurlyeq h$. Then for all $x \in \mathbb{R}$, $f(x) \leq g(x)$ and $g(x) \leq h(x)$. So, by the transitivity of $\leq$, for all $x \in \mathbb{R}$, $f(x) \leq h(x)$. Thus, $f \preccurlyeq h$, and therefore, $\preccurlyeq$ is transitive.

Since $\preccurlyeq$ is reflexive, antisymmetric, and transitive, $({}^{\mathbb{R}}\mathbb{R}, \preccurlyeq)$ is a poset.

Let $f(x) = x$ and $g(x) = x^2$. Then $f(2) = 2$ and $g(2) = 4$. So, $f(2) < g(2)$. Therefore, $g \not\preccurlyeq f$. We also have $f\left(\frac{1}{2}\right) = \frac{1}{2}$ and $g\left(\frac{1}{2}\right) = \frac{1}{4}$. So, $g\left(\frac{1}{2}\right) < f\left(\frac{1}{2}\right)$. Therefore, $f \not\preccurlyeq g$. So, f and g are incomparible with respect to $\preccurlyeq$. Therefore, $(^\mathbb{R}\mathbb{R}, \preccurlyeq)$ is **not** a linearly ordered set.

The same example from the last paragraph gives us $f \preccurlyeq^* g$ and $g \preccurlyeq^* f$. But $f \neq g$. So, $\preccurlyeq^*$ is **not** antisymmetric, and therefore, $(^\mathbb{R}\mathbb{R}, \preccurlyeq^*)$ is **not** a poset.

11. Prove that the function $f: \mathbb{N} \to \mathbb{Z}$ defined by $f(n) = \begin{cases} \dfrac{n}{2} & \text{if } n \text{ is even} \\ -\dfrac{n+1}{2} & \text{if } n \text{ is odd} \end{cases}$ is a bijection.

Proof: First note that if n is even, then there is $k \in \mathbb{Z}$ with $n = 2k$, and so, $\frac{n}{2} = \frac{2k}{2} = k \in \mathbb{Z}$, and if n is odd, there is $k \in \mathbb{Z}$ with $n = 2k + 1$, and so, $-\frac{n+1}{2} = -\frac{(2k+1)+1}{2} = -\frac{2k+2}{2} = -\frac{2(k+1)}{2} = -(k+1) \in \mathbb{Z}$. So, f does take each natural number to an integer.

Now, suppose that $n, m \in \mathbb{N}$ with $f(n) = f(m)$. If n and m are both even, we have $\frac{n}{2} = \frac{m}{2}$, and so, $2 \cdot \frac{n}{2} = 2 \cdot \frac{m}{2}$. Thus, $n = m$. If n and m are both odd, we have $-\frac{n+1}{2} = -\frac{m+1}{2}$, and so, $\frac{n+1}{2} = \frac{m+1}{2}$. Thus, $2 \cdot \frac{n+1}{2} = 2 \cdot \frac{m+1}{2}$. So, $n + 1 = m + 1$, and therefore, $n = m$. If n is even and m is odd, then we have $\frac{n}{2} = -\frac{m+1}{2}$. So, $2 \cdot \frac{n}{2} = 2\left(-\frac{m+1}{2}\right)$. Therefore, $n = -(m + 1)$. Since $m \in \mathbb{N}$, $m \geq 0$. So, $m + 1 \geq 1$. Therefore, $n = -(m + 1) \leq -1$, contradicting $n \in \mathbb{N}$. So, it is impossible for n to be even, m to be odd, and $f(n) = f(m)$. Similarly, we cannot have n odd and m even. So, f is an injection.

Now, let $k \in \mathbb{Z}$. If $k \geq 0$, then $2k \in \mathbb{N}$ and $f(2k) = \frac{2k}{2} = k$. If $k < 0$, then $-2k > 0$, and so, we have $-2k - 1 \in \mathbb{N}$. Then $f(-2k - 1) = -\frac{(-2k-1)+1}{2} = -\frac{-2k}{2} = k$. So, f is a surjection.

Since f is both an injection and a surjection, f is a bijection. $\square$

12. Define a partition $\boldsymbol{P}$ of $\mathbb{N}$ such that $\boldsymbol{P} \sim \mathbb{N}$ and for each $X \in \boldsymbol{P}, X \sim \mathbb{N}$.

Proof: For each $n \in \mathbb{N}$, let P_n be the set of natural numbers ending with exactly n zeros and let $\boldsymbol{P} = \{P_n \mid n \in \mathbb{N}\}$. For example, $5231 \in P_0$, $0 \in P_1$, and $26{,}200 \in P_2$. Let's define $\widetilde{m,n}$ to be the natural number consisting of m 1's followed by n 0's. For example, $\widetilde{3,0} = 111$ and $\widetilde{2,5} = 1{,}100{,}000$. For each $n \in \mathbb{N}$, $\{\widetilde{m,n} \mid m \in \mathbb{N}\} \subseteq P_n$ showing that each P_n is equinumerous to $\mathbb{N}$. Also, if $k \in P_n \cap P_m$, then k ends with exactly n zeros and exactly m zeros, and so, $n = m$. Therefore, $\boldsymbol{P}$ is pairwise disjoint. This also shows that the function $f: \mathbb{N} \to \boldsymbol{P}$ defined by $f(n) = P_n$ is a bijection. So, $\boldsymbol{P} \sim \mathbb{N}$. Finally, if $k \in \mathbb{N}$, then there is $n \in \mathbb{N}$ such that k ends with exactly n zeros. So, $\bigcup \boldsymbol{P} = \mathbb{N}$. $\square$

13. Prove that a countable union of countable sets is countable.

Proof: For each $n \in \mathbb{N}$, let A_n be a countable set. By replacing each A_n by $A_n \times \{n\}$, we can assume that $\{A_n \mid n \in \mathbb{N}\}$ is a pairwise disjoint collection of sets ($A_n \sim A_n \times \{n\}$ via the bijection f sending x to (x, n)). By Problem 12, there is a partition $\boldsymbol{P}$ of $\mathbb{N}$ such that $\boldsymbol{P} \sim \mathbb{N}$ and for each $X \in \boldsymbol{P}$, $X \sim \mathbb{N}$. Let's say $\boldsymbol{P} = \{P_n \mid n \in \mathbb{N}\}$. Since each A_n is countable, for each $n \in \mathbb{N}$ there are injections $f_n : A_n \to P_n$. Define $f : \bigcup \{A_n \mid n \in \mathbb{N}\} \to \mathbb{N}$ by $f(x) = f_n(x)$ if $x \in A_n$.

Since $\{A_n \mid n \in \mathbb{N}\}$ is pairwise disjoint, f is well-defined.

Suppose that $x, y \in \bigcup \{A_n \mid n \in \mathbb{N}\}$ with $f(x) = f(y)$. There exist $n, m \in \mathbb{N}$ such that $x \in A_n$ and $y \in A_m$. So, $f(x) = f_n(x) \in P_n$ and $f(y) = f_m(y) \in P_m$. Since $f(x) = f(y)$, we have $f_n(x) = f_m(y)$. Since for $n \neq m$, $P_n \cap P_m = \emptyset$, we must have $n = m$. So, we have $f_n(x) = f_n(y)$. Since f_n is injective, $x = y$. Since $x, y \in \bigcup \{A_n \mid n \in \mathbb{N}\}$ were arbitrary, f is an injective function. Therefore, $\bigcup \{A_n \mid n \in \mathbb{N}\}$ is countable. $\qquad \square$

14. Let A and B be sets such that $A \sim B$. Prove that $\mathcal{P}(A) \sim \mathcal{P}(B)$.

Proof: Suppose that $A \sim B$. Then there exists a bijection $h : A \to B$. Define $F : \mathcal{P}(A) \to \mathcal{P}(B)$ by $F(X) = \{h(a) \mid a \in X\}$ for each $X \in \mathcal{P}(A)$.

Suppose $X, Y \in \mathcal{P}(A)$ with $F(X) = F(Y)$. Let $a \in X$. Then $h(a) \in F(X)$. Since $F(X) = F(Y)$, $h(a) \in F(Y)$. So, there is $b \in Y$ such that $h(a) = h(b)$. Since h is injective, $a = b$. So, $a \in Y$. Since $a \in X$ was arbitrary, $X \subseteq Y$. By a symmetrical argument, $Y \subseteq X$. Therefore, $X = Y$. Since $X, Y \in \mathcal{P}(A)$ were arbitrary, F is injective.

Let $Y \in \mathcal{P}(B)$ and let $X = \{a \in A \mid h(a) \in Y\}$. Then $b \in F(X)$ if and only if $b = h(a)$ for some $a \in X$ if and only if $b \in Y$ (because h is surjective). So, $F(X) = Y$. Since $Y \in \mathcal{P}(B)$ was arbitrary, F is surjective.

Since F is injective and surjective, $\mathcal{P}(A) \sim \mathcal{P}(B)$. $\qquad \square$

LEVEL 4

15. Prove the following:

    (i) $\mathbb{N} \times \mathbb{N} \sim \mathbb{N}$.

    (ii) $\mathbb{Q} \sim \mathbb{N}$.

    (iii)   Any two intervals of real numbers are equinumerous (including $\mathbb{R}$ itself).

    (iv) $^{\mathbb{N}}\mathbb{N} \sim \mathcal{P}(\mathbb{N})$.

Proofs:

    (i) $\mathbb{N} \times \mathbb{N} = \bigcup \{\mathbb{N} \times \{n\} \mid n \in \mathbb{N}\}$. This is a countable union of countable sets. By Problem 13, $\mathbb{N} \times \mathbb{N}$ is countable. $\qquad \square$

(ii) $\mathbb{Q}^+ = \left\{ \frac{a}{b} \,\middle|\, a \in \mathbb{N} \wedge b \in \mathbb{N}^+ \right\} = \bigcup \left\{ \left\{ \frac{a}{b} \,\middle|\, a \in \mathbb{N} \right\} \,\middle|\, b \in \mathbb{N}^+ \right\}$. This is a countable union of countable sets. By Problem 13, $\mathbb{Q}^+$ is countable. Now, $\mathbb{Q} = \mathbb{Q}^+ \cup \{0\} \cup \mathbb{Q}^-$, where $\mathbb{Q}^- = \{q \in \mathbb{Q} \mid -q \in \mathbb{Q}^+\}$. This is again a countable union of countable sets, thus countable. So, $\mathbb{Q} \sim \mathbb{N}$. $\qquad\square$

(iii)   The function $f \colon \mathbb{R} \to (0, \infty)$ defined by $f(x) = 2^x$ is a bijection. So, $\mathbb{R} \sim (0, \infty)$. The function $g \colon (0, \infty) \to (0, 1)$ defined by $g(x) = \frac{1}{x^2 + 1}$ is a bijection. So, $(0, \infty) \sim (0, 1)$. If $a, b \in \mathbb{R}$, the function $h \colon (0, 1) \to (a, b)$ defined by $h(x) = (b - a)x + a$ is a bijection. So, $(0, 1) \sim (a, b)$. It follows that all bounded open intervals are equinumerous with each other and $\mathbb{R}$.

We have, $[a, b] \subseteq (a - 1, b + 1) \sim (a, b) \subseteq [a, b) \subseteq [a, b]$ and $(a, b) \subseteq (a, b] \subseteq [a, b]$. It follows that all bounded intervals are equinumerous with each other and $\mathbb{R}$.

We also have the following.

$$(a, \infty) \subseteq [a, \infty) \subseteq \mathbb{R} \sim (a, a + 1) \subseteq (a, \infty)$$

$$(-\infty, b) \subseteq (-\infty, b] \subseteq \mathbb{R} \sim (b - 1, b) \subseteq (-\infty, b)$$

Therefore, all unbounded intervals are equinumerous with $\mathbb{R}$. It follows that any two intervals of real numbers are equinumerous. $\qquad\square$

(iv) $^{\mathbb{N}}\mathbb{N} \subseteq \mathcal{P}(\mathbb{N} \times \mathbb{N})$ by the definition of $^{\mathbb{N}}\mathbb{N}$. So, $^{\mathbb{N}}\mathbb{N} \preccurlyeq \mathcal{P}(\mathbb{N} \times \mathbb{N})$ by Note 1 following Example 4.20. By (i) above, $\mathbb{N} \times \mathbb{N} \sim \mathbb{N}$. So, by Problem 14, $\mathcal{P}(\mathbb{N} \times \mathbb{N}) \sim \mathcal{P}(\mathbb{N})$. So, $\mathcal{P}(\mathbb{N} \times \mathbb{N}) \preccurlyeq \mathcal{P}(\mathbb{N})$. Since $\preccurlyeq$ is transitive, $^{\mathbb{N}}\mathbb{N} \preccurlyeq \mathcal{P}(\mathbb{N})$.

Now, $\mathcal{P}(\mathbb{N}) \sim {}^{\mathbb{N}}\{0, 1\}$ (see Example 4.15 (part 5)). So, $\mathcal{P}(\mathbb{N}) \preccurlyeq {}^{\mathbb{N}}\{0, 1\}$. Also, $^{\mathbb{N}}\{0, 1\} \subseteq {}^{\mathbb{N}}\mathbb{N}$, and so, by Note 1 following Example 4.20, $^{\mathbb{N}}\{0, 1\} \preccurlyeq {}^{\mathbb{N}}\mathbb{N}$. Since $\preccurlyeq$ is transitive, $\mathcal{P}(\mathbb{N}) \preccurlyeq {}^{\mathbb{N}}\mathbb{N}$.

By the Cantor-Schroeder-Bernstein Theorem, $^{\mathbb{N}}\mathbb{N} \sim \mathcal{P}(\mathbb{N})$. $\qquad\square$

Notes: (1) In the proof of (iii), we used the fact that equinumerosity is an equivalence relation, the Cantor-Schroeder-Bernstein Theorem, and Problem 3 many times without mention. For example, we have $\mathbb{R} \sim (0, \infty)$ and $(0, \infty) \sim (0, 1)$. So, by the transitivity of $\sim$, we have $\mathbb{R} \sim (0, 1)$. As another example, the sequence $(a, \infty) \subseteq [a, \infty) \subseteq \mathbb{R} \sim (a, a + 1) \subseteq (a, \infty)$ together with Note 1 following Example 4.20 gives us that $(a, \infty) \preccurlyeq \mathbb{R}$ and $\mathbb{R} \preccurlyeq (a, \infty)$. By the Cantor-Schroeder-Bernstein Theorem, $(a, \infty) \sim \mathbb{R}$.

(2) Once we showed that for all $a, b \in \mathbb{R}$, $(0, 1) \sim (a, b)$, it follows from the fact that $\sim$ is an equivalence relation that any two bounded open intervals are equinumerous. Indeed, if (a, b) and (c, d) are bounded open intervals, then $(0, 1) \sim (a, b)$ and $(0, 1) \sim (c, d)$. By the symmetry of $\sim$, we have $(a, b) \sim (0, 1)$, and finally, by the transitivity of $\sim$, we have $(a, b) \sim (c, d)$.

(3) It's easy to prove that two specific intervals of real numbers are equinumerous using just the fact that any two bounded open intervals are equinumerous with each other, together with the fact that $\mathbb{R} \sim (0, 1)$. For example, to show that $[3, \infty)$ is equinumerous with $(-2, 5]$, simply consider the following sequence: $[3, \infty) \subseteq \mathbb{R} \sim (0, 1) \sim (-2, 5) \subseteq (-2, 5] \subseteq (-2, 6) \sim (3, 4) \subseteq [3, \infty)$.

16. Prove that if $A \sim B$ and $C \sim D$, then $^A C \sim {}^B D$.

Proof: Suppose that $A \sim B$ and $C \sim D$. Then there exist bijections $h: A \to B$ and $k: C \to D$. Define $F: {}^A C \to {}^B D$ by $F(f)(b) = k\left(f\left(h^{-1}(b)\right)\right)$.

Suppose $f, g \in {}^A C$ with $F(f) = F(g)$. Let $a \in A$ and let $b = h(a)$. We have $F(f)(b) = F(g)(b)$, or equivalently, $k\left(f\left(h^{-1}(b)\right)\right) = k\left(g\left(h^{-1}(b)\right)\right)$. Since k is injective, $f\left(h^{-1}(b)\right) = g\left(h^{-1}(b)\right)$. Since $b = h(a)$, $a = h^{-1}(b)$. So, $f(a) = g(a)$. Since $a \in A$ was arbitrary, $f = g$. Since $f, g \in {}^A C$ were arbitrary, F is injective.

Now, let $g \in {}^B D$ and let's define $f \in {}^A C$ by $f(a) = k^{-1}\left(g(h(a))\right)$. Let $b \in B$. Then we have $F(f)(b) = k\left(f\left(h^{-1}(b)\right)\right) = k\left(k^{-1}\left(g\left(h(h^{-1}(b))\right)\right)\right) = g(b)$. Since $b \in B$ was arbitrary, we have $F(f) = g$. Since $g \in {}^B D$ was arbitrary, F is surjective.

Since F is injective and surjective, ${}^A C \sim {}^B D$. $\qquad\square$

LEVEL 5

17. Let X be a nonempty set of sets and let f be a function such that $\bigcup X \subseteq \operatorname{dom} f$. Prove each of the following:

    (i) $f[\bigcup X] = \bigcup\{f[A] \mid A \in X\}$

    (ii) $f[\bigcap X] \subseteq \bigcap\{f[A] \mid A \in X\}$

    (iii) $f^{-1}[\bigcup X] = \bigcup\{f^{-1}[A] \mid A \in X\}$

    (iv) $f^{-1}[\bigcap X] = \bigcap\{f^{-1}[A] \mid A \in X\}$

Proofs:

(i)   Let $y \in f[\bigcup X]$. Then there is $x \in \bigcup X$ such that $f(x) = y$. Since $x \in \bigcup X$, there is $B \in X$ such that $x \in B$. So, $y = f(x) \in f[B]$. Therefore, $y \in \bigcup\{f[A] \mid A \in X\}$. Since $y \in f[\bigcup X]$ was arbitrary, we see that $f[\bigcup X] \subseteq \bigcup\{f[A] \mid A \in X\}$.

    Now, let $y \in \bigcup\{f[A] \mid A \in X\}$. Then there is $B \in X$ such that $y \in f[B]$. So, there is $x \in B$ such that $y = f(x)$. By Problem 29 (part (i)) from Problem Set 1, $B \subseteq \bigcup X$. Since $x \in B$ and $B \subseteq \bigcup X$, $x \in \bigcup X$. Thus, $y = f(x) \in f[\bigcup X]$. Since $y \in \bigcup\{f[A] \mid A \in X\}$ was arbitrary, we see that $\bigcup\{f[A] \mid A \in X\} \subseteq f[\bigcup X]$.

    Since $f[\bigcup X] \subseteq \bigcup\{f[A] \mid A \in X\}$ and $\bigcup\{f[A] \mid A \in X\} \subseteq f[\bigcup X]$, it follows that $f[\bigcup X] = \bigcup\{f[A] \mid A \in X\}$. $\qquad\square$

(ii)   Let $y \in f[\bigcap X]$. Then there is $x \in \bigcap X$ such that $f(x) = y$. Let $B \in X$. Since $x \in \bigcap X$, $x \in B$. So, $y = f(x) \in f[B]$. Since $B \in X$ was arbitrary, $y \in \bigcap\{f[A] \mid A \in X\}$. Since $y \in f[\bigcap X]$ was arbitrary, we see that $f[\bigcap X] \subseteq \bigcap\{f[A] \mid A \in X\}$. $\qquad\square$

(iii) $x \in f^{-1}[\bigcup X]$ if and only if $f(x) \in \bigcup X$ if and only if there is $A \in X$ such that $f(x) \in A$ if and only if there is $A \in X$ such that $x \in f^{-1}[A]$ if and only if $x \in \bigcup\{f^{-1}[A] \mid A \in X\}$. Therefore, $f^{-1}[\bigcup X] = \bigcup\{f^{-1}[A] \mid A \in X\}$. $\qquad\square$

55

(iv) $x \in f^{-1}[\cap X]$ if and only if $f(x) \in \cap X$ if and only for all $A \in X$, $f(x) \in A$ if and only if for all $A \in X$, $x \in f^{-1}[A]$ if and only if $x \in \cap\{f^{-1}[A] \mid A \in X\}$. Therefore, we see that $f^{-1}[\cap X] = \cap\{f^{-1}[A] \mid A \in X\}$.   □

18. Prove that for any sets A, B, and C, $^{B \times C}A \sim {}^C(^BA)$.

Proof: Let A, B, and C be sets, and define $F: {}^{B \times C}A \to {}^C(^BA)$ by $F(f)(c)(b) = f(b,c)$.

Suppose $f, g \in {}^{B \times C}A$ with $F(f) = F(g)$. Let $c \in C$. Since $F(f) = F(g)$, $F(f)(c) = F(g)(c)$. So, for all $b \in B$, $F(f)(c)(b) = F(g)(c)(b)$. So, for all $b \in B$, $f(b,c) = g(b,c)$. Since $c \in C$ was arbitrary, for all $b \in B$ and $c \in C$, $f(b,c) = g(b,c)$. Therefore, $f = g$. Since $f, g \in {}^{B \times C}A$ were arbitrary, F is injective.

Let $k \in {}^C(^BA)$ and define $f \in {}^{B \times C}A$ by $f(b,c) = k(c)(b)$. Then $F(f)(c)(b) = f(b,c) = k(c)(b)$. So, $F(f) = k$. Since $k \in {}^C(^BA)$ was arbitrary, F is surjective.

Since F is injective and surjective, $^{B \times C}A \sim {}^C(^BA)$.   □

19. Prove the following:

(i) $\mathcal{P}(\mathbb{N}) \sim S(\mathbb{N})$ (recall that $S(\mathbb{N}) = \{f \in {}^{\mathbb{N}}\mathbb{N} \mid f \text{ is a bijection}\}$).

(ii) $^{\mathbb{N}}\mathbb{R} \not\sim {}^{\mathbb{R}}\mathbb{N}$.

Proofs:

(i)   Let $S = S(\mathbb{N}) = \{f \in {}^{\mathbb{N}}\mathbb{N} \mid f \text{ is a bijection}\}$. Then $S \subseteq {}^{\mathbb{N}}\mathbb{N}$. So $S \preccurlyeq {}^{\mathbb{N}}\mathbb{N}$ by Note 1 following Example 4.20. By part (iv) of Problem 15, $^{\mathbb{N}}\mathbb{N} \sim \mathcal{P}(\mathbb{N})$. So, $^{\mathbb{N}}\mathbb{N} \preccurlyeq \mathcal{P}(\mathbb{N})$. By the transitivity of $\preccurlyeq$, $S \preccurlyeq \mathcal{P}(\mathbb{N})$.

Now, define $F: \mathcal{P}(\mathbb{N}) \to S$ by $F(A) = f_A$, where f_A is defined as follows: if $n \notin A$, then $f_A(2n) = 2n$ and $f_A(2n + 1) = 2n + 1$; if $n \in A$, then $f_A(2n) = 2n + 1$ and $f_A(2n + 1) = 2n$.

To see that F is injective, suppose that $A, B \in \mathcal{P}(\mathbb{N})$ and $A \neq B$. Without loss of generality, suppose that there is $n \in A \setminus B$. Then $f_A(2n) = 2n + 1$ and $f_B(2n) = 2n$. So, $f_A \neq f_B$. Thus, $F(A) \neq F(B)$, and therefore, F is injective.

Since $S \preccurlyeq \mathcal{P}(\mathbb{N})$ and $\mathcal{P}(\mathbb{N}) \preccurlyeq S$, by the Cantor-Schroeder-Bernstein Theorem, $\mathcal{P}(\mathbb{N}) \sim S$.   □

(ii) By part (iii) of Problem 15, $\mathbb{R} \sim [0, 1)$. By Example 4.21, $[0, 1) \sim \mathcal{P}(\mathbb{N})$. So, by the transitivity of $\sim$, $\mathbb{R} \sim \mathcal{P}(\mathbb{N})$. By Problem 16, $^{\mathbb{N}}\mathbb{R} \sim {}^{\mathbb{N}}\mathcal{P}(\mathbb{N})$.

Using previous equinumerosity results, we get the following:

$^{\mathbb{N}}\mathbb{R} \sim {}^{\mathbb{N}}\mathcal{P}(\mathbb{N}) \sim {}^{\mathbb{N}}(^{\mathbb{N}}2) \sim {}^{\mathbb{N} \times \mathbb{N}}2 \sim {}^{\mathbb{N}}2 \sim \mathcal{P}(\mathbb{N}) \sim \mathbb{R} \prec \mathcal{P}(\mathbb{R}) \sim {}^{\mathbb{R}}2 \subseteq {}^{\mathbb{R}}\mathbb{N}$. It follows that $^{\mathbb{N}}\mathbb{R} \prec {}^{\mathbb{R}}\mathbb{N}$.   □

Note: To help us understand the function F defined above, let's draw a visual representation of $F(\mathbb{E})$, where $\mathbb{E}$ is the set of even natural numbers.

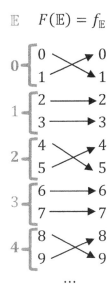

$$\mathbb{E} \quad F(\mathbb{E}) = f_{\mathbb{E}}$$

Along the left of the image we have listed the natural numbers $0, 1, 2, 3, 4, \ldots$ (we stopped at 4, but our intention is that they keep going). The elements of $\mathbb{E}$ are $0, 2, 4, \ldots$ We highlighted these in bold. We associate each natural number n with the pair $\{2n, 2n + 1\}$. For example, $2 \cdot 4 = 8$ and $2 \cdot 4 + 1 = 9$. So, we associate 4 with the pair of natural numbers $\{8, 9\}$. We used left braces to indicate that association. The arrows give a visual representation of $f_{\mathbb{E}}$. Since $0 \in \mathbb{E}$, $f_{\mathbb{E}}$ swaps the corresponding pair 0 and 1. Since $1 \notin \mathbb{E}$, $f_{\mathbb{E}}$ leaves the corresponding pair 2 and 3 fixed. And so on, down the line...

The configuration of $f_{\mathbb{O}}$, where $\mathbb{O}$ is the set of odd natural numbers would be the opposite of the configuration for the evens. For example, 0 and 1 would remain fixed, while 2 and 3 would be swapped.

LEVEL 1

1. Use the Principle of Mathematical Induction to prove each of the following:

   (i) $2^n > n$ for all natural numbers $n \geq 1$.

   (ii) $0 + 1 + 2 + \cdots + n = \frac{n(n+1)}{2}$ for all natural numbers.

   (iii) $n! > 2^n$ for all natural numbers $n \geq 4$ (where $n! = 1 \cdot 2 \cdots n$ for all natural numbers $n \geq 1$).

   (iv) $2^n \geq n^2$ for all natural numbers $n \geq 4$.

Proofs:

(i) **Base Case** $(k = 1)$: $2^1 = 2 > 1$.

Inductive Step: Let $k \in \mathbb{N}$ with $k \geq 1$ and assume that $2^k > k$. Then we have

$$2^{k+1} = 2^k \cdot 2^1 = 2^k \cdot 2 > k \cdot 2 = 2k = k + k \geq k + 1.$$

Therefore, $2^{k+1} > k + 1$.

By the Principle of Mathematical Induction, $2^n > n$ for all natural numbers $n \geq 1$. □

(ii) **Base Case** $(k = 0)$: $0 = \frac{0(0+1)}{2}$.

Inductive Step: Let $k \in \mathbb{N}$ and assume that $0 + 1 + 2 + \cdots + k = \frac{k(k+1)}{2}$. Then we have

$$0 + 1 + 2 + \cdots + k + (k + 1) = \frac{k(k + 1)}{2} + (k + 1) = (k + 1)\left(\frac{k}{2} + 1\right) = (k + 1)\left(\frac{k}{2} + \frac{2}{2}\right)$$

$$= (k + 1)\left(\frac{k + 2}{2}\right) = \frac{(k + 1)(k + 2)}{2} = \frac{(k + 1)\big((k + 1) + 1\big)}{2}$$

By the Principle of Mathematical Induction, $0 + 1 + 2 + \cdots + n = \frac{n(n+1)}{2}$ for all natural numbers n. □

(iii) **Base Case** $(k = 4)$: $4! = 1 \cdot 2 \cdot 3 \cdot 4 = 24 > 16 = 2^4$.

Inductive Step: Let $k \in \mathbb{N}$ with $k \geq 4$ and assume that $k! > 2^k$. Then we have

$$(k + 1)! = (k + 1)k! > (k + 1)2^k \geq (4 + 1) \cdot 2^k = 5 \cdot 2^k \geq 2 \cdot 2^k = 2^1 \cdot 2^k = 2^{1+k} = 2^{k+1}.$$

Therefore, $(k + 1)! > 2^{k+1}$.

By the Principle of Mathematical Induction, $n! > 2^n$ for all natural numbers $n \geq 4$. □

(iv) **Base Case** $(k = 4)$: $2^4 = 16 = 4^2$. So, $2^4 \geq 4^2$.

Inductive Step: Let $k \in \mathbb{N}$ with $k \geq 4$ and assume that $2^k \geq k^2$. Then we have

$$2^{k+1} = 2^k \cdot 2^1 \geq k^2 \cdot 2 = 2k^2 = k^2 + k^2.$$

By Theorem 5.11, $k^2 > 2k + 1$. So, we have $2^{k+1} > k^2 + 2k + 1 = (k+1)^2$.

Therefore, $2^{k+1} \geq (k+1)^2$.

By the Principle of Mathematical Induction, $2^n \geq n^2$ for all $n \in \mathbb{N}$ with $n \geq 4$. $\qquad\square$

Note: Let's take one last look at number (iv). $2^0 = 1 \geq 0 = 0^2$. So, the statement in (iv) is true for $k = 0$. Also, $2^1 = 2 \geq 1 = 1^2$ and $2^2 = 4 = 2^2$. So, the statement is true for $k = 1$ and $k = 2$. However, $2^3 = 8$ and $3^2 = 9$. So, the statement is false for $k = 3$. It follows that $2^n \geq n^2$ for all natural numbers n except $n = 3$.

2. A natural number n is **divisible** by a natural number k, written $k|n$, if there is another natural number b such that $n = kb$. Prove that $n^3 - n$ is divisible by 3 for all natural numbers n.

Proof by Mathematical Induction:

Base Case ($k = 0$): $0^3 - 0 = 0 = 3 \cdot 0$. So, $0^3 - 0$ is divisible by 3.

Inductive Step: Let $k \in \mathbb{N}$ and assume that $k^3 - k$ is divisible by 3. Then $k^3 - k = 3b$ for some integer b. Now,

$$(k+1)^3 - (k+1) = (k+1)[(k+1)^2 - 1] = (k+1)[(k+1)(k+1) - 1]$$

$$= (k+1)(k^2 + 2k + 1 - 1) = (k+1)(k^2 + 2k) = k^3 + 2k^2 + k^2 + 2k = k^3 + 3k^2 + 2k$$

$$= k^3 - k + k + 3k^2 + 2k = (k^3 - k) + 3k^2 + 3k = 3b + 3(k^2 + k) = 3(b + k^2 + k).$$

Since $\mathbb{Z}$ is closed under addition and multiplication, $b + k^2 + k \in \mathbb{Z}$. Therefore, $(k+1)^3 - (k+1)$ is divisible by 3.

By the Principle of Mathematical Induction, $n^3 - n$ is divisible by 3 for all $n \in \mathbb{N}$. $\qquad\square$

Note: Notice our use of SACT (see Note 1 after Example 1.16) in the beginning of the last line of the sequence of equations. We needed $k^3 - k$ to appear, but the $-k$ was nowhere to be found. So, we simply threw it in, and then repaired the damage by adding k right after it.

3. Let $z = -4 - i$ and $w = 3 - 5i$. Compute each of the following:

    (i) $z + w$

    (ii) zw

    (iii) Im w

Solutions:

   (i) $z + w = (-4 - i) + (3 - 5i) = (-4 + 3) + (-1 - 5)i = \mathbf{-1 - 6i}$.

   (ii) $zw = (-4 - i)(3 - 5i) = (-12 - 5) + (20 - 3)i = \mathbf{-17 + 17i}$.

   (iii) Im $w = $ Im $(3 - 5i) = \mathbf{-5}$.

4. Prove each of the following. (You may assume that $<$ is a strict linear ordering of $\mathbb{N}$.)

    (i)   Addition is commutative in $\mathbb{N}$.

    (ii)   The set of natural numbers is closed under multiplication.

    (iii)   1 is a multiplicative identity in $\mathbb{N}$.

    (iv)   Multiplication is distributive over addition in $\mathbb{N}$.

    (v)   Multiplication is associative in $\mathbb{N}$.

    (vi)   Multiplication is commutative in $\mathbb{N}$.

    (vii)   For all natural numbers m, n, and k, if $m + k = n + k$, then $m = n$.

    (viii) For all natural numbers m, n, and k, if $mk = nk$, then $m = n$.

    (ix)   For all natural numbers m and n, $m < n$ if and only if there is a natural number $k > 0$ such that $n = m + k$.

    (x)   For all natural numbers m, n, and k, $m < n$ if and only if $m + k < n + k$.

    (xi)   For all natural numbers m and n, if $m > 0$ and $n > 0$, then $mn > 0$.

Proofs:

(i)   We first prove by induction on n that $1 + n = n + 1$.

Base Case $(k = 0)$: By definition of addition of natural numbers, we have $1 + 0 = 1$. By Theorem 5.8, we have $0 + 1 = 1$. Therefore, $1 + 0 = 0 + 1$.

Inductive Step: Let $k \in \mathbb{N}$ and assume that $1 + k = k + 1$. Then we have

$$1 + (k + 1) = (1 + k) + 1 = (k + 1) + 1.$$

For the first equality, we used the definition of addition of natural numbers. For the second equality, we used the inductive hypothesis.

By the Principle of Mathematical Induction, for all natural numbers n, $1 + n = n + 1$.

We are now ready to use induction to prove the result. Assume that m is a natural number.

Base Case $(k = 0)$:   By definition of addition of natural numbers, $m + 0 = m$. By Theorem 5.8, $0 + m = m$. Therefore, $m + 0 = 0 + m$.

Inductive Step: Let $k \in \mathbb{N}$ and assume that $m + k = k + m$. Then we have

$$m + (k + 1) = (m + k) + 1 = (k + m) + 1 = k + (m + 1) = k + (1 + m) = (k + 1) + m.$$

For the first and third equalities, we used the definition of addition of natural numbers (or Theorem 5.9). For the second equality, we used the inductive hypothesis. For the fourth equality, we used the preliminary result that we proved above. For the fifth equality, we used Theorem 5.9.

By the Principle of Mathematical Induction, for all natural numbers n, $m + n = n + m$.

Since m was an arbitrary natural number, we have shown that for all natural numbers m and n, we have $m + n = n + m$. $\qquad\square$

(ii)   Assume that m is a natural number.

Base Case $(k = 0)$: $m \cdot 0 = 0$, which is a natural number.

Inductive Step: Let k be a natural number and assume that mk is also a natural number. Then $m(k + 1) = mk + m$. Since mk and m are both natural numbers, by Theorem 5.7, $mk + m$ is a natural number.

By the Principle of Mathematical Induction, mn is a natural number for all natural numbers n.

Since m was an arbitrary natural number, we have shown that the product of any two natural numbers is a natural number. $\qquad\square$

(iii)   Assume that m is a natural number.

We have $m \cdot 1 = m(0 + 1) = m \cdot 0 + m = 0 + m = m$. For the first and fourth equalities, we used Theorem 5.8. For the second and third equalities, we used the definition of multiplication of natural numbers.

We prove that $1 \cdot n = n$ by induction on n.

Proof: Base Case $(k = 0)$: $1 \cdot 0 = 0$ by the definition of multiplication of natural numbers.

Inductive Step: Let $k \in \mathbb{N}$ and assume that $1 \cdot k = k$. Then

$$1(k + 1) = 1 \cdot k + 1 = k + 1.$$

For the first equality, we used the definition of multiplication of natural numbers. For the second equality, we used the inductive hypothesis.

By the Principle of Mathematical Induction, for all natural numbers n, $1 \cdot n = n$. $\qquad\square$

(iv)   Let m and n be natural numbers. We first prove that for all $t \in \mathbb{N}$, $(m + n) \cdot t = mt + nt$ (we say that multiplication is **right distributive** over addition in $\mathbb{N}$).

Base Case $(k = 0)$: $(m + n) \cdot 0 = 0$ by the definition of multiplication of natural numbers. Similarly, $m \cdot 0 = 0$ and $n \cdot 0 = 0$. So, $m \cdot 0 + n \cdot 0 = 0$. Therefore, $(m + n) \cdot 0 = m \cdot 0 + n \cdot 0$.

Inductive Step: Let $k \in \mathbb{N}$ and assume that $(m + n) \cdot k = mk + nk$. Then

$$(m + n)(k + 1) = (m + n) \cdot k + (m + n) = (mk + nk) + (m + n)$$
$$= (mk + m) + (nk + n) = m(k + 1) + n(k + 1).$$

For the first and fourth equalities, we used the definition of multiplication of natural numbers. For the second equality, we used the inductive hypothesis. For the third equality we used the fact that addition is associative and commutative in $\mathbb{N}$ several times.

By the Principle of Mathematical Induction, for all natural numbers t, $(m + n) \cdot t = mt + nt$.

We next prove that $n \cdot 0 = 0$ and $0 \cdot n = 0$ for all natural numbers n.

$n \cdot 0 = 0$ by the definition of multiplication of natural numbers.

We prove that $0 \cdot n = 0$ by induction on n.

Base Case $(k = 0)$: By definition of multiplication of natural numbers, we have $0 \cdot 0 = 0$.

Inductive Step: Let $k \in \mathbb{N}$ and assume that $0 \cdot k = 0$. Then we have

$$0 \cdot (k + 1) = 0 \cdot k + 0 = 0 + 0 = 0.$$

For the first equality, we used the definition of multiplication of natural numbers. For the second equality, we used the inductive hypothesis. For the third equality, we used the definition of addition of natural numbers.

By the Principle of Mathematical Induction, for all natural numbers n, $0 \cdot n = n$.

Let m be a natural number. We prove that for all $n \in \mathbb{N}$, $mn = nm$ (we say that multiplication is **commutative** in $\mathbb{N}$).

Base Case $(k = 0)$: $m \cdot 0 = 0$ by the definition of multiplication of natural numbers. We just proved that $0 \cdot m = 0$. Therefore, $m \cdot 0 = 0 \cdot m$

Inductive Step: Let $k \in \mathbb{N}$ and assume that $mk = km$. Then

$$m(k + 1) = mk + m = km + m = (k + 1)m.$$

For the first equality, we used the definition of multiplication of natural numbers. For the second equality, we used the inductive hypothesis. For the third equality we used the fact that multiplication is right distributive over addition in $\mathbb{N}$ (proved above).

By the Principle of Mathematical Induction, for all natural numbers n, $mn = nm$.

Finally, let $m, n, t \in \mathbb{N}$. Then $m(n + t) = (n + t)m = nm + tm = mn + mt$. This shows that multiplication is distributive over addition in $\mathbb{N}$. □

    (v)   Assume that m and n are natural numbers

Base Case $(k = 0)$: $(mn) \cdot 0 = 0 = m \cdot 0 = m(n \cdot 0)$ by the definition of multiplication of natural numbers.

Inductive Step: Let $k \in \mathbb{N}$ and assume that $(mn)k = m(nk)$. Then

$$(mn)(k + 1) = (mn)k + mn = m(nk) + mn = mn + m(nk)$$
$$= m(n + nk) = m(nk + n) = m\big(n(k + 1)\big).$$

For the first and sixth equalities, we used the definition of multiplication of natural numbers. For the second equality, we used the inductive hypothesis. For the third and fifth equalities, we used the fact that addition is commutative in $\mathbb{N}$. For the fourth equality, we used the fact that multiplication is distributive over addition in $\mathbb{N}$.

By the Principle of Mathematical Induction, for all natural numbers t, $(mn)t = m(nt)$. This shows that multiplication is associative in $\mathbb{N}$. □

    (vi)   This was already proved in (iv) above. □

(vii)   Let $m, n \in \mathbb{N}$. We prove by induction on k that $m + k = n + k \rightarrow m = n$.

Base Case ($k = 0$ and $k = 1$): If $m + 0 = n + 0$, then since $m + 0 = m$ and $n + 0 = n$ (by definition of addition of natural numbers), $m = n$. Next, suppose $m + 1 = n + 1$. Then $m \cup \{m\} = n \cup \{n\}$. If $n \neq m$, then either $n \in m$ or $m \in n$. Without loss of generality, assume that $n \in m$. Since $\in$ is antisymmetric on $\mathbb{N}$ and $n \neq m$, we must have $m \notin n$. Thus, $m = n$, contrary to our assumption that $n \neq m$. This contradiction shows that $m = n$.

Inductive Step: Let $t \in \mathbb{N}$, assume that $m + t = n + t \rightarrow m = n$, and let $m + (t + 1) = n + (t + 1)$. By the definition of addition in $\mathbb{N}$, $(m + t) + 1 = (n + t) + 1$. By the base case, $m + t = n + t$. By the inductive hypothesis, $m = n$.

By the Principle of Mathematical Induction, for all natural numbers m, n, and k, if $m + k = n + k$, then $m = n$. $\qquad\square$

(viii)   Let $m, n \in \mathbb{N}$. We prove by induction on k that $mk = nk \rightarrow m = n$.

Base Case ($k = 0$): If $m \cdot 0 = n \cdot 0$, then since $m \cdot 0 = 0$ and $n \cdot 0 = 0$ (by definition of multiplication of natural numbers), $m = n$.

Inductive Step: Let $t \in \mathbb{N}$, assume that $mt = nt \rightarrow m = n$, and let $m(t + 1) = n(t + 1)$. By the definition of multiplication in $\mathbb{N}$, $mt + 1 = nt + 1$. By (vii), $mt = nt$. By the inductive hypothesis, we have $m = n$.

By the Principle of Mathematical Induction, for all natural numbers m, n, and k, if $mk = nk$, then $m = n$. $\qquad\square$

(ix)   Let $m \in \mathbb{N}$. We prove by induction on n that if $m < n$, there is $k > 0$ such that $n = m + k$.

Base Case ($t = 0$): If $m < 0$, then $m \in \emptyset$, which is impossible. So, the conclusion is vacuously true.

Inductive Step: Let $t \in \mathbb{N}$ and assume that if $m < t$, there is $k > 0$ such that $t = m + k$. Assume that $m < t + 1$. Then $m < t$ or $m = t$. If $m < t$, then $t + 1 = (m + k) + 1 = m + (k + 1)$. If $m = t$, then $t + 1 = m + 1$.

By the Principle of Mathematical Induction, for all $n \in \mathbb{N}$, if $m < n$, there is $k > 0$ so that $n = m + k$.

Now, let $n, m \in \mathbb{N}$. We prove by induction on $k > 0$ that if $n = m + k$, then $m < n$.

Base Case ($t = 1$): If $n = m + 1 = m \cup \{m\}$, then since $m \in \{m\}$, $m \in n$, and so, $m < n$.

Inductive Step: Assume that if $n = m + t$, then $m < n$. Let $n = m + (t + 1)$. Then since addition is commutative and associative in $\mathbb{N}$, $n = m + (1 + t) = (m + 1) + t$. By the inductive hypothesis, we have $m + 1 < n$. Since $m < m + 1$ and $<$ is transitive on $\mathbb{N}$, $m < n$.

By the Principle of Mathematical Induction, if $k > 0$ and $n = m + k$, then $m < n$. $\qquad\square$

(x)   Let $m, n, k \in \mathbb{N}$.

By (ix), $m < n$ if and only if there is a natural number $t > 0$ such that $n = m + t$. Now, $n + k = (m + t) + k = m + (t + k) = m + (k + t) = (m + k) + t$. So, if $m < n$, then there is a natural number $t > 0$ such that $n + k = (m + k) + t$. Thus, by (ix), $m + k < n + k$. Conversely, if $m + k < n + k$, then there is a natural number t such that $n + k = (m + k) + t = (m + t) + k$. By (vii), $n = m + t$. So, by (ix) again, $m < n$. $\qquad\square$

(xi)   Let $m \in \mathbb{N}$ with $m > 0$. We prove by induction on n that $n > 0 \to mn > 0$.

Base Case $(k = 1)$: If $n = 1$, then $m \cdot 1 = m \cdot 0 + m = 0 + m = m > 0$.

Inductive Step: Let $k \in \mathbb{N}$ with $k > 0$ and assume that $mk > 0$. Then $m(k + 1) = mk + k$. Since $mk > 0$, by (x), $mk + k > 0 + k = k > 0$. So, $m(k + 1) > 0$.

By the Principle of Mathematical Induction, for all natural numbers m and n, if $m > 0$ and $n > 0$, then $mn > 0$. $\qquad\square$

5.   A set A is **transitive** if $\forall x(x \in A \to x \subseteq A)$ (in words, every element of A is also a subset of A). Prove that every natural number is transitive.

Proof by Mathematical Induction:

Base Case $(k = 0)$: $0 = \emptyset$. Since $\emptyset$ has no elements, it is vacuously true that every element of $\emptyset$ is a subset of $\emptyset$.

Inductive Step: Assuming that k is transitive, let $j \in k + 1 = k \cup \{k\}$ and $m \in j$. Then $j \in k$ or $j \in \{k\}$. If $j \in k$, then we have $m \in j \in k$. Since k is transitive, $m \in k$. Therefore, $m \in k \cup \{k\} = k + 1$. If $j \in \{k\}$, then $j = k$. So, $m \in k$, and again, $m \in k \cup \{k\} = k + 1$.

By the Principle of Mathematical Induction, every natural number is transitive. $\qquad\square$

6.   Determine if each of the following sequences are Cauchy sequences. Are any of the Cauchy sequences equivalent?

   (i) $(x_n) = \left(1 + \dfrac{1}{n+1}\right)$

   (ii) $(y_n) = (2^n)$

   (iii) $(z_n) = \left(1 - \dfrac{1}{2n+1}\right)$

Solutions:

   (i)   **Cauchy**

   (ii)   **Not Cauchy**

   (iii)   **Cauchy**

(x_n) and (z_n) are equivalent.

7.   Each of the following complex numbers are written in exponential form. Rewrite each complex number in standard form: (i) $e^{\pi i}$; (ii) $e^{-\frac{5\pi}{2}i}$; (iii) $3e^{\frac{\pi}{4}i}$; (iv) $2e^{\frac{\pi}{3}i}$; (v) $\sqrt{2}e^{\frac{7\pi}{6}i}$; (vi) $\pi e^{-\frac{5\pi}{4}i}$; (vii) $e^{\frac{19\pi}{12}}$

Solutions:

   (i) $e^{\pi i} = \cos \pi + i \sin \pi = -1 + 0i = -\mathbf{1}.$

   (ii) $e^{-\frac{5\pi}{2}i} = \cos\left(-\dfrac{5\pi}{2}\right) + i \sin\left(-\dfrac{5\pi}{2}\right) = \cos\dfrac{5\pi}{2} - i \sin\dfrac{5\pi}{2} = 0 - 1i = -\boldsymbol{i}.$

(iii) $\quad 3e^{\frac{\pi}{4}i} = 3\left(\cos\frac{\pi}{4} + i\sin\frac{\pi}{4}\right) = 3\left(\frac{\sqrt{2}}{2} + \frac{\sqrt{2}}{2}i\right) = \frac{3\sqrt{2}}{2} + \frac{3\sqrt{2}}{2}\boldsymbol{i}.$

(iv) $\quad 2e^{\frac{\pi}{3}i} = 2\left(\cos\frac{\pi}{3} + i\sin\frac{\pi}{3}\right) = 2\left(\frac{1}{2} + \frac{\sqrt{3}}{2}i\right) = \boldsymbol{1 + \sqrt{3}i}.$

(v) $\quad \sqrt{2}e^{\frac{7\pi}{6}i} = \sqrt{2}\left(\cos\frac{7\pi}{6} + i\sin\frac{7\pi}{6}\right) = \sqrt{2}\left(-\frac{\sqrt{3}}{2} - \frac{1}{2}i\right) = -\frac{\sqrt{6}}{2} - \frac{\sqrt{2}}{2}\boldsymbol{i}.$

(vi) $\quad \pi e^{-\frac{5\pi}{4}i} = \pi\left(\cos\left(-\frac{5\pi}{4}\right) + i\sin\left(-\frac{5\pi}{4}\right)\right) = \pi\left(\cos\frac{5\pi}{4} - i\sin\frac{5\pi}{4}\right) = -\frac{\pi\sqrt{2}}{2} + \frac{\pi\sqrt{2}}{2}\boldsymbol{i}.$

(vii) $\quad e^{\frac{19\pi}{12}} = \cos\frac{19\pi}{12} + i\sin\frac{19\pi}{12} = \frac{-\sqrt{2}+\sqrt{6}}{4} + \frac{-\sqrt{2}-\sqrt{6}}{4}\boldsymbol{i}.$

8. Each of the following complex numbers are written in standard form. Rewrite each complex number in exponential form: (i) $-1 - i$; (ii) $\sqrt{3} + i$; (iii) $1 - \sqrt{3}i$; (iv) $\left(\frac{\sqrt{6}+\sqrt{2}}{4}\right) + \left(\frac{\sqrt{6}-\sqrt{2}}{4}\right)i.$

Solutions:

(i) $\quad r^2 = (-1)^2 + (-1)^2 = 1 + 1 = 2.$ So, $r = \sqrt{2}.$ $\tan\theta = \frac{-1}{-1} = 1.$ So, $\theta = \pi + \frac{\pi}{4} = \frac{5\pi}{4}.$
Therefore, $-1 - i = \sqrt{2}e^{\frac{5\pi}{4}i} = \sqrt{2}e^{-\frac{3\pi}{4}i}.$

(ii) $\quad r^2 = \left(\sqrt{3}\right)^2 + 1^2 = 3 + 1 = 4.$ So, $r = 2.$ $\tan\theta = \frac{1}{\sqrt{3}}.$ So, $\theta = \frac{\pi}{6}.$ Therefore, we have
$\sqrt{3} + i = \boldsymbol{2e^{\frac{\pi}{6}i}}.$

(iii) $\quad r^2 = 1^2 + \left(-\sqrt{3}\right)^2 = 1 + 3 = 4.$ So, $r = 2.$ $\tan\theta = \frac{-\sqrt{3}}{1}.$ So, $\theta = -\frac{\pi}{3}.$ Therefore, we have
$1 - \sqrt{3}i = \boldsymbol{2e^{-\frac{\pi}{3}i}}.$

(iv) $\quad r^2 = \left(\frac{\sqrt{6}+\sqrt{2}}{4}\right)^2 + \left(\frac{\sqrt{6}-\sqrt{2}}{4}\right)^2 = \frac{6+2+2\sqrt{12}}{16} + \frac{6+2-2\sqrt{12}}{16} = \frac{16}{16} = 1.$ So, $r = 1.$ By part 2 of
Problem 2, $\theta = \frac{\pi}{12}.$ Therefore, $\left(\frac{\sqrt{6}+\sqrt{2}}{4}\right) + \left(\frac{\sqrt{6}-\sqrt{2}}{4}\right)i = 1e^{\frac{\pi}{12}i} = \boldsymbol{e^{\frac{\pi}{12}i}}.$

9. Write the following complex numbers in standard form: (i) $\left(\frac{\sqrt{2}}{2} + \frac{\sqrt{2}}{2}i\right)^4$; (ii) $\left(1 + \sqrt{3}i\right)^5.$

Solutions:

(i) If $z = \frac{\sqrt{2}}{2} + \frac{\sqrt{2}}{2}i$, then $r = \sqrt{\left(\frac{\sqrt{2}}{2}\right)^2 + \left(\frac{\sqrt{2}}{2}\right)^2} = \sqrt{\frac{2}{4} + \frac{2}{4}} = 1$ and $\tan\theta = \frac{\frac{\sqrt{2}}{2}}{\frac{\sqrt{2}}{2}} = 1$, so that $\theta = \frac{\pi}{4}.$
So, in exponential form, $z = e^{\frac{\pi}{4}i}.$ Therefore, $\left(\frac{\sqrt{2}}{2} + \frac{\sqrt{2}}{2}i\right)^4 = \left(e^{\frac{\pi}{4}i}\right)^4 = e^{\pi i} = \boldsymbol{-1}.$

(ii) If $z = 1 + \sqrt{3}i$, then $r = \sqrt{1^2 + \left(\sqrt{3}\right)^2} = \sqrt{1+3} = \sqrt{4} = 2$ and $\tan\theta = \frac{\sqrt{3}}{1} = \sqrt{3}$, so that
$\theta = \frac{\pi}{3}.$ So, in exponential form, $z = 2e^{\frac{\pi}{3}i}.$ So, $\left(1 + \sqrt{3}i\right)^5 = \left(2e^{\frac{\pi}{3}i}\right)^5 = 2^5 e^{\frac{5\pi}{3}i} = \boldsymbol{16 - 16\sqrt{3}i}.$

10. Prove that if $n \in \mathbb{N}$ and A is a nonempty subset of n, then A has a least element.

Proof by Mathematical Induction:

Base Case $(k = 0)$: $0 = \emptyset$. The only subset of $\emptyset$ is $\emptyset$. So, the statement is vacuously true.

Inductive Step: Assume that every nonempty subset of the natural number k has a least element. We will show that every nonempty subset of $k + 1 = k \cup \{k\}$ has a least element.

Let A be a nonempty subset of $k + 1$. Then $A \setminus \{k\} \subseteq k$. If $A \setminus \{k\} \neq \emptyset$, then by the inductive hypothesis, $A \setminus \{k\}$ has a least element, say j. Since $j \in k$, j is the least element of A. If $A \setminus \{k\} = \emptyset$, then k is the only element of A, and therefore, it is the least element of A.

By the Principle of Mathematical Induction, if $n \in \mathbb{N}$ and A is a nonempty subset of n, then A has a least element. $\qquad\square$

11. Prove POMI $\to$ WOP.

Proof: Assume POMI, let A be a nonempty subset of $\mathbb{N}$, and choose $n \in A$. If $n \cap A = \emptyset$, then n is the least element of A (If $m \in A$ with $m \in n$, then $m \in n \cap A$, contradicting $n \cap A = \emptyset$). Otherwise, $n \cap A$ is a nonempty subset of n, and so, by Problem 5, $n \cap A$ has a least element m. Then m is the least element of A (If $k \in A$ with $k \in m$, then $k \in n$ by Problem 4, and so, m is not the least element of $n \cap A$). $\qquad\square$

12. Prove that $<_{\mathbb{Z}}$ is a well-defined strict linear ordering on $\mathbb{Z}$. You may use the fact that $<_{\mathbb{N}}$ is a well-defined strict linear ordering on $\mathbb{N}$.

Proof: We first show that $<_{\mathbb{Z}}$ is well-defined. Suppose that $(a, b) \sim (a', b')$ and $(c, d) \sim (c', d)$. Since $(a, b) \sim (a', b')$, $a + b' = b + a'$. Since $(c, d) \sim (c', d')$, $c + d' = d + c'$.

We need to check that $[(a, b)] <_{\mathbb{Z}} [(c, d)]$ if and only if $[(a', b')] <_{\mathbb{Z}} [(c', d')]$. We have

$[(a, b)] <_{\mathbb{Z}} [(c, d)]$ if and only if $a + d <_{\mathbb{N}} b + c$ if and only if $a + d + b' + c' <_{\mathbb{N}} b + c + b' + c'$ if and only if $a + b' + d + c' <_{\mathbb{N}} b + c + b' + c'$ if and only if $b + a' + c + d' <_{\mathbb{N}} b + c + b' + c'$ if and only if $b + c + a' + d' <_{\mathbb{N}} b + c + b' + c'$ if and only if $a' + d' < b' + c'$ if and only if $[(a', b')] <_{\mathbb{Z}} [(c', d')]$, as desired.

Next, we show that $<_{\mathbb{Z}}$ is antireflexive. To see this, note that $a + b \not<_{\mathbb{N}} a + b$ because $\not<_{\mathbb{N}}$ is antireflexive. So, $a + b \not<_{\mathbb{N}} b + a$. Therefore, $[(a, b)] \not<_{\mathbb{Z}} [(a, b)]$.

To see that $<_{\mathbb{Z}}$ is antisymmetric, suppose that $[(a, b)] <_{\mathbb{Z}} [(c, d)]$ and $[(c, d)] <_{\mathbb{Z}} [(a, b)]$. Then we have $a + d <_{\mathbb{N}} b + c$ and $c + b <_{\mathbb{N}} d + a$, or equivalently, $b + c <_{\mathbb{N}} a + d$. This is impossible, and so, it is vacuously true that $<_{\mathbb{Z}}$ is antisymmetric.

To see that $<_\mathbb{Z}$ is transitive, suppose that $[(a,b)] <_\mathbb{Z} [(c,d)]$ and $[(c,d)] <_\mathbb{Z} [(e,f)]$. Then we have $a + d <_\mathbb{N} b + c$ and $c + f <_\mathbb{N} d + e$. By adding each side of these two inequalities we get the inequality $a + d + c + f <_\mathbb{N} b + c + d + e$. Cancelling c and d from each side of this last inequality yields $a + f <_\mathbb{N} b + e$. Therefore, $[(a,b)] <_\mathbb{Z} [(e,f)]$.

Finally, we check that trichotomy holds. Suppose $[(a,b)] \not<_\mathbb{Z} [(c,d)]$ and $[(a,b)] \neq [(c,d)]$. Then $a + d \not<_\mathbb{N} b + c$ and $a + d \neq b + c$. Since trichotomy holds for $<_\mathbb{N}$, we have $b + c <_\mathbb{N} a + d$, or equivalently, $c + b <_\mathbb{N} d + a$. Therefore, $[(c,d)] <_\mathbb{Z} [(a,b)]$. □

LEVEL 4

13. Prove that $3^n - 1$ is even for all natural numbers n.

Proof by Mathematical Induction:

Base Case $(k = 0)$: $3^0 - 1 = 1 - 1 = 0 = 2 \cdot 0$. So, $3^0 - 1$ is even.

Inductive Step: Let $k \in \mathbb{N}$ and assume that $3^k - 1$ is even. Then $3^k - 1 = 2b$ for some integer b. Now,

$$3^{k+1} - 1 = 3^k \cdot 3^1 - 1 = 3^k \cdot 3 - 1 = 3^k \cdot 3 - 3^k + 3^k - 1 = 3^k(3 - 1) + (3^k - 1)$$

$$= 3^k \cdot 2 + 2b = 2 \cdot 3^k + 2b = 2(3^k + b).$$

Since $\mathbb{N}$ is closed under multiplication, $3^k \in \mathbb{N}$. Since $\mathbb{N}$ is closed under addition, $3^k + b \in \mathbb{N}$. Therefore, $3^{k+1} - 1$ is even.

By the Principle of Mathematical Induction, $3^n - 1$ is even for all $n \in \mathbb{N}$. □

Notes: Notice our use of SACT (see Note 1 after Example 1.16) in the middle of the first line of the sequence of equations. We needed $3^k - 1$ to appear, so we added 3^k, and then subtracted 3^k to the left of it.

14. Prove that the Principle of Mathematical Induction is equivalent to the following statement:

(⋆) Let $P(n)$ be a statement and suppose that (i) $P(0)$ is true and (ii) for all $k \in \mathbb{N}$, $P(k) \to P(k + 1)$. Then $P(n)$ is true for all $n \in \mathbb{N}$.

Proof: Recall that the Principle of Mathematical Induction says the following: Let S be a set of natural numbers such that (i) $0 \in S$ and (ii) for all $k \in \mathbb{N}$, $k \in S \to k + 1 \in S$. Then $S = \mathbb{N}$.

Suppose that the Principle of Mathematical Induction is true and let $P(n)$ be a statement such that $P(0)$ is true, and for all $k \in \mathbb{N}$, $P(k) \to P(k + 1)$. Define $S = \{n \mid (P(n)\}$. Since $P(0)$ is true, $0 \in S$. If $k \in S$, then $P(k)$ is true. So, $P(k + 1)$ is true, and therefore, $k + 1 \in S$. By the Principle of Mathematical Induction, $S = \mathbb{N}$. So, $P(n)$ is true for all $n \in \mathbb{N}$.

Now, suppose that (⋆) holds, and let S be a set of natural numbers such that $0 \in S$, and for all $k \in \mathbb{N}$, $k \in S \to k + 1 \in S$. Let $P(n)$ be the statement $n \in S$. Since $0 \in S$, $P(0)$ is true. If $P(k)$ is true, then $k \in S$. So, $k + 1 \in S$, and therefore, $P(k + 1)$ is true. By (⋆), $P(n)$ is true for all n. So, for all $n \in \mathbb{N}$, we have $n \in S$. In other words, $\mathbb{N} \subseteq S$. Since we were given $S \subseteq \mathbb{N}$, we have $S = \mathbb{N}$. □

15. Let $r \in \mathbb{N}$. Prove that the Principle of Mathematical Induction implies the following statement:

$(\star_r)$ Let $P(n)$ be a statement and suppose that (i) $P(r)$ is true and (ii) for all $k \in \mathbb{N}$ with $k \geq r$, $P(k) \rightarrow P(k+1)$. Then $P(n)$ is true for all $n \in \mathbb{N}$ with $n \geq r$.

Proof: Suppose that the Principle of Mathematical Induction is true and let $P(n)$ be a statement such that $P(r)$ is true, and for all $k \in \mathbb{N}$ with $k \geq r$, $P(k) \rightarrow P(k+1)$. Define $S = \{n \mid (P(n+r)\}$. Since $P(r) = P(0+r)$ is true, $0 \in S$. If $k \in S$, then $P(k+r)$ is true. So, $P\big((k+1)+r\big) = P(k+r+1)$ is true, and therefore, $k+1 \in S$. By the Principle of Mathematical Induction, $S = \mathbb{N}$. So, $P(n+r)$ is true for all $n \in \mathbb{N}$. Therefore, $P(n)$ is true for all $n \in \mathbb{N}$ with $n \geq r$.

16. Prove that addition of integers is well-defined.

Proof: Suppose that $(a,b) \sim (a',b')$ and $(c,d) \sim (c',d)$. Since $(a,b) \sim (a',b')$, $a+b' = b+a'$. Since $(c,d) \sim (c',d')$, $c+d' = d+c'$.

We need to check that $(a+c, b+d) \sim (a'+c', b'+d')$, or equivalently, we need to check that $(a+c)+(b'+d') = (b+d)+(a'+c')$

Since $a+b' = b+a'$ and $c+d' = d+c'$, we have

$$(a+c)+(b'+d') = (a+b')+(c+d') = (b+a')+(d+c') = (b+d)+(a'+c').$$

Therefore, $(a+c, b+d) = (a'+c', b'+d')$, as desired.

17. Prove that addition and multiplication of rational numbers are well-defined.

Proof: Suppose that $\frac{a}{b} = \frac{a'}{b'}$ and $\frac{c}{d} = \frac{c'}{d'}$. Since $\frac{a}{b} = \frac{a'}{b'}$, we have $ab' = ba'$. Since $\frac{c}{d} = \frac{c'}{d'}$, we have $cd' = dc'$.

We first need to check that $\frac{a}{b} + \frac{c}{d} = \frac{a'}{b'} + \frac{c'}{d'}$, or equivalently, $\frac{ad+bc}{bd} = \frac{a'd'+b'c'}{b'd'}$.

Since $ab' = ba'$ and $cd' = dc'$, we have

$$(ad+bc)(b'd') = adb'd' + bcb'd' = ab'dd' + cd'bb' = ba'dd' + dc'bb'$$
$$= bda'd' + bdb'c' = (bd)(a'd' + b'c').$$

Therefore, $\frac{ad+bc}{bd} = \frac{a'd'+b'c'}{b'd'}$, as desired.

We next need to check that $\frac{a}{b} \cdot \frac{c}{d} = \frac{a'}{b'} \cdot \frac{c'}{d'}$, or equivalently, $\frac{ac}{bd} = \frac{a'c'}{b'd'}$.

Since $ab' = ba'$ and $cd' = dc'$, we have

$$(ac)(b'd') = (ab')(cd') = (ba')(dc') = (bd)(a'c')$$

Therefore, $\frac{ac}{bd} = \frac{a'c'}{b'd'}$, as desired. $\qquad\square$

18. Let $A = \{(x_n) \mid (x_n) \text{ is a Cauchy sequence of rational numbers}\}$ and define the relation R on A by $(x_n)R(y_n)$ if and only if for every $k \in \mathbb{N}^+$, there is $K \in \mathbb{N}$ such that $n > K$ implies $|x_n - y_n| < \frac{1}{k}$. Prove that R is an equivalence relation on A.

Proof: Let $(x_n) \in A$, let $k \in \mathbb{N}^+$ and let $K = 0$. Then $n > K$ implies $|x_n - x_n| = 0 < \frac{1}{k}$. So, $(x_n)R(x_n)$, and therefore, R is reflexive.

Since $|x_n - y_n| = |y_n - x_n|$, it is clear that R is symmetric.

Let $(x_n), (y_n), (z_n) \in A$ with $(x_n)R(y_n)$ and $(y_n)R(z_n)$ and let $k \in \mathbb{N}^+$. Since $(x_n)R(y_n)$, there is $K_1 \in \mathbb{N}$ such that $n > K_1$ implies $|x_n - y_n| < \frac{1}{2k}$. Since $(y_n)R(z_n)$, there is $K_2 \in \mathbb{N}$ such that $n > K_2$ implies $|y_n - z_n| < \frac{1}{2k}$. Let $K = \max\{K_1, K_2\}$. Let $n > K$. Since $K \geq K_1$, $n > K_1$, and therefore, we have $|x_n - y_n| < \frac{1}{2k}$. Since $K \geq K_2$, $n > K_2$, and therefore, we have $|y_n - z_n| < \frac{1}{2k}$. It follows that

$$|x_n - z_n| = |x_n - y_n + y_n - z_n| \leq |x_n - y_n| + |y_n - z_n| < \frac{1}{2k} + \frac{1}{2k} = 2 \cdot \frac{1}{2k} = \frac{1}{k}.$$

So, $(x_n)R(z_n)$, and therefore, R is transitive.

Since R is reflexive, symmetric, and transitive, it follows that R is an equivalence relation. $\square$

19. Prove that $\{A \in \mathcal{P}(\mathbb{N}) \mid A \text{ is finite}\}$ is countable and $\{A \in \mathcal{P}(\mathbb{N}) \mid A \text{ is infinite}\}$ is uncountable.

Proof: We first show that $X = \{A \in \mathcal{P}(\mathbb{N}) \mid A \text{ is finite}\}$ is countable. For each $n \in \mathbb{N}$, let $A_n = \{A \in \mathcal{P}(\mathbb{N}) \mid |A| \leq n\}$. Since $X = \bigcup\{A_n \mid n \in \mathbb{N}\}$, by Problem 13 from Problem Set 4, it suffices to show that for each $n \in \mathbb{N}$, A_n is countable. We show this by induction on $n \in \mathbb{N}$. $A_0 = \{\emptyset\}$, which is certainly countable. $\{\{n\} \mid n \in \mathbb{N}\}$ is clearly equinumerous to $\mathbb{N}$ via the function sending $\{n\}$ to n. Therefore, we see that $A_1 = A_0 \cup \{\{n\} \mid n \in \mathbb{N}\}$ is countable. Let $k \in \mathbb{N}$ and assume that A_k is countable. For each $n \in \mathbb{N}$, the set $B_k^n = \{A \cup \{n\} \mid A \in A_k\}$ is countable. By Problem 13 from Problem Set 4, the set $B_{k+1} = \bigcup\{B_k^n \mid n \in \mathbb{N}\}$ is countable. So, $A_{k+1} = A_0 \cup B_{k+1}$ is countable. By the principle of mathematical induction, for each $n \in \mathbb{N}$, A_n is countable. It follows that $X = \{A \in \mathcal{P}(\mathbb{N}) \mid A \text{ is finite}\}$ is countable.

Let $Y = \{A \in \mathcal{P}(\mathbb{N}) \mid A \text{ is infinite}\}$. Since every subset of $\mathbb{N}$ is either finite or infinite, $\mathcal{P}(\mathbb{N}) = X \cup Y$. If Y were countable, then since X is countable, by Problem 13 from Problem Set 4, $\mathcal{P}(\mathbb{N})$ would be countable, which we know it is not. Therefore, Y is uncountable. $\square$

Note: Computing A_1 in the proof above was not necessary. $B_0^n = \{A \cup \{n\} \mid A \in A_0\} = \{\{n\}\}$. Therefore, $B_1 = \bigcup\{B_0^n \mid n \in \mathbb{N}\} = \{\{n\} \mid n \in \mathbb{N}\}$. So, $A_1 = A_0 \cup B_1 = A_0 \cup \{\{n\} \mid n \in \mathbb{N}\}$. This is the same set that we wrote out explicitly in the proof.

20. Consider triangle AOP, where $O = (0,0)$, $A = (1,0)$, and P is the point on the unit circle so that angle POA has radian measure $\frac{\pi}{3}$. Prove that triangle AOP is equilateral, and then use this to prove that $W\left(\frac{\pi}{3}\right) = \left(\frac{1}{2}, \frac{\sqrt{3}}{2}\right)$. You may use the following facts about triangles: (i) The interior angle measures of a triangle sum to π radians; (ii) Two sides of a triangle have the same length if and only if the interior angles of the triangle opposite these sides have the same measure; (iii) If two sides of a triangle have the same length, then the line segment beginning at the point of intersection of those two sides and terminating on the opposite base midway between the endpoints of that base is perpendicular to that base.

Proof: Let's start by drawing the unit circle together with triangle AOP. We also draw line segment PE, where E is midway between O and A. By (iii), PE is perpendicular to OA.

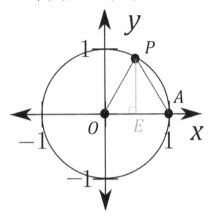

Since OP and OA are both radii of the circle, they have the same length. By (ii), angles OAP and OPA have the same measure. By (i), the sum of these measures is $\pi - \frac{\pi}{3} = \frac{3\pi}{3} - \frac{\pi}{3} = \frac{2\pi}{3}$. So, each of angles OAP and OPA measure $\frac{\pi}{3}$ radians. It follows from (ii) again that triangle AOP is equilateral.

Now, $OP = 1$ because OP is a radius of the unit circle and $OE = \frac{1}{2}$ because OA is a radius of the unit circle and E is midway between O and A. Since triangle OEP is a right triangle with hypotenuse OP, by the Pythagorean Theorem, $PE^2 = OP^2 - OE^2 = 1^2 - \left(\frac{1}{2}\right)^2 = 1 - \frac{1}{4} = \frac{3}{4}$. So, $PE = \sqrt{\frac{3}{4}} = \frac{\sqrt{3}}{\sqrt{4}} = \frac{\sqrt{3}}{2}$. It follows that $W\left(\frac{\pi}{3}\right) = \left(\frac{1}{2}, \frac{\sqrt{3}}{2}\right)$. $\qquad\square$

21. Prove that $W\left(\frac{\pi}{6}\right) = \left(\frac{\sqrt{3}}{2}, \frac{1}{2}\right)$. You can use facts (i), (ii), and (iii) described in Problem 20.

Proof: Let's start by drawing a picture similar to what we drew in Problem 20. We draw P and Q on the unit circle and A on the positive x-axis so that angle AOP has radian measure $\frac{\pi}{6}$, angle AOQ has radian measure $-\frac{\pi}{6}$, and A is right in the middle of the line segment joining P and Q.

70

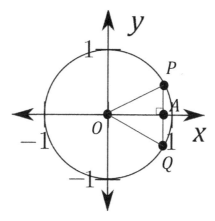

By reasoning similar to what was done in Problem 1, we see that triangle POQ is equilateral and OA is perpendicular to PQ.

Now, $OP = 1$ because OP is a radius of the unit circle and $PA = \frac{1}{2}$ because A is midway between P and Q. Since triangle POA is a right triangle with hypotenuse OP, by the Pythagorean Theorem, $OA^2 = OP^2 - AP^2 = 1^2 - \left(\frac{1}{2}\right)^2 = 1 - \frac{1}{4} = \frac{3}{4}$. Therefore, $OA = \sqrt{\frac{3}{4}} = \frac{\sqrt{3}}{\sqrt{4}} = \frac{\sqrt{3}}{2}$. It follows that $W\left(\frac{\pi}{6}\right) = \left(\frac{\sqrt{3}}{2}, \frac{1}{2}\right)$. $\qquad\square$

22. Let θ and ϕ be the radian measures of angles A and B, respectively. Prove the following identity:
$$\cos(\theta - \phi) = \cos\theta \cos\phi + \sin\theta \sin\phi$$

Proof: Let's draw a picture of the unit circle together with angles θ, ϕ, and $\theta - \phi$ in standard position, and label the corresponding points on the unit circle.

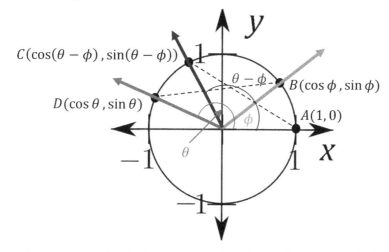

Since the arcs moving counterclockwise from A to C and from B to D both have radian measure $\theta - \phi$, it follows that $AC = BD$, and so, using the Pythagorean Theorem twice, we have
$$(\cos(\theta - \phi) - 1)^2 + (\sin(\theta - \phi) - 0)^2 = (\cos\theta - \cos\phi)^2 + (\sin\theta - \sin\phi)^2$$

The left-hand side of this equation is equal to:

71

$$(\cos(\theta - \phi) - 1)^2 + (\sin(\theta - \phi) - 0)^2$$
$$= \cos^2(\theta - \phi) - 2\cos(\theta - \phi) + 1 + \sin^2(\theta - \phi)$$
$$= (\cos^2(\theta - \phi) + \sin^2(\theta - \phi)) - 2\cos(\theta - \phi) + 1$$
$$= 1 - 2\cos(\theta - \phi) + 1 \text{ (by the Pythagorean Identity)}$$
$$= 2 - 2\cos(\theta - \phi)$$

The right-hand side of this equation is equal to:

$$(\cos\theta - \cos\phi)^2 + (\sin\theta - \sin\phi)^2$$
$$= \cos^2\theta - 2\cos\theta\cos\phi + \cos^2\phi + \sin^2\theta - 2\sin\theta\sin\phi + \sin^2\phi$$
$$= (\cos^2\theta + \sin^2\theta) + (\cos^2\phi + \sin^2\phi) - 2\cos\theta\cos\phi - 2\sin\theta\sin\phi$$
$$= 1 + 1 - 2\cos\theta\cos\phi - 2\sin\theta\sin\phi$$
$$= 2 - 2\cos\theta\cos\phi - 2\sin\theta\sin\phi$$

Therefore, we have $2 - 2\cos(\theta - \phi) = 2 - 2\cos\theta\cos\phi - 2\sin\theta\sin\phi$. Subtracting 2 from each side of this equation gives us $-2\cos(\theta - \phi) = -2\cos\theta\cos\phi - 2\sin\theta\sin\phi$. Multiplying each side of this last equation by $-\frac{1}{2}$ gives us $\cos(\theta - \phi) = \cos\theta\cos\phi + \sin\theta\sin\phi$, as desired. □

23. Let θ and ϕ be the radian measure of angles A and B, respectively. Prove the following identities:
(i) $\cos(\theta + \phi) = \cos\theta\cos\phi - \sin\theta\sin\phi$; (ii) $\cos(\pi - \theta) = -\cos\theta$; (iii) $\cos\left(\frac{\pi}{2} - \theta\right) = \sin\theta$;
(iv) $\sin\left(\frac{\pi}{2} - \theta\right) = \cos\theta$; (v) $\sin(\theta + \phi) = \sin\theta\cos\phi + \cos\theta\sin\phi$; (vi) $\sin(\pi - \theta) = -\sin\theta$.

Proofs:

(i) $\cos(\theta + \phi) = \cos(\theta - (-\phi)) = \cos\theta\cos(-\phi) + \sin\theta\sin(-\phi)$ (by Problem 13)
$$= \cos\theta\cos\phi - \sin\theta\sin\phi \text{ (by the Negative Identities)}. □$$

(ii) $\cos(\pi - \theta) = \cos\pi\cos\theta + \sin\pi\sin\theta = (-1)\cos\theta + 0\cdot\sin\theta = -\cos\theta.$ □

(iii) $\cos\left(\frac{\pi}{2} - \theta\right) = \cos\frac{\pi}{2}\cos\theta + \sin\frac{\pi}{2}\sin\theta = 0\cdot\cos\theta + 1\cdot\sin\theta = \sin\theta.$ □

(iv) $\sin\left(\frac{\pi}{2} - \theta\right) = \cos\left(\frac{\pi}{2} - \left(\frac{\pi}{2} - \theta\right)\right) = \cos\left(\frac{\pi}{2} - \frac{\pi}{2} + \theta\right) = \cos\theta.$ □

(v) $\sin(\theta + \phi) = \cos\left(\frac{\pi}{2} - (\theta + \phi)\right) = \cos\left(\left(\frac{\pi}{2} - \theta\right) - \phi\right)$
$$= \cos\left(\frac{\pi}{2} - \theta\right)\cos\phi + \sin\left(\frac{\pi}{2} - \theta\right)\sin\phi = \sin\theta\cos\phi + \cos\theta\sin\phi. □$$

(vi) $\sin(\pi - \theta) = \sin\pi\cos\theta + \cos\pi\sin\theta = 0\cdot\cos\theta + (-1)\sin\theta = -\sin\theta.$ □

24. The Principle of Strong Induction is the following statement:

> ($\star\star$) Let $P(n)$ be a statement and suppose that (i) $P(0)$ is true and (ii) for all $k \in \mathbb{N}$, $\forall j \leq k \left(P(j)\right) \to P(k+1)$. Then $P(n)$ is true for all $n \in \mathbb{N}$.

Use the Principle of Mathematical Induction to prove the Principle of Strong Induction.

Proof: Let $P(n)$ be a statement such that $P(0)$ is true, and for all $k \in \mathbb{N}$, $\forall j \leq k \left(P(j)\right) \to P(k+1)$. Let $Q(n)$ be the statement $\forall j \leq n \left(P(j)\right)$.

Base case: $Q(0) \equiv \forall j \leq 0 \left(P(j)\right) \equiv P(0)$. Since $P(0)$ is true and $Q(0) \equiv P(0)$, $Q(0)$ is also true.

Inductive step: Suppose that $Q(k)$ is true. Then $\forall j \leq k \left(P(j)\right)$ is true. Therefore, $P(k+1)$ is true. So $Q(k) \wedge P(k+1)$ is true. But notice that

$$Q(k+1) \equiv \forall j \leq k+1 \left(P(j)\right) \equiv \forall j \leq k \left(P(j)\right) \wedge P(k+1) \equiv Q(k) \wedge P(k+1).$$

So, $Q(k+1)$ is true.

By the Principle of Mathematical Induction (($\star$) from Problem 14), $Q(n)$ is true for all $n \in \mathbb{N}$. This implies that $P(n)$ is true for all $n \in \mathbb{N}$. $\qquad\square$

25. Use the Principle of Mathematical Induction to prove that for every $n \in \mathbb{N}$, if S is a set with $|S| = n$, then S has 2^n subsets. (Hint: Use Problem 28 from Problem Set 1.)

Proof: Base Case ($k = 0$): Let S be a set with $|S| = 0$. Then $S = \emptyset$, and the empty set has exactly 1 subset, namely itself. So, the number of subsets of S is $1 = 2^0$.

Inductive Step: Assume that for any set S with $|S| = k$, S has 2^k subsets.

Now, let A be a set with $|A| = k + 1$, let d be any element from A, and let $S = A \setminus \{d\}$ (S is the set consisting of all elements of A except d). $|S| = k$, and so, by the inductive hypothesis, S has 2^k subsets. Let $B = \{X \mid X \subseteq A \wedge d \notin X\}$ and $C = \{X \mid X \subseteq A \wedge d \in X\}$. B is precisely the set of subsets of S, and so $|B| = 2^k$. By Problem 28 from Lesson 1, $|B| = |C|$ and therefore, $|C| = 2^k$. Also, B and C have no elements in common and every subset of A is in either B or C. So, the number of subsets of A is equal to $|B| + |C| = 2^k + 2^k = 2 \cdot 2^k = 2^1 \cdot 2^k = 2^{1+k} = 2^{k+1}$.

By the Principle of Mathematical Induction, given any $n \in \mathbb{N}$, if S is a set with $|S| = n$, then S has 2^n subsets. $\qquad\square$

Notes: (1) Recall from Lesson 1 that $|S| = n$ means that the set S has n elements.

(2) Also, recall from Lesson 1 that if S is a set, then the **power set** of S is the set of subsets of S.

$$\mathcal{P}(S) = \{X \mid X \subseteq S\}$$

In this problem, we proved that a set with n elements has a power set with 2^n elements. Symbolically, we have $|S| = n \to |\mathcal{P}(S)| = 2^n$.

26. Provide a formal definition of generalized commutativity. Then prove that if $\star$ is a binary operation that is commutative in a set S, then $\star$ satisfies generalized commutativity in S.

Definition: An operation $\star$ satisfies **generalized commutativity** in a set S if for any $n \in \mathbb{N}^+$, for all $x_1, \ldots, x_n \in S$, and any bijection $f: \{1, 2, \ldots, n\} \to \{1, 2, \ldots, n\}$, we have

$$\prod_{i=1}^{n} x_{f(i)} = \prod_{i=1}^{n} x_i.$$

Proof: Suppose that $\star$ is commutative in S. We will prove by induction that for all $n \in \mathbb{N}$ with $n \geq 1$, for all $x_1, \ldots, x_n \in S$, and any bijection $f: \{1, 2, \ldots, n\} \to \{1, 2, \ldots, n\}$, we have

$$\prod_{i=1}^{n} x_{f(i)} = \prod_{i=1}^{n} x_i.$$

The base case $(k = 1)$ is obvious. So, assume that the statement is true for some $k \geq 1$, and let $x_1, \ldots x_{k+1} \in S$, let $f: \{1, 2, \ldots, k+1\} \to \{1, 2, \ldots, k+1\}$ be a bijection, and suppose $f(j) = k + 1$.

We have

$$\prod_{i=1}^{k+1} x_{f(i)} = \prod_{i=1}^{j-1} x_{f(i)} \star x_{f(j)} \star \prod_{i=1}^{k+1-j} x_{f(j+i)} = \prod_{i=1}^{j-1} x_{f(i)} \star \prod_{i=1}^{k+1-j} x_{f(j+i)} \star x_{f(j)}.$$

Now, define $g: \{1, 2, \ldots, k\} \to \{1, 2, \ldots, k\}$ by $g(i) = f(i)$ if $i < j$ and $g(i) = f(i+1)$ if $i \geq j$. Then we have

$$\prod_{i=1}^{k+1} x_{f(i)} = \prod_{i=1}^{j-1} x_{g(i)} \star \prod_{i=1}^{k+1-j} x_{g(j-1+i)} \star x_{k+1} = \prod_{i=1}^{k} x_{g(i)} \star x_{k+1} = \prod_{i=1}^{k} x_i \star x_{k+1} = \prod_{i=1}^{k+1} x_i.$$

The inductive hypothesis was used in the third equality above.

By the Principle of Mathematical Induction, for all $m, n \in \mathbb{N}^+$, for all $x_1, \ldots, x_n \in S$, and any bijection $f: \{1, 2, \ldots, n\} \to \{1, 2, \ldots, n\}$, we have

$$\prod_{i=1}^{n} x_{f(i)} = \prod_{i=1}^{n} x_i. \qquad \square$$

27. Prove that addition of real numbers is well-defined and that the sum of two real numbers is a real number.

Proof: Suppose that $[(x_n)] = [(z_n)]$ and $[(y_n)] = [(w_n)]$. To prove that addition is well-defined, we need to show that $[(x_n + y_n)] = [(z_n + w_n)]$.

Let $k \in \mathbb{N}^+$. Since $[(x_n)] = [(z_n)]$, there is $K_1 \in \mathbb{N}$ such that $n > K_1$ implies $|x_n - z_n| < \frac{1}{2k}$. Since $[(y_n)] = [(w_n)]$, there is $K_2 \in \mathbb{N}$ such that $n > K_2$ implies $|y_n - w_n| < \frac{1}{2k}$. Let $K = \max\{K_1, K_2\}$. Let $n > K$. Since $K \geq K_1$, $n > K_1$, and therefore, we have $|x_n - z_n| < \frac{1}{2k}$. Since $K \geq K_2$, $n > K_2$, and therefore, we have $|y_n - w_n| < \frac{1}{2k}$. It follows that

$$|(x_n + y_n) - (z_n + w_n)| = |(x_n - z_n) + (y_n - w_n)| \leq |x_n - z_n| + |y_n - w_n| < \frac{1}{2k} + \frac{1}{2k} = \frac{1}{k}.$$

So, $[(x_n + y_n)] = [(z_n + w_n)]$, as desired.

We now prove that the sum of two real numbers is a real number. Let $[(x_n)]$ and $[(y_n)]$ be real numbers. Since the sum of two rational numbers is a rational number, for each $n \in \mathbb{N}$, we have $x_n + y_n \in \mathbb{Q}$. We need to show that $(x_n + y_n)$ is a Cauchy sequence. To see this, let $k \in \mathbb{N}^+$. Since (x_n) is a Cauchy sequence, there is $K_1 \in \mathbb{N}$ such that $m \geq n > K_1$ implies $|x_m - x_n| < \frac{1}{2k}$. Since (y_n) is a Cauchy sequence, there is $K_2 \in \mathbb{N}$ such that $m \geq n > K_2$ implies $|y_m - y_n| < \frac{1}{2k}$. Let $K = \max\{K_1, K_2\}$ and let $k \in \mathbb{N}^+$. Suppose that $m \geq n > K$. Since $K \geq K_1$, we have $|x_m - x_n| < \frac{1}{2k}$. Since $K \geq K_2$, we have $|y_m - y_n| < \frac{1}{2k}$. So,

$$|(x_m + y_m) - (x_n + y_n)| = |(x_m - x_n) + (y_m - y_n)| \leq |x_m - x_n| + |y_m - y_n| < \frac{1}{2k} + \frac{1}{2k} = \frac{1}{k}.$$

Therefore, $(x_n + y_n)$ is a Cauchy sequence. $\square$

28. Using the formal definitions of $\mathbb{N}$, $\mathbb{Z}$, $\mathbb{Q}$, and $\mathbb{R}$ provided in this lesson, prove each of the following:

    (i) $(\mathbb{N}, +, \cdot)$ is a commutative semiring, but not a ring.

    (ii) $(\mathbb{Z}, +, \cdot)$ is a commutative ring, but not a field.

    (iii) $(\mathbb{R}, +, \cdot)$ is a field.

Proofs:

(i)   By Theorem 5.7, addition on the set of natural numbers is a binary operation.

     By Theorem 5.9, addition is associative in $\mathbb{N}$.

     By part (i) of Problem 4 above, addition is commutative in $\mathbb{N}$.

     By Theorem 5.8 and the notes that follow it, 0 is an additive identity in $\mathbb{N}$.

     So, $(\mathbb{N}, +)$ is a commutative monoid.

     By part (ii) of Problem 4 above, multiplication on the set of natural numbers is a binary operation.

     By part (v) of Problem 4 above, multiplication is associative in $\mathbb{N}$.

     By part (vi) of Problem 4 above, multiplication is commutative in $\mathbb{N}$.

     By part (iii) of Problem 4 above, 1 is a multiplicative identity.

So, $(\mathbb{N}, \cdot)$ is a commutative monoid.

By part (iv) of Problem 4 above, multiplication is distributive over addition in $\mathbb{N}$.

By the definition of multiplication of natural numbers, for all $n \in \mathbb{N}$, $n \cdot 0 = 0$. Since multiplication is commutative in $\mathbb{N}$, $0 \cdot n = n \cdot 0 = 0$.

Therefore, $(\mathbb{N}, +, \cdot)$ is a semiring.

We now show that 1 has no additive inverse in $\mathbb{N}$ (in fact, the only natural number with an additive inverse is 0). Indeed, suppose toward contradiction that $n \in \mathbb{N}$ with $n + 1 = 0$. Since $n + 1 = n^+ = n \cup \{n\}$, and $n \in n \cup \{n\}$, we must have $n \in 0 = \emptyset$. But the empty set has no elements. This contradiction proves that there is no natural number n such that $n + 1 = 0$. So, 1 has no additive inverse in $\mathbb{N}$. Therefore, the inverse property fails and $(\mathbb{N}, +)$ is **not** a group. So, $(\mathbb{N}, +, \cdot)$ is **not** a ring. $\qquad \square$

(ii)   By Problem 16 above, addition of integers is well-defined.

By part (i) above, if $a, b \in \mathbb{N}$, then $a + c, b + d \in \mathbb{N}$. So, $[(a, b)], [(c, d)] \in \mathbb{Z}$ implies that $[(a, b)] + [(c, d)] = [(a + c, b + d)] \in \mathbb{Z}$, showing that $\mathbb{Z}$ is closed under addition.

To see that $+$ is associative in $\mathbb{Z}$, observe that for $a, b, c, d, e, f \in \mathbb{N}$, we have

$$([(a, b)] + [(c, d)]) + [(e, f)] = [(a + c, b + d)] + [(e, f)] = [((a + c) + e, (b + d) + f)]$$
$$= [(a + (c + e), b + (d + f))] = [(a, b)] + [(c + e, d + f)] = [(a, b)] + ([(c, d)] + [(e, f)])$$

For the first, second, fourth and fifth equalities, we simply used the definition of addition of integers. For the third equality, we used the associativity of addition in $\mathbb{N}$.

To see that $+$ is commutative in $\mathbb{Z}$, observe that for $a, b, c, d \in \mathbb{N}$, we have

$$[(a, b)] + [(c, d)] = [(a + c, b + d)] = [(c + a, d + b)] = [(c, d)] + [(a, b)].$$

For the first and third equalities, we simply used the definition of addition of integers. For the second equality, we used the commutativity of addition in $\mathbb{N}$.

$[(0, 0)]$ is an additive identity in $\mathbb{Z}$ because for $a, b \in \mathbb{N}$, we have:
$$[(0, 0)] + [(a, b)] = [(0 + a, 0 + b)] = [(a, b)]$$
$$[(a, b)] + [(0, 0)] = [(a + 0, b + 0)] = [(a, b)].$$

If $a, b \in \mathbb{N}$, then the inverse of $[(a, b)]$ is $[(b, a)]$ because we have
$$[(a, b)] + [(b, a)] = [(a + b, b + a)] = [(0, 0)]$$
$$[(b, a)] + [(a, b)] = [(b + a, a + b)] = [(0, 0)].$$

So, $(\mathbb{Z}, +)$ is a commutative group.

By Problem 29, multiplication of integers is well-defined.

By part (i) above, if $a, b, c, d \in \mathbb{N}$, then $ac + bd, ad + bc \in \mathbb{N}$. So, $[(a, b)], [(c, d)] \in \mathbb{Z}$ implies that $[(a, b)] \cdot [(c, d)] = [(ac + bd, ad + bc)] \in \mathbb{Z}$, showing that $\mathbb{Z}$ is closed under multiplication.

To see that $\cdot$ is associative in $\mathbb{Z}$, observe that for $a, b, c, d, e, f \in \mathbb{N}$, we have

$$([(a,b)] \cdot [(c,d)]) \cdot [(e,f)] = [(ac + bd, ad + bc)] \cdot [(e,f)]$$
$$= \left[((ac + bd)e + (ad + bc)f, (ac + bd)f + (ad + bc)e) \right]$$
$$= [(ace + bde + adf + bcf, acf + bdf + ade + bce)]$$
$$= [(ace + adf + bcf + bde, acf + ade + bce + bdf)]$$
$$= \left[(a(ce + df) + b(cf + de), a(cf + de) + b(ce + df)) \right]$$
$$= [(a,b)] \cdot [(ce + df, cf + de)] = [(a,b)] \cdot ([(c,d)] \cdot [(e,f)])$$

For the first, second, sixth, and seventh equalities, we used the definition of multiplication of integers. For the third and fifth equalities, we used the distributivity of multiplication over addition in $\mathbb{N}$. For the fourth equality, we used the commutativity of addition in $\mathbb{N}$. Associativity of both addition and multiplication in $\mathbb{N}$ were used in writing the fourth and fifth expresions, as is evidenced by the lack of parentheses.

To see that $\cdot$ is commutative in $\mathbb{Z}$, observe that for $a, b, c, d \in \mathbb{N}$, we have

$$[(a,b)] \cdot [(c,d)] = [(ac + bd, ad + bc)] = [(ca + db, cb + da)] = [(c,d)] \cdot [(a,b)].$$

For the first and third equalities, we used the definition of multiplication of integers. For the second equality, we used the commutativity of both addition and multiplication in $\mathbb{N}$.

$[(1,0)]$ is an multiplicative identity in $\mathbb{Z}$ because for $a, b \in \mathbb{N}$, we have:

$$[(1,0)] \cdot [(a,b)] = [(1a + 0b, 1b + 0a)] = [(a,b)]$$
$$[(a,b)] \cdot [(1,0)] = [(a \cdot 1 + b \cdot 0, a \cdot 0 + b \cdot 1)] = [(a,b)].$$

So, $(\mathbb{Z}, \cdot)$ is a commutative monoid.

We next check left distributivity. For $a, b, c, d, e, f \in \mathbb{N}$, we have

$$[(a,b)]([(c,d)] + [(e,f)]) = [(a,b)] \cdot [(c + e, d + f)]$$
$$= \left[(a(c + e) + b(d + f), a(d + f) + b(c + e)) \right]$$
$$= [((ac + ae) + (bd + bf), (ad + af) + (bc + be))]$$
$$= [((ac + bd) + (ae + bf), (ad + bc) + (af + be))]$$
$$= [(ac + bd, ad + bc)] + [(ae + bf, af + be)] = [(a,b)] \cdot [(c,d)] + [(a,b)] \cdot [(e,f)].$$

For the first, second, fifth and sixth equalities, we simply used the definitions of addition and multiplication of integers. For the third equality, we used the distributivity of multiplication over addition in $\mathbb{N}$. For the fourth equality, we used the associativity and commutativity of addition in $\mathbb{N}$.

Since multiplication is commutative in $\mathbb{Z}$, right distributivity follows immediately from left distributivity:

$$([(c,d)] + [(e,f)])[(a,b)] = [(a,b)]([(c,d)] + [(e,f)])$$
$$= [(a,b)] \cdot [(c,d)] + [(a,b)] \cdot [(e,f)] = [(c,d)] \cdot [(a,b)] + [(e,f)] \cdot [(a,b)].$$

Therefore, $(\mathbb{Z}, +, \cdot)$ is a ring.

To see that $(\mathbb{Z}, +, \cdot)$ is not a field, we will show that 2 has no multiplicative inverse in $\mathbb{Z}$. We first show that 2 has no multiplicative inverse in $\mathbb{N}$. We have $2 \cdot 0 = 0 \neq 1$. We now prove by induction that for all $n \geq 1$, $2n > 1$. The base case is $2 \cdot 1 = 2 > 1$. Assuming $2k > 1$, by parts (iv) and (x) of Problem 4 above, we have $2(k + 1) = 2k + 2 > 1 + 2 > 1$. In particular, we showed that for all $n \in \mathbb{N}$, $2n \neq 1$. Therefore, 2 has no multiplicative inverse in $\mathbb{N}$.

We now prove that $2 = [(2, 0)]$ has no multiplicative inverse in $\mathbb{Z}$. If $[(a, b)]$ is a multiplicative inverse of 2, then we have $2a + 0b = 1$ and $2b + 0a = 0$. The first equation is equivalent to $2a = 1$. However, in the previous paragraph, we showed that 2 has no multiplicative inverse in $\mathbb{N}$. Therefore, the equation $2a = 1$ has no solution, and so, 2 has no multiplicative inverse in $\mathbb{Z}$. □

(iii) By Problem 27, addition of real numbers is well-defined and $\mathbb{R}$ is closed under addition.

To see that $+$ is associative in $\mathbb{R}$, we use associativity of $+$ in $\mathbb{Q}$. If $[(x_n)], [(y_n)], [(z_n)] \in \mathbb{R}$, then

$$([(x_n)] + [(y_n)]) + [(z_n)] = [(x_n + y_n)] + [(z_n)] = [((x_n + y_n) + z_n)]$$
$$= [(x_n + (y_n + z_n))] = [(x_n)] + [(y_n + z_n)] = [(x_n)] + ([(y_n)] + [(z_n)]).$$

To see that $+$ is commutative in $\mathbb{R}$, we use the commutativity of $+$ in $\mathbb{Q}$. If $[(x_n)], [(y_n)] \in \mathbb{R}$, then

$$[(x_n)] + [(y_n)] = [(x_n + y_n)] = [(y_n + x_n)] = [(y_n)] + [(x_n)].$$

To see that $[(0)]$ is the additive identity, using the fact that 0 is the additive identity in $\mathbb{Q}$, we have for $[(x_n)] \in \mathbb{R}$,

$$[(0)] + [(x_n)] = [(0 + x_n)] = [(x_n)] \text{ and } [(x_n)] + [(0)] = [(x_n + 0)] = [(x_n)].$$

The additive inverse of the real number $[(x_n)]$ is $[(-x_n)]$, where for each $n \in \mathbb{N}$, $-x_n$ is the additive inverse of x_n in $\mathbb{Q}$. To see this, simply observe that

$$[(x_n)] + [(-x_n)] = [(x_n + (-x_n))] = [(0)] \text{ and } [(-x_n)] + [(x_n)] = [(-x_n + x_n)] = [(0)].$$

So, $(\mathbb{R}, +)$ is a commutative group.

By Problem 30, multiplication of real numbers is well-defined and $\mathbb{R}$ is closed under multiplication.

To see that $\cdot$ is associative in $\mathbb{R}^*$, we use the associativity of $\cdot$ in $\mathbb{Q}$. If $[(x_n)], [(y_n)], [(z_n)] \in \mathbb{R}^*$, then

$$([(x_n)] \cdot [(y_n)]) \cdot [(z_n)] = [(x_n \cdot y_n)] \cdot [(z_n)] = [((x_n \cdot y_n) \cdot z_n)]$$
$$= [(x_n \cdot (y_n \cdot z_n))] = [x_n] \cdot [(y_n \cdot z_n)] = [(x_n)] \cdot ([(y_n)] \cdot [(z_n)]).$$

To see that $\cdot$ is commutative in $\mathbb{R}^*$, we use the commutativity of $\cdot$ in $\mathbb{Q}$. If $[(x_n)], [(y_n)] \in \mathbb{R}^*$, then $[(x_n)] \cdot [(y_n)] = [(x_n y_n)] = [(y_n x_n)] = [(y_n)] \cdot [(x_n)]$.

To see that $[(1)]$ is the multiplicative identity, using the fact that 1 is the additive identity in $\mathbb{Q}$, we have for $[(x_n)] \in \mathbb{R}$,

$$[(1)] \cdot [(x_n)] = [(1 \cdot x_n)] = [(x_n)] \text{ and } [(x_n)] \cdot [(1)] = [(x_n \cdot 1)] = [(x_n)].$$

The inverse of the real number $[(x_n)]$ is $[(y_n)]$, where for each $n \in \mathbb{N}$, $y_n = \frac{1}{x_n}$ if $x_n \neq 0$ and $y_n = 0$ if $x_n = 0$. We have that $[(x_n)] \cdot [(y_n)] = [(z_n)]$ and $[(y_n)] + [(x_n)] = [(z_n)]$, where z_n is 0 or 1 for all $n \in \mathbb{N}$. We claim that $[(z_n)] = [(1)]$. To see this, note that since $[(x_n)] \neq [(0)]$, there is a $K > 0$ such that for $n > N$, $x_n \neq 0$.

So, $(\mathbb{R}^*, \cdot)$ is a commutative group.

Distributivity is similar to commutativity and associativity. Thus, $(\mathbb{R}, +, \cdot)$ is a field. $\quad\square$

LEVEL 1

1. Let H and K be the subsets of S_3 defined by $H = \{(1), (123), (132)\}$ and $K = \{(1), (12)\}$. Prove that H and K are subgroups of S_3.

Solution: Here is the multiplication table of S_3.

$(S_3, \circ)$	(1)	(12)	(13)	(23)	(123)	(132)
(1)	(1)	(12)	(13)	(23)	(123)	(132)
(12)	(12)	(1)	(132)	(123)	(23)	(13)
(13)	(13)	(123)	(1)	(132)	(12)	(23)
(23)	(23)	(132)	(123)	(1)	(13)	(12)
(123)	(123)	(13)	(23)	(12)	(132)	(1)
(132)	(132)	(23)	(12)	(13)	(1)	(123)

We now show that H and K are subgroups of S_3. The restricted tables look as follows:

$(H, \circ)$	(1)	(123)	(132)
(1)	(1)	(123)	(132)
(123)	(123)	(132)	(1)
(132)	(132)	(1)	(123)

$(K, \circ)$	(1)	(12)
(1)	(1)	(12)
(12)	(12)	(1)

From the tables, we can see that each of H and K are closed under $\circ$. Also, each of H and K contain the identity (1). In H, (123) and (132) are inverses of each other, and in K, (12) is its own inverse. It follows that both H and K are subgroups of S_3.

2. Determine if each of the following subsets of $\mathbb{R}^2$ is a subspace of $\mathbb{R}^2$:

   (i) $A = \{(x, y) \mid x + y = 0\}$

   (ii) $B = \{(x, y) \mid xy = 0\}$

   (iii) $C = \{(x, y) \mid 2x = 3y\}$

   (iv) $D = \{(x, y) \mid x \in \mathbb{Q}\}$

Solutions:

   (i)   Since $0 + 0 = 0$, $(0, 0) \in A$.

   Let $(x, y), (z, w) \in A$. Then $x + y = 0$ and $z + w = 0$. Therefore,

$$(x + z) + (y + w) = (x + y) + (z + w) = 0 + 0 = 0.$$

80

So, $(x, y) + (z, w) = (x + z, y + w) \in A$.

Let $(x, y) \in A$ and $k \in \mathbb{R}$. Then $x + y = 0$. So, $kx + ky = k(x + y) = k \cdot 0 = 0$ (by part (iii) of Problem 10 from Problem Set 2).

So, $k(x, y) = (kx, ky) \in A$.

By Theorem 6.6, A is a subspace of $\mathbb{R}^2$.

(ii) Since $0 \cdot 1 = 0$, we have $(0, 1) \in B$. Since $1 \cdot 0 = 0$, we have $(1, 0) \in B$. Adding these two vectors gives us $(1, 0) + (0, 1) = (1, 1)$. However, $1 \cdot 1 = 1 \neq 0$, and so, $(1, 1) \notin B$. So, B is not closed under addition. Therefore, B is **not** a subspace of $\mathbb{R}^2$.

(iii) Since $2 \cdot 0 = 0$ and $3 \cdot 0 = 0$, $2 \cdot 0 = 3 \cdot 0$. Therefore, $(0, 0) \in C$.

Let $(x, y), (z, w) \in C$. Then $2x = 3y$ and $2z = 3w$. Therefore,
$$2(x + z) = 2x + 2z = 3y + 3w = 3(y + w).$$
So, $(x, y) + (z, w) = (x + z, y + w) \in C$.

Let $(x, y) \in C$ and $k \in \mathbb{R}$. Then $2x = 3y$. So, $2(kx) = k(2x) = k(3y) = 3(ky)$.

So, $k(x, y) = (kx, ky) \in C$.

By Theorem 6.6, A is a subspace of $\mathbb{R}^2$.

(iv) Since $1 \in \mathbb{Q}$, $(1, 0) \in D$. Now, $\sqrt{2}(1, 0) = (\sqrt{2}, 0) \notin D$ because $\sqrt{2} \notin \mathbb{Q}$. So, D is not closed under scalar multiplication. Therefore, D is **not** a subspace of $\mathbb{R}^2$.

3. For each of the following, determine if the given pair of vectors v and w are linearly independent or linearly dependent in the given vector space V:

   (i) $V = \mathbb{Q}^4, v = (3, 2, 2, -1), w = \left(-1, -\frac{2}{3}, -\frac{2}{3}, -\frac{1}{3}\right)$

   (ii) $V = \mathbb{R}^3, v = \left(1, \sqrt{2}, 1\right), w = \left(\sqrt{2}, 2, \sqrt{2}\right)$

   (iii) $V = \mathbb{C}^5, v = (1, i, 2 - i, 0, 3i), w = (-i, 1, -1 - 2i, 0, 3)$

   (iv) $V = M_{22}^{\mathbb{Q}}, v = \begin{bmatrix} a & b \\ \frac{a}{2} & 3b \end{bmatrix}, w = \begin{bmatrix} 1 & \frac{b}{a} \\ \frac{1}{2} & 3 \end{bmatrix} \ (a \neq 0, a \neq b)$

   (v) $V = \{ax^2 + bx + c \mid a, b, c \in \mathbb{R}\}, v = x, w = x^2$

Solutions:

(i) $-3w = -3\left(-1, -\frac{2}{3}, -\frac{2}{3}, -\frac{1}{3}\right) = (3, 2, 2, 1)$. Since $-3(-1) = 3$, but $-3\left(-\frac{1}{3}\right) \neq -1$, v and w are **not** scalar multiples of each other. Therefore, v and w are **linearly independent**.

(ii) $\sqrt{2}v = \sqrt{2}\left(1, \sqrt{2}, 1\right) = \left(\sqrt{2}, 2, \sqrt{2}\right) = w$. So, v and w **are** scalar multiples of each other. Therefore, v and w are **linearly dependent**.

(iii) $-iv = -i(1, i, 2 - i, 0, 3i) = (-i, 1, -1 - 2i, 0, 3) = w$. So, v and w **are** scalar multiples of each other. Therefore, v and w are **linearly dependent**.

81

(iv) $aw = a\begin{bmatrix} 1 & \frac{b}{a} \\ \frac{1}{2} & 3 \end{bmatrix} = \begin{bmatrix} a & b \\ \frac{a}{2} & 3a \end{bmatrix}$. Since $a \cdot 1 = a$, but $a \cdot 3 = 3a \neq 3b$, v and w are **not** scalar

multiples of each other. Therefore, v and w are **linearly independent**.

(v) If $k \in \mathbb{R}$, then $kx \neq x^2$. So, x and x^2 are **not** scalar multiples of each other. Therefore, v and w are **linearly independent**.

LEVEL 2

4. Let G be a group and let $a \in G$. The **centralizer** of a in G is $C_a(G) = \{x \in G \mid ax = xa\}$. Prove that $C_a(G)$ is a subgroup of G. Then define the centralizer $C_a(R)$ of an element a in a ring R analogously and prove that $C_a(R)$ is a subring of R.

Proofs: Let $x, y \in C_a(G)$. Then $a(xy) = (ax)y = (xa)y = x(ay) = x(ya) = (xy)a$. So, $xy \in C_a(G)$. Since $x, y \in G$ were arbitrary, we see that $C_a(G)$ is closed under the group operation. Next, let $x \in C_a(G)$. Then $ax^{-1} = ax^{-1}a^{-1}a = a(ax)^{-1}a = a(xa)^{-1}a = aa^{-1}x^{-1}a = x^{-1}a$. Therefore, $x^{-1} \in C_a(G)$. Since $x \in C_a(G)$ was arbitrary, $C_a(G)$ is closed under taking inverses. Finally, we have $ae = a = ea$, and so, $e \in C_a(G)$. Therefore, $C_a(G)$ is a subgroup of G.

We define $C_a(R) = \{x \in R \mid ax = xa\}$. Let $x, y \in C_a(R)$. Then

$$a(x + y) = ax + ay = xa + ya = (x + y)a.$$
$$a(xy) = (ax)y = (xa)y = x(ay) = x(ya) = (xy)a.$$

It follows that $x + y \in C_a(R)$ and $xy \in C_a(R)$. Since $x, y \in C_a(R)$ were arbitrary, we see that $C_a(R)$ is closed under $+$ and $\cdot$. Next, let $x \in C_a(R)$. Then we have

$$a(-x) = a(-1x) = -1(ax) = -1(xa) = (-1x)a = (-x)a.$$

(Note that we used part (v) of Problem 7 from Problem Set 2 here.) So, $x^{-1} \in C_a(R)$. Since $x \in C_a(R)$ was arbitrary, $C_a(R)$ is closed under taking inverses. Finally, $a \cdot 1 = a = 1a$, and so, $1 \in C_a(R)$. Therefore, $C_a(R)$ is a subring of R. $\square$

5. Let G be a group with H a nonempty subset of G. Prove that H is a subgroup of G if and only if for all $g, h \in H$, $gh^{-1} \in H$.

Proof: Let G be a group with H a nonempty subset of G.

First, let H be a subgroup of G and let $g, h \in H$. Since H has the inverse property, h^{-1} exists in H. Since H is closed under the group operation, $gh^{-1} \in H$. Since $g, h \in H$ were arbitrary, we have shown that for all $g, h \in H$, $gh^{-1} \in H$.

Conversely, suppose that for all $g, h \in H$, $gh^{-1} \in H$. Since $H \neq \emptyset$, there is $g \in H$. Therefore, $e = gg^{-1} \in H$. Now, let $h \in H$. Since $e \in H$, $h^{-1} = eh^{-1} \in H$. Finally, let $g, h \in H$. We just showed that $h^{-1} \in H$. Therefore, $g \star h = g \star (h^{-1})^{-1} \in H$. So, H is closed under $\star$. Thus, H is a subgroup of G. $\square$

6. Let G be a group with H and K subgroups of G. Prove that if G is commutative, then $HK = \{hk \in G \mid h \in H \text{ and } k \in K\}$ is a subgroup of G. Is the result still true if G is not commutative?

Proof: Since $e = ee \in HK$, we see that $HK \neq \emptyset$. Let $x, y \in HK$. There are $h_1, h_2 \in H$ and $k_1, k_2 \in K$ such that $x = h_1 k_1$ and $y = h_2 k_2$. Then we have

$$xy^{-1} = (h_1 k_1)(h_2 k_2)^{-1} = h_1 k_1 k_2^{-1} h_2^{-1} = (h_1 h_2^{-1})(k_1 k_2^{-1}) \in HK.$$

By Problem 5 above, $HK \leq G$.

If G is not commutative, the result can be false. A counterexample is given by $G = S_3$, $H = \{(1), (12)\}$, $K = \{(1), (13)\}$ In this case, $HK = \{(1), (12), (13), (132)\}$ and HK is not closed under the group operation. Indeed, $(132)(132) = (123)$. □

7. Let $X = \{a + bi \mid a, b \in \mathbb{Z}\}$ be the set of Gaussian integers. Prove that X is a subring of $\mathbb{C}$.

Proof: Let $a + bi, c + di \in X$. Then $(a + bi) + (c + di) = (a + c) + (b + d)i$. Since $\mathbb{Z}$ is closed under addition, $a + c \in \mathbb{Z}$ and $b + d \in \mathbb{Z}$. Therefore, $(a + bi) + (c + di) \in X$, and so, X is closed under addition. Also, $(a + bi)(c + di) = (ac - bd) + (ad + bc)i$. Since $\mathbb{Z}$ is closed under multiplication, $ac, bd, ad, bc \in \mathbb{Z}$. Since $\mathbb{Z}$ has the additive inverse property, $-(bd) \in \mathbb{Z}$. Since $\mathbb{Z}$ is closed under addition, we have $ad + bc \in \mathbb{Z}$ and $ac - bd = ac + (-(bd)) \in \mathbb{Z}$. Therefore, $(a + bi)(c + di) \in X$, and so, X is closed under multiplication. The additive inverse of $a + bi$ is $-a - bi = -a + (-b)i$. Since $\mathbb{Z}$ has the additive inverse property, $-a, -b \in \mathbb{Z}$, and so, $-a - bi \in X$. Finally, $1 = 1 + 0i \in X$ because $1, 0 \in \mathbb{Z}$. It follows that X is a subring of $\mathbb{C}$. □

8. Let G be a commutative group with identity e. Prove that each of the following subsets of G is a subgroup of G:

   (i) $H = \{x \in G \mid x^2 = e\}$

   (ii) $K = \{x^2 \mid x \in G\}$

   (iii) $L = \{x \in G \mid x \text{ has finite order}\}$

Solutions:

   (i)   Since $e^2 = e$, $H \neq \emptyset$. Let $x, y \in H$. Then

$$(xy^{-1})^2 = xy^{-1}xy^{-1} = x^2(y^2)^{-1} = e^2(e^2)^{-1} = ee^{-1} = ee = e.$$

       So, $xy^{-1} \in H$. By Problem 5, H is a subgroup of G.

   (ii)   Since $e = e^2$, $e \in K$. So, $K \neq \emptyset$. Let $x^2, y^2 \in K$. Then

$$x^2(y^2)^{-1} = x^2(y^{-1})^2 = xxy^{-1}y^{-1} = xy^{-1}xy^{-1} = (xy^{-1})^2$$

       So, $xy^{-1} \in K$. By Problem 5, K is a subgroup of G.

   (iii) Since $e^1 = e$, e has order 1, and so, $e \in L$. So, $L \neq \emptyset$.

       Let $x, y \in L$. Then there are $m, n \in \mathbb{N}$ such that $x^m = e$ and $y^n = e$. Then we also have $(y^{-1})^n = (y^n)^{-1} = e^{-1} = e$. So,

$$(xy^{-1})^{mn} = x^{mn}(y^{-1})^{mn} = (x^m)^n((y^{-1})^n)^m = e^n e^m = e.$$

So, xy^{-1} has order less than or equal to mn. In particular, xy^{-1} has finite order. Therefore, $xy^{-1} \in L$. By Problem 5, L is a subgroup of G $\qquad\square$

LEVEL 3

9. Let G be a group with H and K subgroups of G, and let $G = H \cup K$. Prove that $H = G$ or $K = G$.

Proof: Let G be a group, let H and K be subgroups of G, and let $G = H \cup K$. Suppose toward contradiction that $H \neq G$ and $K \neq G$. Then there exist $a \in G \setminus H$ and $b \in G \setminus K$. Since $G = H \cup K$, we have $a \in K$ and $b \in H$. Since G is a group, $ab \in G$. So, $ab \in H$ or $ab \in K$. Without loss of generality, let $ab \in H$. Since $b \in H$ and H is a group, $b^{-1} \in H$, and thus, $a = ae = a(bb^{-1}) = (ab)b^{-1} \in H$. This contradicts our assumption that $a \in G \setminus H$. So, we must have $H = G$ or $K = G$. $\qquad\square$

10. Let $\mathbb{Z}[x]_n = \{a_n x^n + a_{n-1}x^{n-1} + \cdots + a_1 x + a_0 \mid a_0, a_1, \ldots, a_n \in \mathbb{Z}\}$. By Problem 17 from Problem Set 2, $(\mathbb{Z}[x]_n, +)$ is a commutative group for $n = 0, 1$, and 2, where addition is defined in the "usual way." Prove that $\mathbb{Z}[x]_0$ is a subgroup of $\mathbb{Z}[x]_1$ and $\mathbb{Z}[x]_1$ is a subgroup of $\mathbb{Z}[x]_2$.

Proof: $\mathbb{Z}[x]_0 = \{a_0 \mid a_0 \in \mathbb{Z}\} = \mathbb{Z}$.

$\mathbb{Z}[x]_1 = \{a_1 x + a_0 \mid a_0, a_1 \in \mathbb{Z}\}$.

$\mathbb{Z}[x]_2 = \{a_2 x^2 + a_1 x + a_0 \mid a_0, a_1, a_2 \in \mathbb{Z}\}$.

Let $a_0 \in \mathbb{Z}[x]_0 = \mathbb{Z}$. Then $a_0 = 0x + a_0 \in \mathbb{Z}[x]_1$. So, $\mathbb{Z}[x]_0 \subseteq \mathbb{Z}[x]_1$. Since $\mathbb{Z}[x]_0$ is a group under addition, $\mathbb{Z}[x]_0 \leq \mathbb{Z}[x]_1$.

Similarly, if $a_1 x + a_0 \in \mathbb{Z}[x]_1$, then $a_1 x + a_0 = 0x^2 + a_1 x + a_0 \in \mathbb{Z}[x]_2$. Therefore, $\mathbb{Z}[x]_1 \subseteq \mathbb{Z}[x]_2$. Since $\mathbb{Z}[x]_1$ is a group under addition, $\mathbb{Z}[x]_1 \leq \mathbb{Z}[x]_2$.

Let A be the set of polynomials of degree 1. Then x and $-x$ are in A, but $x + (-x) = 0 \notin A$. So, A is not closed under addition, and therefore, $(A, +)$ is **not** a group. $\qquad\square$

11. Let V be a vector space over a field $\mathbb{F}$ and let $\boldsymbol{X}$ be a set of subspaces of V. Prove that $\cap \boldsymbol{X}$ is a subspace of V. State and prove the analogous theorems for groups, rings, and fields.

Proof: Let V be a vector space over a field $\mathbb{F}$ and let $\boldsymbol{X}$ a set of subspaces of V. For each $U \in \boldsymbol{X}$, $0 \in U$ because $U \leq V$. So, $0 \in \cap \boldsymbol{X}$. Let $v, w \in \cap \boldsymbol{X}$. For each $U \in \boldsymbol{X}$, $v, w \in U$, and so $v + w \in U$ because $U \leq V$. Therefore, $v + w \in \cap \boldsymbol{X}$. Let $v \in \cap \boldsymbol{X}$ and $k \in \mathbb{F}$. For each $U \in \boldsymbol{X}$, $v \in U$, and so, $kv \in U$ because $U \leq V$. Therefore, $kv \in \cap \boldsymbol{X}$. By Theorem 6.6, $\cap \boldsymbol{X} \leq V$. $\qquad\square$

12. Prove that a finite set with at least two vectors is linearly dependent if and only if one of the vectors in the set can be written as a linear combination of the other vectors in the set.

Proof: Suppose that $S = \{v_1, v_2, \ldots, v_n\}$ is a linearly dependent set with at least two elements. Then there are weights $c_1, c_2, \ldots, c_n$ not all 0 such that $c_1 v_1 + c_2 v_2 + \cdots + c_n v_n = 0$. Without loss of generality, assume that $c_1 \neq 0$. We have $c_1 v_1 = -c_2 v_2 - \cdots - c_n v_n$, and so, $v_1 = -\frac{c_2}{c_1} v_2 - \cdots - \frac{c_n}{c_1} v_n$. So, v_1 can be written as a linear combination of the other vectors in S.

84

Now, suppose that one of the vectors in S can be written as a linear combination of the other vectors in the set. Without loss of generality, assume that $v_1 = c_2 v_2 + \cdots + c_n v_n$. Then we have

$$v_1 - c_2 v_2 - \cdots - c_n v_n = 0.$$

Since the weight of v_1 is 1, this is a nontrivial dependence relation. This shows that S is a linearly dependent set. $\square$

LEVEL 4

13. Let G be a group and let H be a nonempty finite subset of G that is closed under the operation of G. Prove that H is a subgroup of G.

Proof: Let $x \in H$. We need to prove that $x^{-1} \in H$. If $x = e$, then $x^{-1} = e^{-1} = e \in H$. If $x \neq e$, then by closure and induction on $n \in \mathbb{Z}^+$, $x^n \in H$ for all $n \in \mathbb{Z}^+$. Since H is finite, there are $j, k \in \mathbb{Z}^+$ with $j < k$ and $x^j = x^k$. Then $k - j \in \mathbb{Z}^+$ and $x^{k-j} = x^k x^{-j} = x^k x^{-k} = x^0 = e$. Since $x \neq e$, $k - j > 1$, and so, $k - j - 1 \geq 1$. So, $x \cdot x^{k-j-1} = x^{k-j} = e$. So, $x^{k-j-1} = x^{-1}$ and since $k - j - 1 \geq 1$, $x^{k-j-1} \in H$. $\square$

14. Let U and W be subspaces of a vector space V. Determine necessary and sufficient conditions for $U \cup W$ to be a subspace of V.

Theorem: Let U and W be subspaces of a vector space V. Then $U \cup W$ is a subspace of V if and only if $U \subseteq W$ or $W \subseteq U$.

Proof: Let U and W be subspaces of a vector space V. If $U \subseteq W$, then $U \cup W = W$, and so, $U \cup W$ is a subspace of V. Similarly, if $W \subseteq U$, then $U \cup W = U$, and so, $U \cup W$ is a subspace of V.

Suppose that $U \not\subseteq W$ and $W \not\subseteq U$. Let $x \in U \setminus W$ and $y \in W \setminus U$. Suppose that $x + y \in U$. We have $-x \in U$ because U is a subspace of V. So, $y = (-x + x) + y = -x + (x + y) \in U$, contradicting $y \in W \setminus U$. So, $x + y \notin U$. A similar argument shows that $x + y \notin W$. So, $x + y \notin U \cup W$. It follows that $U \cup W$ is not closed under addition, and therefore, $U \cup W$ is **not** a subspace of V. $\square$

Note: The conditional statement $p \rightarrow q$ can be read "q is necessary for p" or "p is sufficient for q." Furthermore, $p \leftrightarrow q$ can be read "p is necessary and sufficient for q" (as well as "q is necessary and sufficient for p.")

So, when we are asked to determine necessary and sufficient conditions for a statement p to be true, we are being asked to find a statement q that is logically equivalent to the statement p.

Usually if we are being asked for necessary and sufficient conditions, the hope is that we will come up with an equivalent statement that is easier to understand and/or visualize than the given statement.

15. Give an example of vector spaces U and V with $U \subseteq V$ such that U is closed under scalar multiplication, but U is not a subspace of V.

Solution: Let $V = \mathbb{R}^2$ and $U = \{(x, y) \mid x = 0 \text{ or } y = 0 \text{ (or both)}\}$. Let $(x, y) \in U$ and $k \in \mathbb{R}$. Then $k(x, y) = (kx, ky)$. If $x = 0$, then $kx = 0$. If $y = 0$, then $ky = 0$. So, $k(x, y) \in U$. So, U is closed under scalar multiplication. Now, $(0, 1)$ and $(1, 0)$ are in U, but $(1, 1) = (0, 1) + (1, 0) \notin U$. So, $U \not\leq V$. $\square$

16. Let S be a set of two or more linearly dependent vectors in a vector space V. Prove that there is a vector v in the set so that span $S =$ span $S \setminus \{v\}$.

Proof: Let $S = \{v_1, v_2, \ldots, v_n\}$ be a set of two or more linearly dependent vectors in V. By Problem 12, one of the vectors in the set can be written as a linear combination of the other vectors in the set. Without loss of generality, assume that v_n can be written as a linear combination of the other vectors in the set, say $v_n = k_1 v_1 + k_2 v_2 + \cdots + k_{n-1} v_{n-1}$. We show that span $S =$ span $S \setminus \{v_n\}$. Let $v \in$ span S. Then there are weights $c_1, c_2, \ldots, c_n$ with $v = c_1 v_1 + c_2 v_2 + \cdots + c_n v_n$. So, we have

$$v = c_1 v_1 + c_2 v_2 + \cdots + c_n v_n = c_1 v_1 + c_2 v_2 + \cdots + c_n(k_1 v_1 + k_2 v_2 + \cdots + k_{n-1} v_{n-1})$$
$$= (c_1 + c_n k_1)v_1 + (c_2 + c_n k_2)v_2 + \cdots + (c_{n-1} + c_n k_{n-1})v_{n-1} \in \text{span } S \setminus \{v_n\}.$$

So, span $S \subseteq$ span $S \setminus \{v_n\}$. Since it is clear that span $S \setminus \{v_n\} \subseteq$ span S, span $S =$ span $S \setminus \{v_n\}$. $\quad\square$

17. Prove that a finite set of vectors S in a vector space V is a basis of V if and only if every vector in V can be written uniquely as a linear combination of the vectors in S.

Proof: Suppose that $S = \{v_1, v_2, \ldots, v_n\}$ is a basis of V. Then span$\{v_1, v_2, \ldots, v_n\} = V$. So, if $v \in V$, then v can be written as a linear combination of the vectors in S. Suppose there are weights $c_1, c_2, \ldots, c_n$ and $d_1, d_2, \ldots, d_n$ such that $v = c_1 v_1 + c_2 v_2 + \cdots + c_n v_n$ and $v = d_1 v_1 d c_2 v_2 + \cdots + d_n v_n$. Then we have $c_1 v_1 + c_2 v_2 + \cdots + c_n v_n = d_1 v_1 d c_2 v_2 + \cdots + d_n v_n$, and so,

$$(c_1 - d_1)v_1 + (c_2 - d_2)v_2 + \cdots + (c_n - d_n)v_n = 0.$$

Since S is a linearly independent set of vectors, $c_1 - d_1 = 0, c_2 - d_2 = 0, \ldots, c_n - d_n = 0$, and therefore, $c_1 = d_1, c_2 = d_2, \ldots, c_n = d_n$. So, the expression of v as a linear combination of the vectors in S is unique.

Now, suppose that each vector in V can be written uniquely as a linear combination of the vectors in S. Since each vector in V can be written as a linear combination of the vectors in S, we have that span$\{v_1, v_2, \ldots, v_n\} = V$. Since $0v_1 + 0v_2 + \cdots + 0v_n = 0$, by the uniqueness condition, the only way $c_1 v_1 + c_2 v_2 + \cdots + c_n v_n = 0$ could be true is if all weights are 0. So, S is linearly independent, and therefore, S is a basis of V.

18. Let $S = \{v_1, v_2, \ldots, v_m\}$ be a set of linearly independent vectors in a vector space V and let $T = \{w_1, w_2, \ldots, w_n\}$ be a set of vectors in V such that span $T = V$. Prove that $m \leq n$.

Proof: If $V = \{0\}$ or S consists of just one vector, then there is nothing to prove. So, let's assume that $V \neq \{0\}$ and S has at least two vectors. Note that since $V \neq \{0\}$, T has at least one vector.

Let $T_0 = T = \{w_1, w_2, \dots, w_n\}$. Since span $T_0 = V$, v_1 can be written as a linear combination of the vectors in T_0. By Problem 12, $\{w_1, w_2, \dots, w_n, v_1\}$ is linearly dependent. Let $c_1, c_2, \dots, c_n, d$ be weights, not all of which are 0, such that $c_1 w_1 + c_2 w_2 + \cdots + c_n w_n + dv_1 = 0$. We claim that for some $i = 1, 2, \dots, n$, $c_i \neq 0$. If $d = 0$, then since one of the weights must be nonzero, some c_i must be nonzero. Suppose $d \neq 0$. If every $c_i = 0$, then $dv_1 = 0$. Since $d \neq 0$, $v_1 = 0$, contradicting the linear independence of S. In both cases, we must have $c_i \neq 0$ for some i. Without loss of generality, assume that $c_1 \neq 0$. Then $w_1 = -\frac{c_2}{c_1} w_2 - \cdots - \frac{c_n}{c_1} w_n - \frac{d}{c_1} v_1$. Let $T_1 = \{w_2, \dots, w_n, v_1\}$. By the proof of Problem 16, we have span $\{w_1, w_2, \dots, w_n, v_1\} \subseteq$ span T_1. So, span $T_1 = V$.

At this point, note that if T had just one vector, then $T_1 = \{v_1\}$. Since span $T_1 = V$, v_2 would be a scalar multiple of v_1, contradicting the linear independence of S. So, T has at least two vectors. If S has only two vectors, then we are done. Otherwise, we continue as follows.

Since span $T_1 = V$, $\{w_2, \dots, w_n, v_1, v_2\}$ is linearly dependent. Let $c_2, \dots, c_n, d_1, d_2$ be weights, not all of which are 0, such that $c_2 w_2 + \cdots + c_n w_n + d_1 v_1 + d_2 v_2 = 0$. We claim that for some $i = 2, \dots, n$, $c_i \neq 0$. If $d_1 = 0$ or $d_2 = 0$, we can use the same argument in the last paragraph to show that some c_i must be nonzero. Suppose $d_1 \neq 0$ and $d_2 \neq 0$. If every $c_i = 0$, then $d_1 v_1 + d_2 v_2 = 0$, contradicting the linear independence of S. In both cases, we must have $c_i \neq 0$ for some i. Without loss of generality, assume that $c_2 \neq 0$. Then $w_2 = -\frac{c_3}{c_2} w_3 - \cdots - \frac{c_n}{c_2} w_n - \frac{d_1}{c_2} v_1 - \frac{d_2}{c_2} v_2$. Let $T_2 = \{w_3, \dots, w_n, v_1, v_2\}$. By the proof of Problem 16, we have span $\{w_2, \dots, w_n, v_1, v_2\} \subseteq$ span T_2. So, span $T_2 = V$.

Observe that if T had just two vectors, then $T_2 = \{v_1, v_2\}$. Since span $T_2 = V$, v_3 could be written as a linear combination of v_1 and v_2, contradicting the linear independence of S. So, T has at least three vectors. If S has only three vectors, then we are done. Otherwise, we continue in the same way.

Assuming $T_{j-1} = \{w_j, \dots, w_n, v_1, v_2, \dots v_{j-1}\}$ and span $T_{j-1} = V$, we have $\{w_j, \dots, w_n, v_1, v_2, \dots v_{j-1}, v_j\}$ linearly dependent. Once again, reindexing the w_i's if necessary, and letting $T_j = \{w_{j+1}, \dots, w_n, v_1, v_2, \dots v_{j-1}, v_j\}$, by an argument just like that given in the first paragraph, we can show that span $\{w_j, \dots, w_n, v_1, v_2, \dots, v_j\} \subseteq$ span T_j. So, span $T_j = V$.

If $j < m$ and T had just j vectors, then $T_j = \{v_1, v_2, \dots, v_j\}$. Since span $T_j = V$, v_{j+1} could be written as a linear combination of the vectors $v_1, v_2, \dots, v_j$, contradicting the linear independence of S. So, T has at least $j + 1$ vectors. If $j = m$, we have shown that $m \leq n$. Otherwise, we continue in the same way. This procedure terminates in m steps. $\square$

19. Let B be a basis of a vector space V with n vectors. Prove that any other basis of V also has n vectors.

Proof: Let B be a basis of V with n vectors. Let B' be another basis of V with m vectors. Let B. Since B' is a basis of V, B' is a linearly independent set of vectors in V. Since B is a basis of V, span $B = V$. By Problem 18, $m \leq n$. Similarly, we have that B is a linearly independent set of vectors in V and span $B' = V$. So, $n \leq m$. Since $m \leq n$ and $n \leq m$, we have $m = n$. So, B' has n vectors. $\square$

Problem Set 7

LEVEL 1

1. Let H and K be the subgroups of S_3 defined by $H = \{(1), (123), (132)\}$ and $K = \{(1), (12)\}$ (see Problem 1 from Problem Set 6). Determine which of these is a normal subgroup of S_3.

Solution: K is **not** normal in S_3 because $(13)(12)(13)^{-1} = (13)(12)(13) = (23)$ and $(23) \notin K$.

We now show that $H \lhd S_3$. We do this by brute force:

$$(12)(123)(12) = (132), \ (13)(123)(13) = (132), \ (23)(123)(23) = (132),$$
$$(12)(132)(12) = (123), \ (13)(132)(13) = (123), \ (23)(132)(23) = (123).$$

We do not need to check conjugation by the elements in H because we already know that H is a subgroup of S_3. We see that for all $g \in S_3$ and $h \in H$, we have $ghg^{-1} \in H$, and therefore, $H \lhd S_3$.

2. Let V and W be vector spaces over $\mathbb{R}$. Determine if each of the following functions is a linear transformation:

   (i) $f: \mathbb{R} \to \mathbb{R}$ defined by $f(x) = 2x + 1$

   (ii) $g: \mathbb{R} \to \mathbb{R}^2$ defined by $g(x) = (2x, 3x)$

   (iii) $h: \mathbb{R}^3 \to \mathbb{R}^3$ defined by $h\big((x, y, z)\big) = (x + y, x + z, z - y)$

Solutions:

(i) $f(0) = 2 \cdot 0 + 1 = 1 \neq 0$. Since the image of 0 under a linear transformation is 0, f is **not** a linear transformation.

(ii) $g(ax + by) = \big(2(ax + by), 3(ax + by)\big) = (2ax + 2by, 3ax + 3by)$
$$= (2ax, 3ax) + (2by, 3by) = a(2x, 3x) + b(2y, 3y) = ag(x) + bg(y).$$

By Theorem 7.7, g is a linear transformation.

(iii) $h\big(a(x, y, z) + b(s, t, w)\big) = h\big((ax + bs, ay + bt, az + bw)\big)$
$$= (ax + bs + ay + bt, ax + bs + az + bw, az + bw - ay - bt)$$
$$= (ax + ay, ax + az, az - ay) + (bs + bt, bs + bw, bw - bt)$$
$$a(x + y, x + z, z - y) + b(s + t, s + w, w - t) = ah\big((x, y, z)\big) + bh\big((s, t, w)\big).$$

By Theorem 7.7, h is a linear transformation.

3. Compute each of the following:

(i) $\begin{bmatrix} 2 & 0 & -3 \\ 0 & 1 & 4 \end{bmatrix} \cdot \begin{bmatrix} 1 & 1 & 3 & 0 \\ 1 & -4 & 2 & 0 \\ 2 & 0 & 1 & -4 \end{bmatrix}$

(ii) $[3 \ -1 \ 5] \cdot \begin{bmatrix} -4 \\ -7 \\ 2 \end{bmatrix}$

(iii) $\begin{bmatrix} -4 \\ -7 \\ 2 \end{bmatrix} \cdot [3 \ -1 \ 5]$

(iv) $\begin{bmatrix} a & b & c \\ d & e & f \\ g & h & i \end{bmatrix} \cdot \begin{bmatrix} 1 & 0 & 1 \\ 0 & 2 & 0 \\ 3 & 1 & 4 \end{bmatrix}.$

Solutions:

(i) $\begin{bmatrix} 2 & 0 & -3 \\ 0 & 1 & 4 \end{bmatrix} \cdot \begin{bmatrix} 1 & 1 & 3 & 0 \\ 1 & -4 & 2 & 0 \\ 2 & 0 & 1 & -4 \end{bmatrix} = \begin{bmatrix} -4 & 2 & 3 & 12 \\ 9 & -4 & 6 & -16 \end{bmatrix}.$

(ii) $[3 \ -1 \ 5] \cdot \begin{bmatrix} -4 \\ -7 \\ 2 \end{bmatrix} = -12 + 7 + 10 = \mathbf{5}.$

(iii) $\begin{bmatrix} -4 \\ -7 \\ 2 \end{bmatrix} \cdot [3 \ -1 \ 5] = \begin{bmatrix} -12 & 4 & -20 \\ -21 & 7 & -35 \\ 6 & -2 & 10 \end{bmatrix}.$

(iv) $\begin{bmatrix} a & b & c \\ d & e & f \\ g & h & i \end{bmatrix} \cdot \begin{bmatrix} 1 & 0 & 1 \\ 0 & 2 & 0 \\ 3 & 1 & 4 \end{bmatrix} = \begin{bmatrix} a+3c & 2b+c & a+4c \\ d+3f & 2e+f & d+4f \\ g+3i & 2h+i & g+4i \end{bmatrix}.$

LEVEL 2

4. Let $(R, +, \cdot)$ be a ring and define addition and multiplication on $R \times R$ componentwise, as was done in Problem 13 from Problem Set 2. Prove that $(R, +, \cdot)$ is isomorphic to a subring of $(R \times R, +, \cdot)$.

Proof: Let $S = \{(x, x) \mid x \in R\}$. Then $S \subseteq R \times R$, $(0, 0) \in S$, and $(1, 1) \in S$. If $(x, x), (y, y) \in S$, then we have $(x, x) - (y, y) = (x - y, x - y) \in S$ and $(x, x) \cdot (y, y) = (xy, xy) \in S$. So, S is a subring of $R \times R$ (note that we used Problem 4 from Problem Set 6 here).

Define $f: R \to S$ by $f(x) = (x, x)$. Clearly, f is bijective. If $x, y \in R$, we have

$$f(x + y) = (x + y, x + y) = (x, x) + (y, y) = f(x) + f(y).$$
$$f(xy) = (xy, xy) = (x, x) \cdot (y, y) = f(x) \cdot f(y).$$

So, f is a homomorphism. Therefore, $f: R \cong S$. $\qquad \square$

89

5. Let z and w be complex numbers. Prove the following:

(i) $\overline{z+w} = \bar{z} + \bar{w}$

(ii) $\overline{zw} = \bar{z} \cdot \bar{w}$

(iii) $\overline{\left(\dfrac{z}{w}\right)} = \dfrac{\bar{z}}{\bar{w}}$

Proofs:

(i) Let $z = a + bi$ and $w = c + di$. Then we have

$$\overline{z+w} = \overline{(a+bi)+(c+di)} = \overline{(a+c)+(b+d)i} = (a+c)-(b+d)i$$
$$= (a-bi)+(c-di) = \overline{a+bi}+\overline{c+di} = \bar{z}+\bar{w}. \qquad \square$$

(ii) Let $z = a + bi$ and $w = c + di$. Then we have

$$\overline{zw} = \overline{(a+bi)(c+di)} = \overline{(ac-bd)+(ad+bc)i} = (ac-bd)-(ad+bc)i$$
$$= (a-bi)(c-di) = \overline{(a+bi)}\,\overline{(c+di)} = \bar{z}\cdot\bar{w}. \qquad \square$$

(iii) Let $z = a + bi$ and $w = c + di$. Then we have

$$\overline{\left(\frac{z}{w}\right)} = \overline{\frac{(a+bi)}{(c+di)}} = \overline{\frac{(a+bi)}{(c+di)}\cdot\frac{(c-di)}{(c-di)}} = \overline{\frac{(a+bi)(c-di)}{(c+di)(c-di)}} = \overline{\frac{(ac+bd)+(-ad+bc)i}{c^2+d^2}}$$

$$= \overline{\frac{(ac+bd)}{c^2+d^2}+\frac{(-ad+bc)}{c^2+d^2}i} = \frac{(ac+bd)}{c^2+d^2}-\frac{(-ad+bc)}{c^2+d^2}i = \frac{(ac+bd)+(ad-bc)i}{c^2+d^2}$$

$$= \frac{(a-bi)(c+di)}{(c-di)(c+di)} = \frac{(a-bi)}{(c-di)}\cdot\frac{(c+di)}{(c+di)} = \frac{a-bi}{c-di} = \frac{\overline{a+bi}}{\overline{c+di}} = \frac{\bar{z}}{\bar{w}}$$

$$\square$$

6. Consider $\mathbb{C}$ as a vector space over itself. Give an example of a function $f: \mathbb{C} \to \mathbb{C}$ such that f is additive, but **not** a linear transformation. Then give an example of vector spaces V and W and a homogenous function $g: V \to W$ that is **not** a linear transformation.

Solution: Define $f: \mathbb{C} \to \mathbb{C}$ by $f(z) = \operatorname{Re} z$. If $z = x + yi$ and $w = u + vi$, then

$$f(z+w) = f\big((x+yi)+(u+vi)\big) = f\big((x+u)+(y+v)i\big)$$
$$= x+u = \operatorname{Re} z + \operatorname{Re} w = f(z) + f(w).$$

So, f is additive.

Now, $f(i \cdot 1) = f(i) = 0$ and $i \cdot f(1) = i \cdot 1 = i$. So, $f(i \cdot 1) \neq i \cdot f(1)$. Therefore, f is **not** homogenous.

So, f is **not** a linear transformation.

Let $V = \mathbb{R}^2$ and $W = \mathbb{R}$, considered as vector spaces over the field $\mathbb{R}$. Define $g: \mathbb{R}^2 \to \mathbb{R}$ by $g\big((v,w)\big) = (v^3 + w^3)^{\frac{1}{3}}$. Then for $k \in \mathbb{R}$, we have

$$g\big(k(v,w)\big) = g\big((kv, kw)\big) = ((kv)^3 + (kw)^3)^{\frac{1}{3}} = (k^3 v^3 + k^3 w^3)^{\frac{1}{3}} = \big(k^3(v^3 + w^3)\big)^{\frac{1}{3}}$$
$$= (k^3)^{\frac{1}{3}}(v^3 + w^3)^{\frac{1}{3}} = k(v^3 + w^3)^{\frac{1}{3}} = k \cdot g\big((v,w)\big).$$

Therefore, g is homogeneous.

Now, we have

$$g\big((1,0)\big) + g\big((0,1)\big) = (1^3 + 0^3)^{\frac{1}{3}} + (0^3 + 1)^{\frac{1}{3}} = 1 + 1 = 2.$$
$$g\big((1,0) + (0,1)\big) = g\big((1,1)\big) = (1^3 + 1^3)^{\frac{1}{3}} = 2^{\frac{1}{3}}.$$

So, $g\big((1,0) + (0,1)\big) \neq g\big((1,0)\big) + g\big((0,1)\big)$, and therefore, g is **not** additive.

So, g is **not** a linear transformation.

LEVEL 3

7. Prove that there are exactly two ring homomorphisms from $\mathbb{Z}$ to itself.

Proof: The identity function $i_{\mathbb{Z}}: \mathbb{Z} \to \mathbb{Z}$ and the zero function $0: \mathbb{Z} \to \mathbb{Z}$ are both ring homomorphisms from $\mathbb{Z}$ to itself. We show that these are the only ones.

Let $f: \mathbb{Z} \to \mathbb{Z}$ be a ring homomorphism and suppose that $f(1) = n$. Then we also have

$$f(1) = f(1 \cdot 1) = f(1) \cdot f(1) = n \cdot n = n^2.$$

So, $n^2 = n$. Therefore, $n^2 - n = 0$, and so, $n(n - 1) = 0$. It follows that $n = 0$ or $n = 1$.

Now, it is easy to show that $f(k) = k \cdot f(1)$ for all $k \in \mathbb{Z}$. For $k \in \mathbb{N}$, use the principle of mathematical induction. Then if $k < 0$, we have $f(k) = f\big(-(-k)\big) = -f(-k) = -(-k)f(1) = kf(1)$. $f(0) = 0$ follows from Theorem 7.2.

So, if $f(1) = 0$, then for all $k \in \mathbb{Z}$, $f(k) = kf(1) = k \cdot 0 = 0$. In this case, f is the zero function.

If $f(1) = 1$, then for all $k \in \mathbb{Z}$, $f(k) = kf(1) = k \cdot 1 = k$. In this case, f is the identity function. $\quad\square$

8. Prove each of the following:

    (i)   Ring isomorphism is an equivalence relation.

    (ii)   If we let $\mathrm{Aut}(R)$ be the set of automorphisms of a ring R, then $(\mathrm{Aut}(R), \circ)$ is a group, where $\circ$ is composition. $\mathrm{Aut}(R)$ is called the **automorphism group** of R.

    (iii) Let R be a ring and for each $x \in R$, define the function $\phi_x: R \to R$ by $\phi_x(y) = xyx^{-1}$. Let $\mathrm{Inn}(R) = \{\phi_x \mid x \in R\}$. Prove that $\mathrm{Inn}(R)$ is a normal subgroup of $\mathrm{Aut}(R)$. $\mathrm{Inn}(R)$ is called the **inner automorphism group** of R.

Proofs:

(i) Since the proof for groups is almost the same as the proof for rings (but a little easier), I will give the details only for rings.

$i_R: R \to R$ is a bijection and if $x, y \in R$, then $i_R(x + y) = x + y = i_R(x) + i_R(y)$ and $i_R(xy) = xy = i_R(x)i_R(y)$. Also, $i_R(1_R) = 1_R$. So, i_R is an isomorphism from R to itself. Therefore, $\cong$ is reflexive.

Suppose that $f: R \to S$ is an isomorphism from R to S. We already know that $f^{-1}: S \to R$ is a bijection from S to R. Let $x, y \in S$ and let $z, w \in R$ with $f(z) = x$ and $f(w) = y$. Then $f(z + w) = f(z) + f(w) = x + y$, and so, $f^{-1}(x + y) = z + w = f^{-1}(x) + f^{-1}(y)$. Also, $f(zw) = f(z)f(w) = xy$, so that $f^{-1}(xy) = zw = f^{-1}(x)f^{-1}(y)$. Finally, $f^{-1}(1_S) = 1_R$. Therefore, f^{-1} is an isomorphism from S to R, and so, $\cong$ is symmetric.

Suppose that $f: R \to S, g: S \to T$ are isomorphisms. We already know that $g \circ f: R \to T$ is a bijection. If $x, y \in R$, then we have

$$(g \circ f)(x + y) = g(f(x + y)) = g(f(x) + f(y))$$
$$= g(f(x)) + g(f(y)) = (g \circ f)(x) + (g \circ f)(y)$$

and

$$(g \circ f)(xy) = g(f(xy)) = g(f(x) \cdot f(y))$$
$$= g(f(x)) \cdot g(f(y)) = (g \circ f)(x) \cdot (g \circ f)(y).$$

Also, $(g \circ f)(1_R) = g(f(1_R)) = g(1_S) = 1_T$. So, $g \circ f$ is an isomorphism from R to T, and so, $\cong$ is transitive.

Since $\cong$ is reflexive, symmetric, and transitive, $\cong$ is an equivalence relation. □

(ii) Let R be a ring and let $f, g \in \text{Aut}(R)$. Then $g \circ f$ is an automorphism by the proof of transitivity from part (i). So $\text{Aut}(R)$ is closed under $\circ$. We proved that $\circ$ is associative in $S(R)$ in Theorem 4.11. Since $\text{Aut}(R) \subseteq S(R)$, $\circ$ is associative in $\text{Aut}(R)$ as well. We proved that i_R satisfies $i_R \circ f = f$ and $f \circ i_R = f$ for all $f \in \text{Aut}(R)$ in the same example and we proved i_R is an automorphism in part (i) above. Let $f \in \text{Aut}(R)$. By Theorem 4.9, we have $f^{-1} \circ f = f \circ f^{-1} = i_R$, and we proved that f^{-1} is an automorphism in part (i) above. It follows that $(\text{Aut}(R), \circ)$ is a group. □

(iii) We first show that for each $x \in R$, ϕ_x is an automorphism of R. So, let $x, y, z \in R$. Then

$$\phi_x(y + z) = x(y + z)x^{-1} = (xy + xz)x^{-1} = xyx^{-1} + xzx^1 = \phi_x(y) + \phi_x(z)$$

$$\phi_x(yz) = x(yz)x^{-1} = xy \cdot 1 \cdot zx^{-1} = (xyx^{-1})(xzx^{-1}) = \phi_x(y) \cdot \phi_x(z)$$

$$\phi_x(1) = x1x^{-1} = xx^{-1} = 1$$

It follows that $\text{Inn}(R) \subseteq \text{Aut}(R)$. Now, for all $y \in R$, $\phi_e(y) = eye^{-1} = ye = y$. So, ϕ_e is the identity automorphism of R. It follows that $\text{Inn}(R)$ contains the identity of $\text{Aut}(R)$. Let $\phi_x, \phi_y \in \text{Inn}(R)$. Then for all $z \in R$,

$$(\phi_x \circ \phi_y)(z) = \phi_x(\phi_y(z)) = \phi_x(yzy^{-1}) = xyzy^{-1}x^{-1} = (xy)z(xy)^{-1} = \phi_{xy}(z).$$

So, $\phi_x \circ \phi_y = \phi_{xy} \in \text{Inn}(R)$ and therefore, $\text{Inn}(R)$ is closed under composition. Let $\phi_x \in \text{Inn}(R)$. Then for all $z \in R$,

$$(\phi_x \circ \phi_{x^{-1}})(z) = \phi_x(\phi_{x^{-1}}(z)) = \phi_x(x^{-1}zx) = xx^{-1}zxx^{-1} = z = \phi_e(z).$$

So, $\phi_x \circ \phi_{x^{-1}} = \phi_e$. It follows that $(\phi_x)^{-1} = \phi_{x^{-1}} \in \text{Inn}(R)$. So, $\text{Inn}(R)$ is closed under taking inverses. Therefore, $\text{Inn}(R) \leq \text{Aut}(R)$.

Finally, let $f \in Aut(R)$, $\phi_x \in Inn(R)$, and $y \in R$. Then

$$(f \circ \phi_x \circ f^{-1})(y) = f\left(\phi_x(f^{-1}(y))\right) = f(xf^{-1}(y)x^{-1})$$

$$= f(x)f(f^{-1}(y))f(x^{-1}) = f(x)y(f(x))^{-1} = \phi_{f(x)}(y).$$

So, $f \circ \phi_x \circ f^{-1} = \phi_{f(x)} \in Inn(R)$. Therefore, $\text{Inn}(R) \lhd \text{Aut}(R)$.　　　□

9. Prove that a commutative ring R is a field if and only if the only ideals of R are $\{0\}$ and R.

Proof: Let R be a commutative ring. If R is a field then by part 7 of Example 7.22, the only ideals of R are $\{0\}$ and R.

Conversely, assume that the only ideals of R are $\{0\}$ and R. Let $a \in R$ with $a \neq 0$, and let $I = \{ax \mid x \in R\}$ b ethe principal ideal generated by a. By part 3 of Example 7.22, I is an ideal of R.

Since $a = ae \in I$ and $a \neq 0$, $I \neq \{0\}$. By assumption, we must have $I = R$. Since $1 \in R$, $1 \in I$. Therefore, there is $b \in R$ such that $ab = 1$. So, $b = a^{-1}$. Since $a \neq 0$ was arbitrary, we have shown that R has the multiplicative inverse property, and therefore, R is a field.　　　□

10. Prove that if X is a nonempty set of normal subgroups of a group G then $\cap X$ is a normal subgroup of G. Similarly, prove that if X is a nonempty set of ideals of a ring R, then $\cap X$ is an ideal of R. Is the union of normal subgroups always a normal subgroup? Is the union of ideals always an ideal?

Proofs: Let X be a nonempty set of normal subgroups of a group G. Since for all $H \in X$, $e \in H$, $e \in \cap X$, and so, $\cap X \neq \emptyset$. Let $g, h \in \cap X$. Then for all $H \in X$, $g, h \in H$. By Problem 5 from Problem Set 6, for all $H \in X$, $gh^{-1} \in H$. So, $gh^{-1} \in \cap X$. Again, by Problem 5 from Problem Set 6, $\cap X$ is a subgroup of G. Now, let $h \in \cap X$, and let $g \in G$. Then for all $H \in X$, $h \in H$, and since each H is a normal subgroup of G, $ghg^{-1} \in H$. So, $ghg^{-1} \in \cap X$. Therefore, $\cap X$ is a normal subgroup of G.　　　□

Let X be a nonempty set of ideals of a ring R. Since for all $I \in X$, $0 \in I$, $0 \in \cap X$, and so, $\cap X \neq \emptyset$. Let $x, y \in \cap X$. Then for all $I \in X$, $x, y \in I$. By Problem 5 from Problem Set 6, for all $I \in X$, $x - y \in I$. So, $x - y \in \cap X$. Again, by Problem 5 from Problem Set 6, $(\cap X, +)$ is a subgroup of $(R, +)$. Now, let $x \in \cap X$, and let $y \in R$. Then for all $I \in X$, $x \in I$, and since each I is an ideal of R, $xy \in I$. So, $xy \in \cap X$. Therefore, $\cap X$ absorbs R, and so, $\cap X$ is an ideal of R.　　　□

Since $(\mathbb{Z}, +)$ is a commutative group, all subgroups are normal. In particular $(2\mathbb{Z}, +)$ and $(3\mathbb{Z}, +)$ are normal subgroups of $(\mathbb{Z}, +)$. Now, $2, 3 \in (2\mathbb{Z}, +) \cup (3\mathbb{Z}, +)$, but $2 + 3 = 5 \notin (2\mathbb{Z}, +) \cup (3\mathbb{Z}, +)$. So, $(2\mathbb{Z}, +) \cup (3\mathbb{Z}, +)$ is not closed under addition and is therefore not a subgroup of $(\mathbb{Z}, +)$.

Since $(2\mathbb{Z}, +, \cdot)$ and $(3\mathbb{Z}, +, \cdot)$ are ideals of $(\mathbb{Z}, +, \cdot)$, the same argument in the last paragraph shows that the union of ideals is **not** always an ideal.

11. Let $P = \{ax^2 + bx + c \mid a, b, c \in \mathbb{R}\}$ be the vector space of polynomials of degree at most 2 with real coefficients (see part 3 of Example 2.19 from Lesson 2). Define the linear transformation $D: P \to P$ by $D(ax^2 + bx + c) = 2ax + b$. Find the matrix of T with respect to each of the following bases:

    (i)   The standard basis $B = \{1, x, x^2\}$

    (ii) $C = \{x + 1, x^2 + 1, x^2 + x\}$

Solutions:

(i) $D(1) = 0 = 0x^2 + 0x + 0$, $D(x) = 1 = 0x^2 + 0x + 1$, and $D(x^2) = 2x = 0x^2 + 2x + 0$.

Therefore, $\mathcal{M}_T = \begin{bmatrix} 0 & 0 & 0 \\ 0 & 0 & 2 \\ 0 & 1 & 0 \end{bmatrix}$.

(ii) We have the following:

$$D(x + 1) = 1 = \frac{1}{2}(x + 1) + \frac{1}{2}(x^2 + 1) - \frac{1}{2}(x^2 + x)$$
$$D(x^2 + 1) = 2x = 1(x + 1) - 1(x^2 + 1) + 1(x^2 + x)$$
$$D(x^2 + x) = 2x + 1 = \frac{3}{2}(x + 1) - \frac{1}{2}(x^2 + 1) + \frac{1}{2}(x^2 + x)$$

Therefore, $\mathcal{M}_T(C) = \begin{bmatrix} \frac{1}{2} & 1 & \frac{3}{2} \\ \frac{1}{2} & -1 & -\frac{1}{2} \\ -\frac{1}{2} & 1 & \frac{1}{2} \end{bmatrix}$.

Notes: (1) In part (ii), it's a little more challenging to express the images of basis elements as a linear combination of basis elements. For example, how do we express 1 as a linear combination of $x + 1$, $x^2 + 1$, and $x^2 + x$. Well, we need to find weights c_1, c_2, and c_3 such that

$$1 = c_1(x + 1) + c_2(x^2 + 1) + c_3(x^2 + x).$$

We rewrite each side of this equation as a linear combination of x^2, x, and 1 as follows:

$$1 = c_1 x + c_1 + c_2 x^2 + c_2 + c_3 x^2 + c_3 x$$
$$0x^2 + 0x + 1 = (c_2 + c_3)x^2 + (c_1 + c_3)x + (c_1 + c_2)$$

Since $x^2, x, 1$ are linearly independent, we must have $c_2 + c_3 = 0$, $c_1 + c_3 = 0$, and $c_1 + c_2 = 1$. Subtracting the first equation from the third equation gives $c_1 - c_3 = 1$. Adding this equation to the second equation gives $2c_1 = 1$. Dividing by 2, we get $c_1 = \frac{1}{2}$. Using this value for c_1 and the second and third equations, we get $c_2 = \frac{1}{2}$ and $c_3 = -\frac{1}{2}$. This is how we wrote $D(x + 1)$ as a linear combination of $x + 1$, $x^2 + 1$, and $x^2 + x$ in the solution above.

The computations for $D(x^2 + 1)$ and $D(x^2 + x)$ can be done similarly.

(2) In a computational linear algebra course, you learn a procedure for solving systems of linear equations called Gauss-Jordan reduction. This procedure will always allow you to express arbitrary vectors as linear combinations of basis vectors. In fact, a single Gauss-Jordan reduction can be used to express the images of as many vectors as we like as a linear combination of basis vectors. Performing tedious computations like this lies outside the scope of this book and so, we leave it for the interested reader to investigate themselves.

12. Let V and W be vector spaces with V finite-dimensional, let $U \leq V$, and let $T \in \mathcal{L}(U, W)$. Prove that there is an $S \in \mathcal{L}(V, W)$ such that $S(v) = T(v)$ for all $v \in U$.

Proof: Suppose that $U \leq V$ with $\dim V = n$. Let $B = \{v_1, v_2, \ldots, v_k\}$ be a basis of U. Since $v_1, v_2, \ldots, v_k$ are linearly independent, we can extend B to a basis B' of V, say $B' = \{v_1, v_2, \ldots, v_k, v_{k+1}, \ldots, v_n\}$. Define S by $S(c_1 v_1 + \cdots + c_n v_n) = T(c_1 v_1 + \cdots + c_k v_k)$. Since every vector in V can be written as a linear combination of the vectors in B', $\text{dom } S = V$. Also, $\text{ran } S \subseteq \text{ran } T \subseteq W$. So, $S: V \to W$. Since T is linear, so is S. If $v \in U$, then v can be written as a linear combination of the vectors in B, say $v = c_1 v_1 + \cdots c_k v_k$. Then we have

$$S(v) = S(c_1 v_1 + \cdots + c_k v_k) = S(c_1 v_1 + \cdots + c_k v_k + 0 v_{k+1} + \cdots + 0 v_n)$$
$$= T(c_1 v_1 + \cdots + c_k v_k) = T(v). \qquad \square$$

LEVEL 4

13. Let G and H be groups and let $f: G \to H$ be a homomorphism. Prove each of the following:

    (i)   If G is commutative, then $f[G]$ is commutative.

    (ii)   If $n \in \mathbb{Z}$ and $x \in G$, then $f(x^n) = (f(x))^n$.

    (iii) If G is cyclic, then $f[G]$ is cyclic.

    (iv) If f is an isomorphism, then $f[Z(G)] = Z(H)$, where $Z(G)$ is the center of G (in other words, $Z(G) = \{x \in G \mid xz = zx \text{ for all } z \in G \}$).

Proofs:

    (i)   Suppose that G is commutative and let $x, y \in f[G]$. Then there are $g, h \in G$ such that $f(g) = x$ and $f(h) = y$. So, $xy = f(g)f(h) = f(gh) = f(hg) = f(h)f(g) = yx$. Since $x, y \in f[G]$ were arbitrary, $f[G]$ is commutative. $\qquad \square$

    (ii)   If $n = 0$, then $f(x^0) = f(e) = e = (f(x))^0$. For $n \in \mathbb{Z}^+$, we use induction on n.

    Base case $(k = 1)$: $f(x^1) = f(x) = (f(x))^1$.

    Inductive step: Assume that $k \in \mathbb{Z}^+$ and $f(x^k) = (f(x))^k$. Then

$$f(x^{k+1}) = f(x^k x) = f(x^k)f(x) = (f(x))^k f(x) = (f(x))^{k+1}.$$

    By the Principle of Mathematical Induction, $f(x^n) = (f(x))^n$ for all $n \in \mathbb{Z}^+$.

    Finally, if $n \in \mathbb{Z}^+$, then $f(x^{-n}) = f((x^n)^{-1}) = (f(x^n))^{-1} = ((f(x))^n)^{-1} = (f(x))^{-n}$.

So, for all $n \in \mathbb{Z}$, $f(x^n) = \left(f(x)\right)^n$. □

(iii) Suppose that G is cyclic with generator x. We will show that $f[G]$ is cyclic with generator $f(x)$. Let $y \in f[G]$. Then there is $g \in G$ with $f(g) = y$. Since G is generated by x, there is $n \in \mathbb{Z}$ with $g = x^n$. Then $y = f(g) = f(x^n) = \left(f(x)\right)^n \in \langle f(x) \rangle$ (by part (ii) above). So, $f[G] \subseteq \langle f(x) \rangle$. Conversely, if $y \in \langle f(x) \rangle$, then there is $n \in \mathbb{Z}$ with $y = \left(f(x)\right)^n$. Since $x \in G$, $f(x) \in f[G]$. By the Note following Theorem 7.18, $f[G]$ is a subgroup of H. So, $y = \left(f(x)\right)^n \in f[G]$. Therefore, $\langle f(x) \rangle \subseteq f[G]$. Thus, $\langle f(x) \rangle = f[G]$. □

(iv) Let $y \in f[Z(G)]$. Then there is $x \in Z(G)$ with $y = f(x)$. Since $x \in Z(G)$, $xz = zx$ for all $z \in G$. So, $f(x)f(z) = f(xz) = f(zx) = f(z)f(x)$ for all $z \in G$. Since $y = f(x)$, we see that $yf(z) = f(z)y$ for all $z \in G$. So, $y \in Z(f[G])$. Since $y \in f[Z(G)]$ was arbitrary, we have $f[Z(G)] \subseteq Z(f[G]) = Z(H)$ (because $f[G] = H$).

Conversely, let $y \in Z(H)$. Since f is an isomorphism, there is $x \in G$ with $y = f(x)$. Let $w \in G$ and let $z = f(w)$. Then

$$xw = f^{-1}(y)f^{-1}(z) = f^{-1}(yz) = f^{-1}(zy) = f^{-1}(z)f^{-1}(y) = wx.$$

So, $x \in Z(G)$. Therefore, $y = f(x) \in f[Z(G)]$. Since $y \in Z(H)$ was arbitrary, we have $Z(H) \subseteq f[Z(G)]$. So, $f[Z(G)] = Z(H)$. □

14. Prove that each of the following pairs of groups are **not** isomorphic.

  (i) $(\mathbb{Q}, +)$ and $(\mathbb{Z}, +)$.

  (ii) $(\mathbb{Q}, +)$ and $(\mathbb{Q}^+, \cdot)$.

Proofs:

(i) Suppose toward contradiction that $f: \mathbb{Q} \to \mathbb{Z}$ is an isomorphism. Since f is surjective, there is $q \in \mathbb{Q}$ such that $f(q) = 1$. Then $2f\left(\frac{q}{2}\right) = f\left(\frac{q}{2}\right) + f\left(\frac{q}{2}\right) = f\left(\frac{q}{2} + \frac{q}{2}\right) = f(q) = 1$. If we let $x = f\left(\frac{q}{2}\right)$, then we see that $f\left(\frac{q}{2}\right)$ is a solution of the equation $2x = 1$. But this equation has no solution in $\mathbb{Z}$. Therefore, there is no such isomorphism. □

(ii) Suppose toward contradiction that $f: \mathbb{Q} \to \mathbb{Q}^+$ is an isomorphism. Since f is surjective, there is $q \in \mathbb{Q}$ such that $f(q) = 2$. Then $\left(f\left(\frac{q}{2}\right)\right)^2 = f\left(\frac{q}{2}\right)f\left(\frac{q}{2}\right) = f\left(\frac{q}{2} + \frac{q}{2}\right) = f(q) = 2$. If we let $x = f\left(\frac{q}{2}\right)$, then we see that $f\left(\frac{q}{2}\right)$ is a solution of the equation $x^2 = 2$. But this equation has no solution in $\mathbb{Q}$. So, there is no such isomorphism. □

15. Let $T: V \to W$ be a linear transformation and let $v_1, v_2, \ldots, v_n \in V$. Prove the following:

  (i) If T is injective and $v_1, v_2, \ldots, v_n$ are linearly independent in V, then $T(v_1), T(v_2), \ldots, T(v_n)$ are linearly independent in W.

  (ii) If T is surjective and $\text{span}\{v_1, v_2, \ldots, v_n\} = V$, then $\text{span}\{T(v_1), T(v_2), \ldots, T(v_n)\} = W$.

Proofs:

(i) Let T be injective and assume that $v_1, v_2, \ldots, v_n$ are linearly independent. Let $c_1, \ldots, c_n \in \mathbb{F}$ be such that $c_1 T(v_1) + \cdots + c_n T(v_n) = 0$. Since T is a linear transformation, $T(c_1 v_1 + \cdots + c_n v_n) = 0$. Since T is injective and $T(0) = 0$, we have $c_1 v_1 + \cdots + c_n v_n = 0$. By the linear independence of $v_1, v_2, \ldots, v_n$, $c_1 = c_2 = \cdots = c_n = 0$. So, $T(v_1), T(v_2), \ldots, T(v_n)$ are linearly independent. $\square$

(ii) Let T be surjective and assume that $\mathrm{span}\{v_1, v_2, \ldots, v_n\} = V$. Let $w \in W$. Since T is surjective, there is $v \in V$ such that $T(v) = w$. Since $\mathrm{span}\{v_1, v_2, \ldots, v_n\} = V$, $v = c_1 v_1 + \cdots c_n v_n$ for some $c_1, \ldots, c_n \in \mathbb{F}$. Then $T(v) = T(c_1 v_1 + \cdots + c_n v_n) = c_1 T(v_1) + \cdots + T(v_n)$. Therefore, $w = T(v)$ is in $\mathrm{span}\{T(v_1), T(v_2), \ldots, T(v_n)\}$. So, $W \subseteq \mathrm{span}\{T(v_1), T(v_2), \ldots, T(v_n)\}$. Since $T: V \to W$ and W is closed under taking linear combinations, we have $\mathrm{span}\{T(v_1), T(v_2), \ldots, T(v_n)\} \subseteq W$. Thus, we have $\mathrm{span}\{T(v_1), T(v_2), \ldots, T(v_n)\} = W$. $\square$

16. Let V and W be vector spaces over a field F. Prove that $\mathcal{L}(V, W)$ is a vector space over F, where addition and scalar multiplication are defined as in Theorem 7.8.

Proof: We first prove that $(\mathcal{L}(V, W), +)$ is a commutative group.

(Closure) Let $S, T \in \mathcal{L}(V, W)$, let $v, w \in V$, and let $a, b \in F$. Then

$$(S + T)(av + bw) = S(av + bw) + T(av + bw) = aS(v) + bS(w) + aT(v) + bT(w)$$
$$= a\big(S(v) + T(v)\big) + b\big(S(w) + T(w)\big) = a(S + T)(v) + b(S + T)(w).$$

So, $S + T \in \mathcal{L}(V, W)$.

(Associativity) Let $S, T, U \in \mathcal{L}(V, W)$ and let $v \in V$. Since addition is associative in W, we have

$$\big((S + T) + U\big)(v) = (S + T)(v) + U(v) = \big(S(v) + T(v)\big) + U(v)$$
$$= S(v) + \big(T(v) + U(v)\big) = S(v) + (T + U)(v) = \big(S + (T + U)\big)(v).$$

So, $(S + T) + U = S + (T + U)$.

(Commutativity) Let $S, T \in \mathcal{L}(V, W)$ and let $v \in V$. Since addition is commutative in W, we have

$$(S + T)(v) = S(v) + T(v) = T(v) + S(v) = (T + S)(v).$$

So, $S + T + T + S$.

(Identity) Define $0: V \to W$ by $0(v) = 0$ for all $v \in V$. Then for all $v, w \in V$ and $a, b \in F$,

$$0(av + bw) = 0 = 0 + 0 = a \cdot 0 + b \cdot 0 = a0(v) + b0(w).$$

So, $0 \in \mathcal{L}(V, W)$.

For any $T \in \mathcal{L}(V, W)$ and $v \in V$, we have $(T + 0)(v) = T(v) + 0(v) = T(v) + 0 = T(v)$ and we have $(0 + T)(v) = 0(v) + T(v) = 0 + T(v) = T(v)$. So, $T + 0 = 0 + T = T$.

(Inverse) Let $T \in \mathcal{L}(V, W)$ and define S by $S(v) = -T(v)$ for all $v \in V$. Then for all $v, w \in V$ and $a, b \in \mathbb{F}$,

$$S(av + bw) = -T(av + bw) = -\big(aT(v) + bT(w)\big) = a\big(-T(v)\big) + b\big(-T(w)\big) = aS(v) + bS(w).$$

So, $S \in \mathcal{L}(V, W)$. If $v \in V$, then

$$(T + S)(v) = T(v) + S(v) = T(v) + \big(-T(v)\big) = 0 = 0(v).$$
$$(S + T)(v) = S(v) + T(v) = -T(v) + T(v) = 0 = 0(v).$$

So, $T + S = S + T = 0$. Therefore, $S = -T$.

Now, let's prove that $\mathcal{L}(V, W)$ has the remaining vector space properties.

(Closure under scalar multiplication) Let $k \in F$, let $T \in \mathcal{L}(V, W)$, let $v, w \in V$, and let $a, b \in F$. Then

$$(kT)(av + bw) = kT(av + bw) = k\big(aT(v) + bT(w)\big) = k(aT(v)) + k(bT(w))$$
$$= (ka)T(v) + (kb)T(w) = (ak)T(v) + (bk)\big(T(w)\big) = a\big(kT(v)\big) + b\big(kT(w)\big)$$
$$= a(kT)(v) + b(kT)(w).$$

So, $kT \in \mathcal{L}(V, W)$.

(Scalar multiplication identity) Let 1 be the multiplicative identity of F, let $T \in \mathcal{L}(V, W)$, and let $v \in V$. Then $(1T)(v) = 1T(v) = T(v)$. So, $1T = T$.

(Associativity of scalar multiplication) Let $j, k \in F$, let $T \in \mathcal{L}(V, W)$, and let $v \in V$. Then since multiplication is associative in W, we have

$$\big((jk)T\big)(v) = (jk)T(v) = j\big(kT(v)\big) = j(kT)(v) = \big(j(kT)\big)(v).$$

So, $(jk)T = j(kT)$.

(Distributivity of 1 scalar over 2 vectors) Let $k \in F$, let $S, T \in \mathcal{L}(V, W)$, and let $v \in V$. Since multiplication is distributive over addition in W, we have

$$\big(k(S + T)\big)(v) = k(S + T)(v) = k\big(S(v) + T(v)\big) = kS(v) + kT(v)$$
$$= (kS)(v) + (kT)(v) = (kS + kT)(v).$$

So, $k(S + T) = kS + kT$.

(Distributivity of 2 scalars over 1 vector) Let $j, k \in F$, let $S \in \mathcal{L}(V, W)$, and let $v \in V$. Since multiplication is distributive over addition in W, we have

$$\big((j + k)S\big)(v) = (j + k)S(v) = jS(v) + kS(v) = (jS)(v) + (kS)(v) = (jS + kS)(v).$$

So, $(j + k)S = jS + kS$. $\qquad\square$

17. Let V be a vector space over a field F. Prove that $\mathcal{L}(V)$ is a linear algebra over F, where addition and scalar multiplication are defined as in Theorem 7.8 and vector multiplication is given by composition of linear transformations.

Proof: By Problem 16, $(\mathcal{L}(V), +)$ is a vector space over F. We now go through the properties for vector multiplication.

(Closure) We showed right before Example 7.19 that if V, W, and U are vector spaces over F, and $T: V \to W$, $S: W \to U$ are linear transformations, then the composition $S \circ T: V \to W$ is a linear transformation. If $S, T \in \mathcal{L}(V)$, then $V = W = U$, and so, $S \circ T: V \to V$. Therefore, $ST = S \circ T \in \mathcal{L}(V)$.

(Associativity) Let $S, T, U \in \mathcal{L}(V)$ and let $v \in V$. Then

$$((ST)U)(v) = (ST)(U(v)) = S\left(T(U(v))\right) = S((TU)(v)) = (S(TU))(v).$$

Since $v \in V$ was arbitrary, $(ST)U = S(TU)$.

(Identity) Define $I: V \to V$ by $I(v) = v$ for all $v \in V$. Then for all $v, w \in V$ and $a, b \in F$,

$$I(av + bw) = av + bw = aI(v) + bI(w).$$

So, $I \in \mathcal{L}(V)$.

For any $T \in \mathcal{L}(V)$ and $v \in V$, we have $(TI)(v) = T(I(v)) = T(v)$ and $(IT)(v) = I(T(v)) = T(v)$. So, $TI = IT = T$.

(Left Distributivity) Let $S, T, U \in \mathcal{L}(V)$ and let $v \in V$. Since multiplication is distributive over addition in V, we have

$$\begin{aligned}
(S(T + U))(v) &= S((T + U)(v)) = S(T(v) + U(v)) = S(T(v)) + S(U(v)) \\
&= (ST)(v) + (SU)(v) = (ST + SU)(v).
\end{aligned}$$

Since $v \in V$ was arbitrary, $S(T + U) = ST + SU$.

(Right Distributivity) Let $S, T, U \in \mathcal{L}(V)$ and let $v \in V$. Since multiplication is distributive over addition in V, we have

$$((S + T)U)(v) = (S + T)(U(v)) = S(U(v)) + T(U(v)) = (SU)(v) + (TU)(v) = (SU + TU)(v).$$

Since $v \in V$ was arbitrary, $(S + T)U = SU + TU$.

(Compatibility of scalar and vector multiplication) Let $S, T \in \mathcal{L}(V)$ and $k \in F$.

$$(k(ST))(v) = k((ST)(v)) = k\left(S(T(v))\right) = (kS)(T(v)) = ((kS)T)(v)$$

So, $k(ST) = (kS)T$.

$$(k(ST))(v) = k\left((ST(v))\right) = k\left(S(T(v))\right) = S\left(k(T(v))\right) = S((kT)(v)) = (S(kT))(v)$$

So, $k(ST) = S(kT)$. $\qquad\square$

18. Let $T: V \to W$ and $S: W \to V$ be linear transformations such that $ST = i_V$ and $TS = i_W$. Prove that S and T are bijections and that $S = T^{-1}$.

Proof: By symmetry, it suffices to show that T is a bijection.

Let $v, w \in V$ and suppose that $T(v) = T(w)$. Since $ST = i_V$,

$$v = i_V(v) = (ST)(v) = S(T(v)) = S(T(w)) = (ST)(w) = i_V(w) = w.$$

Therefore, T is injective.

Let $w \in W$. Since $TS = i_W$, $w = i_W(w) = (TS)(w) = T(S(w))$. So, $w \in \operatorname{ran} T$. Therefore, T is surjective.

Since T is injective and surjective, T is a bijection.

Suppose that $T(v) = w$. Then $v = i_V(v) = (ST)(v) = S(T(v)) = S(w)$. So, $S = T^{-1}$. $\qquad\square$

LEVEL 5

19. Prove that $(^{\mathbb{R}}\mathbb{R}, +, \cdot)$ is a ring, where addition and multiplication are defined pointwise. Then prove that for each $x \in \mathbb{R}$, $I_x = \{f \in {}^{\mathbb{R}}\mathbb{R} \mid f(x) = 0\}$ is an ideal of $^{\mathbb{R}}\mathbb{R}$ and the only ideal of $^{\mathbb{R}}\mathbb{R}$ containing I_x and not equal to I_x is $^{\mathbb{R}}\mathbb{R}$.

Proof: For $f, g \in {}^{\mathbb{R}}\mathbb{R}$, we define $f + g$ and fg to be the functions in $^{\mathbb{R}}\mathbb{R}$ such that for all $x \in \mathbb{R}$,

$$(f + g)(x) = f(x) + g(x) \text{ and } (fg)(x) = f(x) \cdot g(x).$$

Then $f + g$ and fg are in $^{\mathbb{R}}\mathbb{R}$, so that $^{\mathbb{R}}\mathbb{R}$ is closed under addition and multiplication. To see that addition and multiplication are associative in $^{\mathbb{R}}\mathbb{R}$, we have for each $f, g \in {}^{\mathbb{R}}\mathbb{R}$ and each $x \in \mathbb{R}$,

$$\big(f + (g + h)\big)(x) = f(x) + (g + h)(x) = f(x) + \big(g(x) + h(x)\big) = \big(f(x) + g(x)\big) + h(x)$$
$$= (f + g)(x) + h(x) = \big((f + g) + h\big)(x).$$

$$\big(f(gh)\big)(x) = f(x) \cdot (gh)(x) = f(x) \cdot \big(g(x) \cdot h(x)\big) = \big(f(x) \cdot g(x)\big) \cdot h(x)$$
$$= (fg)(x) \cdot h(x) = \big((fg)h\big)(x).$$

Let $0 \in {}^{\mathbb{R}}\mathbb{R}$ be defined by $0(x) = 0$ for all $x \in \mathbb{R}$ and let $1 \in {}^{\mathbb{R}}\mathbb{R}$ be defined by $1(x) = 1$ for all $x \in \mathbb{R}$. Then for all $x \in \mathbb{R}$, we have

$$(0 + f)(x) = 0(x) + f(x) = 0 + f(x) = f(x) \qquad (f + 0)(x) = f(x) + 0(x) = f(x) + 0 = f(x)$$

$$(1f)(x) = 1(x) \cdot f(x) = 1f(x) = f(x) \quad (f \cdot 1)(x) = f(x) \cdot 1(x) = f(x) \cdot 1 = f(x).$$

So, 0 is an additive identity in $^{\mathbb{R}}\mathbb{R}$ and 1 is a multiplicative identity in $^{\mathbb{R}}\mathbb{R}$.

The additive inverse of $f \in {}^{\mathbb{R}}\mathbb{R}$ is $-f$ defined by $(-f)(x) = -f(x)$. Indeed, for each $x \in \mathbb{R}$, we have

$$\big(f + (-f)\big)(x) = f(x) + (-f)(x) = f(x) + \big(-f(x)\big) = 0 = 0(x).$$

To see that addition is commutative in $^{\mathbb{R}}\mathbb{R}$, we have for each $f, g \in {}^{\mathbb{R}}\mathbb{R}$ and each $x \in \mathbb{R}$,

$$(f + g)(x) = f(x) + g(x) = g(x) + f(x) = (g + f)(x).$$

It follows that $(^\mathbb{R}\mathbb{R}, +, \cdot)$ is a ring.

Now, let $x \in \mathbb{R}$ and let $I_x = \{f \in {}^\mathbb{R}\mathbb{R} \mid f(x) = 0\}$. If $f, g \in I_x$, then we have

$$(f + g)(x) = f(x) + g(x) = 0 + 0 = 0.$$

So, I_x is closed under addition.

Since $0(x) = 0$, $0 \in I_x$. So, 0 is an additive identity element for I_x.

If $f \in I_x$, then $(-f)(x) = -f(x) = -0 = 0$, so that $-f \in I_x$. Therefore, I_x has the additive inverse property.

So, $(I_x, +)$ is a subgroup of $(^\mathbb{R}\mathbb{R}, +)$.

Let $f \in I_x$ and $g \in {}^\mathbb{R}\mathbb{R}$. Then for each $x \in \mathbb{R}$, we have $(fg)(x) = f(x)g(x) = 0 \cdot g(x) = 0 = 0(x)$ and $(gf)(x) = g(x)f(x) = g(x) \cdot 0 = 0 = 0(x)$. Therefore, $fg \in I_x$ and $gf \in I_x$. So, I_x absorbs $^\mathbb{R}\mathbb{R}$. It follows that I_x is an ideal of $^\mathbb{R}\mathbb{R}$.

Let K be an ideal containing I_x, such that $K \neq I_x$. Then there is $f \in K \setminus I_x$. Let $g \in {}^\mathbb{R}\mathbb{R} \setminus K$ be arbitrary. Define $h, k \in {}^\mathbb{R}\mathbb{R}$ by $h(z) = \begin{cases} 0 & \text{if } z = x \\ g(z) & \text{if } z \neq x \end{cases}$ and $k(z) = \begin{cases} \frac{g(z)}{f(z)} & \text{if } z = x \\ 0 & \text{if } z \neq x \end{cases}$. Then, we have $g = h + fk$. To see this, observe that if $z \neq x$, then $(h + fk)(z) = h(z) + f(z)k(z) = g(z) + f(z) \cdot 0 = g(z)$ and if $z = x$, then $(h + fk)(z) = (h + fk)(x) = h(x) + f(x)k(x) = 0 + f(x) \cdot \frac{g(x)}{f(x)} = g(x)$.

Now, $h \in I_x$ because $h(x) = 0$. Since $I_x \subseteq K$, $h \in K$. Since $f \in K$ and K is an ideal, $fk \in K$. Since $(K, +)$ is a group, $g = h + fk \in K$. Since $g \in {}^\mathbb{R}\mathbb{R} \setminus K$ was arbitrary, it follows that $K = {}^\mathbb{R}\mathbb{R}$. □

Note: If I is an ideal of a ring R such that the only ideal containing I not equal to I itself is R, then I is called a **maximal ideal** of R. In the solution above, we proved that for each $x \in \mathbb{R}$, I_x is a maximal ideal of $^\mathbb{R}\mathbb{R}$.

20. Let V be a vector space with $\dim V > 1$. Show that $\{T \in \mathcal{L}(V) \mid T \text{ is not invertible}\} \not\leq \mathcal{L}(V)$.

Proof: Let $X = \{T \in \mathcal{L}(V) \mid T \text{ is not invertible}\}$. First suppose that $\dim V = 2$ and let $\{v_1, v_2\}$ be a basis of V. Let T be the linear transformation such that $T(v_1) = v_1$ and $T(v_2) = v_1$. Since T is not injective, T is not invertible. Let U be the linear transformation such that $U(v_1) = 0$ and $U(v_2) = -v_1 + v_2$. Since $v_1 \neq 0$ and $U(0) = 0$, U is not injective, and therefore, U is not invertible. Now, we have $(T + U)(v_1) = T(v_1) + U(v_1) = v_1 + 0 = v_1$, $(T + U)(v_2) = T(v_2) + U(v_2) = v_1 - v_1 + v_2 = v_2$. So, $T + U = i_V$, which is invertible. Therefore, X is not closed under addition, and so, $X \not\leq \mathcal{L}(V)$.

Now, let $\dim V = n > 2$. Let T be the linear transformation such that $T(v_1) = T(v_2) = v_1$ and $T(v_i) = v_i$ for each $i = 3, \ldots, n$. Since T is not injective, T is not invertible. Let U be the linear transformation such that $U(v_2) = -v_1 + v_2$ and $U(v_i) = 0$ for each $i \neq 2$. Since U is not injective, U is not invertible. Now, we have $(T + U)(v_2) = T(v_2) + U(v_2) = v_1 - v_1 + v_2 = v_2$ and for all $i \neq 2$, $(T + U)(v_i) = T(v_i) + U(v_i) = v_i + 0 = v_i$. So, $T + U = i_V$, which is invertible. Therefore, X is not closed under addition, and so $X \not\leq \mathcal{L}(V)$. □

21. Let V be an n-dimensional vector space over a field F. Prove that there is a linear algebra isomorphism $G: \mathcal{L}(V) \to M_{nn}^F$.

Proof: Let $B = \{v_1, \ldots, v_n\}$ be a basis of V and define $G: \mathcal{L}(V) \to M_{nn}^{\mathbb{F}}$ by $G(T) = \mathcal{M}_T(B)$.

Suppose that $G(T) = G(U)$, so that $\mathcal{M}_T(B) = \mathcal{M}_U(B)$. Suppose that $\mathcal{M}_T(B) = \begin{bmatrix} a_{11} & \cdots & a_{1n} \\ \vdots & & \vdots \\ a_{n1} & \cdots & a_{nn} \end{bmatrix}$. Then we also have $\mathcal{M}_U(B) = \begin{bmatrix} a_{11} & \cdots & a_{1n} \\ \vdots & & \vdots \\ a_{n1} & \cdots & a_{nn} \end{bmatrix}$. Let $j \in \{1, 2, \ldots, n\}$. Then we have

$$T(v_j) = a_{1j}v_1 + a_{2j}v_2 + \cdots a_{nj}v_n = U(v_j).$$

Since $j \in \{1, 2, \ldots, n\}$ was arbitrary, for all $j = 1, 2, \ldots, n$, $T(v_j) = U(v_j)$. Since B is a basis of V, for all $v \in V$, $T(v) = U(v)$. Therefore, $T = U$. So, G is injective.

Let $\begin{bmatrix} a_{11} & \cdots & a_{1n} \\ \vdots & & \vdots \\ a_{n1} & \cdots & a_{nn} \end{bmatrix} \in M_{nn}^{\mathbb{F}}$. Define $T \in \mathcal{L}(V)$ on B by $T(v_j) = a_{1j}v_1 + a_{2j}v_2 + \cdots a_{nj}v_n$ for each $j = 1, 2, \ldots, n$. Then clearly $G(T) = \begin{bmatrix} a_{11} & \cdots & a_{1n} \\ \vdots & & \vdots \\ a_{n1} & \cdots & a_{nn} \end{bmatrix}$. So, F is surjective.

Let $T, U \in \mathcal{L}(v)$ and let $a, b \in \mathbb{F}$. Suppose that $G(T) = \begin{bmatrix} a_{11} & \cdots & a_{1n} \\ \vdots & & \vdots \\ a_{n1} & \cdots & a_{nn} \end{bmatrix}$ and $G(U) = \begin{bmatrix} b_{11} & \cdots & b_{1n} \\ \vdots & & \vdots \\ b_{n1} & \cdots & b_{nn} \end{bmatrix}$.

Then for each $j = 1, 2, \ldots, n$, $T(v_j) = a_{1j}v_1 + a_{2j}v_2 + \cdots a_{nj}v_n$, $U(v_j) = b_{1j}v_1 + b_{2j}v_2 + \cdots b_{nj}v_n$. So, $(aT + bU)(v_j) = (aa_{1j} + bb_{1j})v_1 + \cdots + (aa_{nj} + bb_{nj})v_n$. Therefore,

$$G(aT + bU) = \begin{bmatrix} aa_{11} + bb_{11} & \cdots & aa_{1n} + bb_{1n} \\ \vdots & & \vdots \\ aa_{n1} + bb_{n1} & \cdots & aa_{nn} + bb_{nn} \end{bmatrix} = \begin{bmatrix} aa_{11} & \cdots & aa_{1n} \\ \vdots & & \vdots \\ aa_{n1} & \cdots & aa_{nn} \end{bmatrix} + \begin{bmatrix} bb_{11} & \cdots & bb_{1n} \\ \vdots & & \vdots \\ bb_{n1} & \cdots & bb_{nn} \end{bmatrix}$$

$$= a\begin{bmatrix} a_{11} & \cdots & a_{1n} \\ \vdots & & \vdots \\ a_{n1} & \cdots & a_{nn} \end{bmatrix} + b\begin{bmatrix} b_{11} & \cdots & b_{1n} \\ \vdots & & \vdots \\ b_{n1} & \cdots & b_{nn} \end{bmatrix} = aG(T) + bG(U).$$

So, G is a vector space homomorphism (in other words, G is a linear transformation).

Now, let $T, U \in \mathcal{L}(V)$. Suppose that $G(T) = \begin{bmatrix} a_{11} & \cdots & a_{1n} \\ \vdots & & \vdots \\ a_{n1} & \cdots & a_{nn} \end{bmatrix}$ and $G(U) = \begin{bmatrix} b_{11} & \cdots & b_{1n} \\ \vdots & & \vdots \\ b_{n1} & \cdots & b_{nn} \end{bmatrix}$. Then for each $j = 1, 2, \ldots, n$, $T(v_j) = a_{1j}v_1 + a_{2j}v_2 + \cdots + a_{nj}v_n$, $U(v_j) = b_{1j}v_1 + b_{2j}v_2 + \cdots + b_{nj}v_n$.

We have $(TU)(v_j) = T\big(U(v_j)\big) = T(b_{1j}v_1 + b_{2j}v_2 + \cdots + b_{nj}v_n) = c_{1j}v_1 + c_{2j}v_2 + \cdots + c_{nj}v_n$, where $c_{ij} = a_{i1}b_{1j} + a_{i2}b_{2j} + \cdots + a_{in}b_{nj}$. Also, we have

$$\begin{bmatrix} a_{11} & \cdots & a_{1n} \\ \vdots & & \vdots \\ a_{n1} & \cdots & a_{nn} \end{bmatrix} \cdot \begin{bmatrix} b_{11} & \cdots & b_{1n} \\ \vdots & & \vdots \\ b_{n1} & \cdots & b_{nn} \end{bmatrix} = \begin{bmatrix} c_{11} & \cdots & c_{1n} \\ \vdots & & \vdots \\ c_{n1} & \cdots & c_{nn} \end{bmatrix}, \text{ where } c_{ij} = a_{i1}b_{1j} + a_{i2}b_{2j} + \cdots + a_{in}b_{nj}.$$

It follows that $G(TU) = \begin{bmatrix} c_{11} & \cdots & c_{1n} \\ \vdots & & \vdots \\ c_{n1} & \cdots & c_{nn} \end{bmatrix} = \begin{bmatrix} a_{11} & \cdots & a_{1n} \\ \vdots & & \vdots \\ a_{n1} & \cdots & a_{nn} \end{bmatrix} \cdot \begin{bmatrix} b_{11} & \cdots & b_{1n} \\ \vdots & & \vdots \\ b_{n1} & \cdots & b_{nn} \end{bmatrix} = G(T) \cdot G(U).$

Let $i \in \mathcal{L}(V)$ be the identity function, so that $i(v_j) = v_j$ for each $j = 1, 2, \ldots, n$. Then $G(i) = I$, where
$I = \begin{bmatrix} 1 & 0 & \cdots & 0 \\ 0 & 1 & \cdots & 0 \\ \vdots & \vdots & \ddots & \vdots \\ 0 & 0 & \cdots & 1 \end{bmatrix}$, the identity for multiplication of $n \times n$ matrices.

Therefore, G is a ring homomorphism. Since G is both a vector space homomorphism and a ring homomorphism, G is a linear algebra homomorphism. Since G is also bijective, G is a linear algebra isomorphism. □

Problem Set 8

LEVEL 1

1. Write each of the following positive integers as a product of prime factors in canonical form:

   (i) 9

   (ii) 13

   (iii) 21

   (iv) 30

   (v) 44

   (vi) 693

   (vii) 67,500

   (viii) 384,659

   (ix) 9,699,690

Solutions:

   (i) $9 = 3^2$

   (ii) $13 = 13$

   (iii) $21 = 3 \cdot 7$

   (iv) $30 = 2 \cdot 3 \cdot 5$

   (v) $44 = 2^2 \cdot 11$

   (vi) $693 = 3^2 \cdot 7 \cdot 11$

   (vii) $67,500 = 2^2 \cdot 3^3 \cdot 5^4$

   (viii) $384,659 = 11^3 \cdot 17^2$

   (ix) $9,699,690 = 2 \cdot 3 \cdot 5 \cdot 7 \cdot 11 \cdot 13 \cdot 17 \cdot 19$

2. List all prime numbers less than 100.

Solution: $2, 3, 5, 7, 11, 13, 17, 19, 23, 29, 31, 37, 41, 43, 47, 53, 59, 61, 67, 71, 73, 79, 83, 89, 97$

3. Find the gcd and lcm of each of the following sets of numbers:

    (i) $\{4, 6\}$

    (ii) $\{12, 180\}$

    (iii) $\{2, 3, 5\}$

    (iv) $\{14, 21, 77\}$

    (v) $\{720, 2448, 5400\}$

    (vi) $\{2^{17}5^4 11^9 23, 2^5 3^2 7^4 11^3 13\}$

Solutions:

    (i) $\gcd(4, 6) = \mathbf{2}$; $\operatorname{lcm}(4, 6) = \mathbf{12}$.

    (ii) $12 \mid 180$. So, $\gcd(12, 180) = \mathbf{12}$; $\operatorname{lcm}(12, 180) = \mathbf{180}$.

    (iii) $\gcd(2, 3, 5) = \mathbf{1}$; $\operatorname{lcm}(2, 3, 5) = \mathbf{30}$.

    (iv) $\gcd(14, 21, 77) = \mathbf{7}$; $\operatorname{lcm}(14, 21, 77) = 2 \cdot 7 \cdot 3 \cdot 11 = \mathbf{462}$.

    (v) $720 = 2^4 \cdot 3^2 \cdot 5, 2448 = 2^4 \cdot 3^2 \cdot 17, 5400 = 2^3 \cdot 3^3 \cdot 5^2$.

         $\gcd(720, 2448, 5400) = 2^3 \cdot 3^2 = \mathbf{72}$.

         $\operatorname{lcm}(720, 2448, 5400) = 2^4 \cdot 3^3 \cdot 5^2 \cdot 17 = \mathbf{183{,}600}$.

    (vi) $\gcd(2^{17} \cdot 5^4 \cdot 11^9 \cdot 23, 2^5 \cdot 3^2 \cdot 7^4 \cdot 11^3 \cdot 13) = \mathbf{2^5 \cdot 11^3}$.

         $\operatorname{lcm}(2^{17} \cdot 5^4 \cdot 11^9 \cdot 23, 2^5 \cdot 3^2 \cdot 7^4 \cdot 11^3 \cdot 13) = \mathbf{2^{17} \cdot 3^2 \cdot 5^4 \cdot 7^4 \cdot 11^9 \cdot 13 \cdot 23}$.

LEVEL 2

4. Determine if each of the following numbers is prime:

    (i)   101

    (ii)   399

    (iii)   1829

    (iv)   1933

    (v)   8051

    (vi)   13,873

    (vii)   65,623

Solutions:

    (i) $\sqrt{101} < 11$ and 101 is not divisible by 2, 3, 5, and 7. So, 101 is **prime**.

    (ii) $399 = 7 \cdot 57$. So, 399 is **not prime**.

    (iii) $1829 = 31 \cdot 59$. So, 1829 is **not prime**.

(iv) $\sqrt{1933} < 44$ and 1933 is not divisible by 2, 3, 5, 7, 11, 13, 17, 19, 23, 29, 31, 37, 41, and 43. So, 1933 is **prime**.

(v) $8051 = 83 \cdot 97$. So, 8051 is **not prime**.

(vi)   13,873 is **prime** (check that 13,873 is not divisible by any prime number less than 117).

(vii) $65,623 = 137 \cdot 479$. So, 65,623 is **not prime**.

5. Use the Division Algorithm to find the quotient and remainder when 723 is divided by 17.

Solution: $17 \cdot 42 = 714$ and $17 \cdot 43 = 731$. Since $714 < 723 < 731$, the quotient is 42. The remainder is then $723 - 17 \cdot 42 = 723 - 714 = 9$. So, $723 = 17 \cdot \mathbf{42} + \mathbf{9}$. The quotient is $k = \mathbf{42}$ and the remainder is $r = \mathbf{9}$.

6. For $n \in \mathbb{Z}^+$, let $M_n = n! + 1$. Determine if M_n is prime for $n = 1, 2, 3, 4, 5, 6$, and 7.

Solution: $M_1 = 1! + 1 = 1 + 1 = 2$. So, M_1 is prime. $M_2 = 2! + 1 = 2 + 1 = 3$. So, M_2 is prime. $M_3 = 3! + 1 = 6 + 1 = 7$. So, M_3 is prime. $M_4 = 4! + 1 = 24 + 1 = 25$. Since $5 | 25$, M_4 is **not** prime. $M_5 = 5! + 1 = 120 + 1 = 121$. Since $11 | 121$, M_5 is **not** prime. $M_6 = 6! + 1 = 721$. Since $103 | 721$, M_6 is **not** prime. $M_7 = 7! + 1 = 5040 + 1 = 5041$. Since $71 | 5041$, M_7 is **not** prime.

7. Prove that the sum of three integers that are each divisible by 5 is divisible by 5.

Proof: Let m, n, and q be integers that are divisible by 5. Then there are integers j, k, and r such that $m = 5j$, $n = 5k$, and $q = 5r$. So, $m + n + q = 5j + 5k + 5r = 5(j + k) + 5r = 5(j + k + r)$ because multiplication is distributive over addition in $\mathbb{Z}$. Since $\mathbb{Z}$ is closed under addition, we have $j + k + r \in \mathbb{Z}$. Therefore, $m + n + q$ is divisible by 5. $\square$

Note: We are being very relaxed here in our use of associativity. The expression $m + n + q$ makes sense here because addition is associative in $\mathbb{Z}$. In general, $m + n + q$ could mean $(m + n) + q$ or $m + (n + q)$. By associativity, both expressions are equal, and we can leave the parentheses out without causing confusion.

LEVEL 3

8. Prove that if $a, b, c \in \mathbb{Z}$ with $a | b$ and $b | c$, then $a | c$.

Proof: Let $a, b, c \in \mathbb{Z}$ with $a | b$ and $b | c$. Since $a | b$, there is $j \in \mathbb{Z}$ such that $b = aj$. Since $b | c$, there is $k \in \mathbb{Z}$ such that $c = bk$. It follows that $c = bk = (aj)k = a(jk)$ because multiplication is associative in $\mathbb{Z}$. Since $j, k \in \mathbb{Z}$ and $\mathbb{Z}$ is closed under multiplication, $jk \in \mathbb{Z}$. Therefore, $a | c$. $\square$

9. Prove that $n^3 - n$ is divisible by 3 for all natural numbers n.

Proof by Mathematical induction:

Base Case $(k = 0)$: $0^3 - 0 = 0 = 3 \cdot 0$. So, $0^3 - 0$ is divisible by 3.

Inductive Step: Let $k \in \mathbb{N}$ and assume that $k^3 - k$ is divisible by 3. Then $k^3 - k = 3b$ for some integer b. Now,

$$(k + 1)^3 - (k + 1) = (k + 1)[(k + 1)^2 - 1] = (k + 1)[(k + 1)(k + 1) - 1]$$

$$= (k + 1)(k^2 + 2k + 1 - 1) = (k + 1)(k^2 + 2k) = k^3 + 2k^2 + k^2 + 2k = k^3 + 3k^2 + 2k$$

$$= k^3 - k + k + 3k^2 + 2k = (k^3 - k) + 3k^2 + 3k = 3b + 3(k^2 + k) = 3(b + k^2 + k).$$

Here we used the fact that $(\mathbb{Z}, +, \cdot)$ is a ring. Since $\mathbb{Z}$ is closed under addition and multiplication, $b + k^2 + k \in \mathbb{Z}$. Therefore, $(k + 1)^3 - (k + 1)$ is divisible by 3.

By the Principle of Mathematical Induction, $n^3 - n$ is divisible by 3 for all $n \in \mathbb{N}$. □

Notes: (1) Okay...we cheated a little here. Instead of writing out every algebraic step and mentioning every property of the natural numbers we used at each of these steps, we skipped over some of the messy algebra and at the end of it all simply mentioned that all this is okay because $(\mathbb{Z}, +, \cdot)$ is a ring.

For example, we replaced $(k + 1)(k + 1)$ by $k^2 + 2k + 1$. You may remember this "rule" as FOIL (first, inner, outer, last) from your high school classes. We have not yet verified that FOILing is a legal operation in the set of natural numbers. Let's check the details:

$$(k + 1)(k + 1) = (k + 1) \cdot k + (k + 1) \cdot 1 = k \cdot k + k + k + 1 = k^2 + 2k + 1$$

For the first equality, we used left distributivity of multiplication over addition, and for the second equality, we used right distributivity of multiplication over addition, together with the multiplicative identity property and associativity of addition (we've omitted parentheses when adding several terms).

(2) It's a worthwhile exercise to find all the other places in the proof where details were excluded and to fill in those details.

(3) Notice our use of SACT (see Note 1 after Example 1.16) in the beginning of the last line of the sequence of equations. We needed $k^3 - k$ to appear, but the $-k$ was nowhere to be found. So, we simply threw it in, and then repaired the damage by adding k right after it.

10. Use the Euclidean Algorithm to find $\gcd(825, 2205)$. Then express $\gcd(825, 2205)$ as a linear combination of 825 and 2205.

Solution:

$$2205 = 825 \cdot 2 + 555$$
$$825 = 555 \cdot 1 + 270$$
$$555 = 270 \cdot 2 + 15$$
$$270 = 15 \cdot 18 + \mathbf{0}$$

So, $\gcd(825, 2205) = \mathbf{15}$.

Now we have,

$$15 = 555 - 270 \cdot 2 = 555 - (825 - 555 \cdot 1) \cdot 2 = 3 \cdot 555 - 2 \cdot 825$$
$$= 3(2205 - 825 \cdot 2) - 2 \cdot 825 = -\mathbf{8} \cdot \mathbf{825} + 3 \cdot \mathbf{2205}.$$

11. Prove that if $k \in \mathbb{Z}$ with $k > 1$, then $k^3 + 1$ is not prime.

Proof: $k^3 + 1 = (k+1)(k^2 - k + 1)$. Since $k > 1$, $k + 1 > 2$ and $k^2 - k + 1 > 1 - 1 + 1 = 1$. Since neither factor is 1, $k^3 + 1$ is **not** prime. $\square$

12. Prove that $\gcd(a,b) \mid \mathrm{lcm}(a,b)$.

Proof: Since $\gcd(a,b)$ is a divisor of a, $\gcd(a,b) \mid a$. Since $\mathrm{lcm}(a,b)$ is a multiple of a, $a \mid \mathrm{lcm}(a,b)$. By problem 11 in Problem Set 3, $\mid$ is a transitive relation. It follows that $\gcd(a,b) \mid \mathrm{lcm}(a,b)$. $\square$

13. Let $a, b, c \in \mathbb{Z}$. Prove that $\gcd(a,b) = \gcd(a + bc, b)$.

Proof: Let d be a divisor of a and b. Then there are integers j and k such that $a = dj$ and $b = dk$. It follows that $a + bc = dj + (dk)c = d(j + kc)$, so that d is a divisor of $a + bc$.

Now, let e be a divisor of $a + bc$ and b. Then there are integers j and k such that $a + bc = ej$ and $b = ek$. It follows that $a = (a + bc) - bc = ej - (ek)c = e(j - kc)$, so that e is a divisor of a.

So, a and b have the same common divisors as $a + bc$ and b. Therefore $\gcd(ab) = \gcd(a + bc, b)$. $\square$

14. Let $a, b, k, r \in \mathbb{Z}$ with $a = bk + r$. Prove that $\gcd(a,b) = \gcd(r,b)$.

Proof: $\gcd(r,b) = \gcd(a - bk, b) = \gcd(a + b(-k), b) = \gcd(a,b)$ by problem 13. $\square$

LEVEL 4

15. Prove that the product of two odd integers is odd.

Proof: Let m and n be odd integers. Then there are integers j and k such that $m = 2j + 1$ and $n = 2k + 1$. So,

$$m \cdot n = (2j + 1) \cdot (2k + 1) = (2j + 1)(2k) + (2j + 1)(1) = (2k)(2j + 1) + (2j + 1)$$
$$= \big((2k)(2j) + 2k\big) + (2j + 1) = \big(2(k(2j)) + 2k\big) + (2j + 1) = 2(k(2j) + k) + (2j + 1)$$
$$= (2(k(2j) + k) + 2j) + 1 = 2\big((k(2j) + k) + j\big) + 1.$$

Here we used the fact that $(\mathbb{Z}, +, \cdot)$ is a ring. Since $\mathbb{Z}$ is closed under addition and multiplication, we have $(k(2j) + k) + j \in \mathbb{Z}$. Therefore, mn is odd. $\square$

16. Prove that if $a, b, c, d, e \in \mathbb{Z}$ with $a \mid b$ and $a \mid c$, then $a \mid (db + ec)$.

Proof: Let $a, b, c, d, e \in \mathbb{Z}$ with $a \mid b$ and $a \mid c$. Since $a \mid b$, there is $j \in \mathbb{Z}$ such that $b = aj$. Since $a \mid c$, there is $k \in \mathbb{Z}$ such that $c = ak$. Since $(\mathbb{Z}, +, \cdot)$ is a ring, it follows that

$$db + ec = d(aj) + e(ak) = (da)j + (ea)k = (ad)j + (ae)k = a(dj) + a(ek) = a(dj + ek).$$

Since $\mathbb{Z}$ is closed under multiplication, $dj \in \mathbb{Z}$ and $ek \in \mathbb{Z}$. Since $\mathbb{Z}$ is closed under addition, $dj + ek \in \mathbb{Z}$. So, $a \mid (db + ec)$. $\square$

Note: As in Problem 9, we skipped over mentioning every property of the integers we used at each step, and simply mentioned that $(\mathbb{Z}, +, \cdot)$ is a ring. The dedicated reader may want to fill in the details.

17. Prove that $3^n - 1$ is even for all natural numbers n.

Proof by Mathematical induction:

Base Case $(k = 0)$: $3^0 - 1 = 1 - 1 = 0 = 2 \cdot 0$. So, $3^0 - 1$ is even.

Inductive Step: Let $k \in \mathbb{N}$ and assume that $3^k - 1$ is even. Then $3^k - 1 = 2b$ for some integer b. Now,

$$3^{k+1} - 1 = 3^k \cdot 3^1 - 1 = 3^k \cdot 3 - 1 = 3^k \cdot 3 - 3^k + 3^k - 1 = 3^k(3 - 1) + (3^k - 1)$$

$$= 3^k \cdot 2 + 2b = 2 \cdot 3^k + 2b = 2(3^k + b).$$

Here we used the fact that $(\mathbb{Z}, +, \cdot)$ is a ring. Since $\mathbb{Z}$ is closed under multiplication, $3^k \in \mathbb{N}$. Since $\mathbb{Z}$ is closed under addition, $3^k + b \in \mathbb{Z}$. Therefore, $3^{k+1} - 1$ is even.

By the Principle of Mathematical Induction, $3^n - 1$ is even for all $n \in \mathbb{N}$. □

Notes: (1) As in Problem 9, we skipped over mentioning every property of the natural numbers we used at each step, and simply mentioned that $(\mathbb{Z}, +, \cdot)$ is a ring. The dedicated student may want to fill in the details.

(2) Notice our use of SACT (see Note 1 after Example 1.16) in the middle of the first line of the sequence of equations. We needed $3^k - 1$ to appear, so we added 3^k, and then subtracted 3^k to the left of it.

18. Prove the Euclidean Algorithm: Let $a, b \in \mathbb{Z}^+$ with $a \geq b$. Let $r_0 = a$, $r_1 = b$. Apply the Division Algorithm to r_0 and r_1 to find $k_1, r_2 \in \mathbb{Z}^+$ such that $r_0 = r_1 k_1 + r_2$, where $0 \leq r_2 < r_1$. Iterate this process to get $r_j = r_{j+1} k_{j+1} + r_{j+2}$, where $0 \leq r_{j+2} < r_{j+1}$ for $j = 0, 1, \ldots, n - 1$ so that $r_{n+1} = 0$. Then $\gcd(a, b) = r_n$.

Proof: We use the Division Algorithm to get the following sequence of equations:

$$r_0 = r_1 k_1 + r_2, \qquad 0 \leq r_2 < r_1$$
$$r_1 = r_2 k_2 + r_3, \qquad 0 \leq r_3 < r_2$$
$$\cdots$$
$$r_{n-2} = r_{n-1} k_{n-1} + r_n, \qquad 0 \leq r_n < r_{n-1}$$
$$r_{n-1} = r_n k_n + 0$$

Since each remainder r_i is strictly less than the remainder r_{i-1}, after finitely many iterations of the Division Algorithm, we get a remainder of 0.

By problem 14, we have $\gcd(a, b) = \gcd(r_0, r_1) = \gcd(r_1, r_2) = \cdots = \gcd(r_n, 0) = r_n$. □

19. Prove that if $a|c$ and $b|c$, then $\text{lcm}(a, b) \mid c$.

Proof: Suppose that $a|c$ and $b|c$. By the Division Algorithm, there are integers k and r such that $c = \text{lcm}(a, b) \cdot k + r$ with $0 \le r < \text{lcm}(a, b)$. Therefore, we have $r = c - \text{lcm}(a, b) \cdot k$. Since $a|c$ and $a|\text{lcm}(a, b)$, it follows from Problem 16 that $a|r$. Similarly, $b|r$. So r is a multiple of both a and b. Since $0 \le r < \text{lcm}(a, b)$, r must be 0. Thus, $c = \text{lcm}(a, b) \cdot k$ and so, $\text{lcm}(a, b)|c$. $\qquad\square$

20. Suppose that $a, b \in \mathbb{Z}^+$, $\gcd(a, b) = 1$, and $c|ab$. Prove that there are integers d and e such that $c = de$, $d|a$, and $e|b$.

Proof: Suppose that $a, b \in \mathbb{Z}^+$, $\gcd(a, b) = 1$, and $c|ab$. Let $a = p_0^{a_0} p_1^{a_1} \cdots p_n^{a_n}$ and $b = p_0^{b_0} p_1^{b_1} \cdots p_n^{b_n}$ be complete prime factorizations of a and b, let $d = \gcd(a, c)$, and let $e = \gcd(b, c)$. If $d = p_0^{d_0} p_1^{d_1} \cdots p_n^{d_n}$ and $e = p_0^{e_0} p_1^{e_1} \cdots p_n^{e_n}$ are complete prime factorizations of d and e, respectively, then we have $d_i \le a_i$ and $e_i \le b_i$ for each $i = 1, 2, \ldots, n$. It follows that $\gcd(d, e) = 1$, $d|a$, and $e|b$. Every prime power in the prime factorization of c must appear as a factor of d or e. So, $c = de$. $\qquad\square$

21. A **prime triple** is a sequence of three prime numbers of the form p, $p + 2$, and $p + 4$. For example, $3, 5, 7$ is a prime triple. Prove that there are no other prime triples.

Proof: We will show that if $n \in \mathbb{Z}$, then one of $n, n + 2, n + 4$ is divisible by 3. By the Division Algorithm, there are unique integers k and r such that $n = 3k + r$ and $r = 0, 1$, or 2. If $r = 0$, then n is divisible by 3. If $r = 1$, then $n + 2 = (3k + 1) + 2 = 3k + 3 = 3(k + 1)$, and so, $n + 2$ is divisible by 3. Finally, if $r = 2$, then $n + 4 = (3k + 2) + 4 = 3k + 6 = 3(k + 2)$, and so, $n + 4$ is divisible by 3.

So, if p, $p + 2$, $p + 4$ is a prime triple, then either p, $p + 2$, or $p + 4$ must be divisible by 3. The only prime number divisible by 3 is 3. So, $p = 3$, $p + 2 = 3$, or $p + 4 = 3$. If $p = 3$, we get the prime triple $3, 5, 7$. If $p + 2 = 3$, then $p = 1$, which is not prime. If $p + 4 = 3$, then $p = -1$, again not prime. $\qquad\square$

LEVEL 5

22. If $a, b \in \mathbb{Z}^+$ and $\gcd(a, b) = 1$, find the following:

    (i) $\gcd(a, a + 1)$

    (ii) $\gcd(a, a + 2)$

    (iii) $\gcd(3a + 2, 5a + 3)$

    (iv) $\gcd(a + b, a - b)$

    (v) $\gcd(a + 2b, 2a + b)$

Solutions:

    (i)   Since $a + 1 - a = 1$, we see that 1 can be written as a linear combination of a and $a + 1$. Therefore, $\gcd(a, a + 1) = 1$.

    (ii)   Since $a + 2 - a = 2$, we see that 2 can be written as a linear combination of a and $a + 2$. Therefore, $\gcd(a, a + 2) \le 2$. So, $\gcd(a, a + 2) = 1$ or 2.

If a is even, then there is $k \in \mathbb{Z}$ such that $a = 2k$. So, $a + 2 = 2k + 2 = 2(k + 1)$. Thus, we see that $2|a$ and $2|a + 2$. Therefore, if a is even, $\gcd(a, a + 2) = 2$.

If a is odd, then 2 does not divide a. So, $\gcd(a, a + 2)$ cannot be 2, and therefore, must be 1.

(iii)   Since $5(3a + 2) - 3(5a + 3) = 15a + 10 - 15a - 9 = 1$, we see that 1 can be written as a linear combination of $3a + 2$ and $5a + 3$. So, $\gcd(3a + 2, 5a + 3) = 1$.

(iv)   If d divides $a + b$ and $a - b$, then d divides $(a + b) + (a - b) = 2a$ and d divides $(a + b) - (a - b) = 2b$ because by Problem 16 above, d divides any linear combination of $a + b$ and $a - b$. By Theorem 8.18, $\gcd(2a, 2b)$ can be written as a linear combination of $2a$ and $2b$. So, again by Problem 16, $d| \gcd(2a, 2b) = 2$. So, $d = 1$ or $d = 2$.

If a and b are both odd, then both $a + b$ and $a - b$ are even, and so, $\gcd(a + b, a - b) = 2$.

If a and b do not have the same parity (in other words, one is even and the other is odd), then $a + b$ is odd. So, 2 is not a divisor of $a + b$, and therefore, $\gcd(a + b, a - b) = 1$.

a and b cannot both be even because then $\gcd(a, b) \geq 2$.

(v)   If d divides $a + 2b$ and $2a + b$, then d divides $2(a + 2b) - (2a + b) = 3b$ and d divides $2(2a + b) - (a + 2b) = 3a$ because once again by Problem 16 above, d divides any linear combination of $a + 2b$ and $2a + b$. By Theorem 8.18, $\gcd(3a, 3b)$ can be written as a linear combination of $3a$ and $3b$. So, again by Problem 16, $d| \gcd(3a, 3b) = 3$. So, $d = 1$ or $d = 3$.

If we let $a = 2$ and $b = 3$, then we have $a + 2b = 2 + 2 \cdot 3 = 2 + 6 = 8$ and $2a + b = 2 \cdot 2 + 3 = 4 + 3 = 7$. So, $\gcd(a + 2b, 2a + b) = \gcd(8, 7) = 1$.

If we let $a = 2$ and $b = 5$, then we have $a + 2b = 2 + 2 \cdot 5 = 2 + 10 = 12$ and $2a + b = 2 \cdot 2 + 5 = 4 + 5 = 9$. So, $\gcd(a + 2b, 2a + b) = \gcd(12, 9) = 3$.

So, both $\gcd(a + 2b, 2a + b) = 1$ and $\gcd(a + 2b, 2a + b) = 3$ can occur.

23. Find the smallest ideal of $\mathbb{Z}$ containing 6 and 15. Find the smallest ideal of $\mathbb{Z}$ containing 2 and 3. In general, find the smallest ideal of $\mathbb{Z}$ containing j and k, where $j, k \in \mathbb{Z}$.

Solutions: Let I be the smallest ideal of $\mathbb{Z}$ containing 6 and 15. Since $3\mathbb{Z}$ is an ideal of $\mathbb{Z}$ containing 6 and 15, $I \subseteq 3\mathbb{Z}$ because I is the smallest such ideal. If $a \in 3\mathbb{Z}$, then there is an integer k such that $a = 3k$. Since $3 = 15 - 6 - 6$, we have $a = 15k - 6k - 6k \in I$ because $(I, +)$ is a subgroup of $(\mathbb{Z}, +)$. So, $3\mathbb{Z} \subseteq I$. Since $I \subseteq 3\mathbb{Z}$ and $3\mathbb{Z} \subseteq I$, we have $I = 3\mathbb{Z}$.

Let I be the smallest ideal of $\mathbb{Z}$ containing 2 and 3. If $a \in \mathbb{Z}$, then $a = 3a - 2a \in I$ because $(I, +)$ is a subgroup of $(\mathbb{Z}, +)$. So, $\mathbb{Z} \subseteq I$, and therefore, $I = \mathbb{Z}$.

Let I be the smallest ideal of $\mathbb{Z}$ containing j and k, and let $d = \gcd(j, k)$. Since $d\mathbb{Z}$ is an ideal of $\mathbb{Z}$ containing j and k, $I \subseteq d\mathbb{Z}$ because I is the smallest such ideal. If $a \in d\mathbb{Z}$, then there is an integer c such that $a = dc$. By Problem 16, we can write d as a linear combination of j and k, say $d = mj + nk$. So, we have $a = (mj + nk)c = mjc + nkc$. $mjc, nkc \in I$ because I absorbs $\mathbb{Z}$. So, $a = mjc + nkc \in I$ because $(I, +)$ is a subgroup of $(\mathbb{Z}, +)$. Therefore, $d\mathbb{Z} \subseteq I$. Since $I \subseteq d\mathbb{Z}$ and $d\mathbb{Z} \subseteq I$, we have $I = d\mathbb{Z}$, where $d = \gcd(j, k)$.

24. Find all subgroups of $(\mathbb{Z}, +)$ and all submonoids of $(\mathbb{Z}, +)$.

Solutions: Let $n \in \mathbb{N}$. Then $(n\mathbb{Z}, +)$ is a subgroup of $(\mathbb{Z}, +)$. To see this, first note that $0 \in n\mathbb{Z}$ because $0 = n \cdot 0$. Now, let $a, b \in n\mathbb{Z}$. Then there are integers j and k such that $a = nj$ and $b = nk$. It follows that $a - b = nj - nk = n(j - k)$. Since $\mathbb{Z}$ is closed under subtraction, $j - k \in \mathbb{Z}$. So, $a - b \in n\mathbb{Z}$. By problem 4 from Problem Set 5, $(n\mathbb{Z}, +)$ is a subgroup of $(\mathbb{Z}, +)$.

We now show that there are no other subgroups of $(\mathbb{Z}, +)$. Let $(A, +)$ be a subgroup of $(\mathbb{Z}, +)$. If $A \neq \{0\}$, then A must contain a positive integer k, for if $j \in A \setminus \{0\}$, then $-j \in A$ and either j or $-j$ must be positive. By the Well Ordering Principle, A contains a least positive integer n. We will show that $A = n\mathbb{Z}$.

First, if $a \in n\mathbb{Z}$, then there is $b \in \mathbb{Z}$ with $a = nb$. If $b > 0$, then $nb \in A$ because A is closed for addition (this can be proved rigorously using the Principle of Mathematical Induction). If $b < 0$, then $nb = -n(-b) \in \mathbb{Z}$ because $n(-b) \in \mathbb{Z}$ and A is closed under taking inverses. If $b = 0$, then we have $nb = n \cdot 0 = 0$, and $0 \in A$. So, $n\mathbb{Z} \subseteq A$.

Now, let $a \in A$. Since A is closed under taking inverses, we can assume that a is nonnegative. Since $\gcd(n, a)$ can be written as a linear combination of n and a (by Theorem 8.18), and A is a subgroup of $\mathbb{Z}$, it follows that $\gcd(n, a) \in A$. Since $\gcd(n, a)$ is a divisor of n, $\gcd(n, a) \leq n$. Since n is the least positive integer in A, $\gcd(n, a) = 0$ or $\gcd(n, a) = n$. If $\gcd(n, a) = 0$, then $a = 0$. If $\gcd(n, a) = n$, then n is a divisor of a. In either case, $a \in n\mathbb{Z}$. So, $A \subseteq n\mathbb{Z}$.

Since $n\mathbb{Z} \subseteq A$ and $A \subseteq n\mathbb{Z}$, we have $A = n\mathbb{Z}$.

Now, since every subgroup of $(\mathbb{Z}, +)$ is a submonoid of $(\mathbb{Z}, +)$, we have that $(n\mathbb{Z}, +)$ is a submonoid of $(\mathbb{Z}, +)$ for every $n \in \mathbb{N}$. We also have that $(n\mathbb{N}, +)$ is a submonoid of $(\mathbb{Z}, +)$ for each $n \in \mathbb{Z}^+$, where $n\mathbb{N} = \{nk \mid k \in \mathbb{N}\}$. To see this, let $a, b \in n\mathbb{N}$. Then there are natural numbers j and k such that $a = nj$ and $b = nk$. It follows that $a + b = nj + nk = n(j + k)$. Since $\mathbb{N}$ is closed under addition, $j + k \in \mathbb{N}$. So, $a + b \in n\mathbb{N}$. Therefore, $n\mathbb{N}$ is closed under addition. Also, $0 \in n\mathbb{N}$ because $0 = n \cdot 0$. So, $(n\mathbb{N}, +)$ is a submonoid of $(\mathbb{Z}, +)$. Similar reasoning shows that $(-n\mathbb{N}, +)$ is a submonoid of $(\mathbb{Z}, +)$ for each $n \in \mathbb{Z}^+$, where $(-n\mathbb{N}, +) = \{-nk \mid k \in \mathbb{N}\}$.

We now show that there are no other submonoids of $(\mathbb{Z}, +)$. Let $(A, +)$ be a submonoid of $(\mathbb{Z}, +)$. If $A = \{0\}$, then $A = 0\mathbb{Z}$, so assume that $A \neq \{0\}$. If A has only nonnegative integers, then $A = n\mathbb{N}$, where n is the least positive integer in A. The reasoning is similar to what was done above. Similarly, if A has only nonpositive integers, then $A = -n\mathbb{N}$, where $-n\mathbb{N}$ is the least positive integer such that $n \in A$.

Finally, if A has both positive and negative integers, let n be the least element of the set $\{|k| \mid k \in A \wedge k \neq 0\}$. Then $A = n\mathbb{Z}$, again by reasoning similar to what was done above. $\qquad\square$

112

Problem Set 9

LEVEL 1

1. Find the order of 3 in $(\mathbb{Z}_4, +)$.

Solution: $2 \cdot 3 \equiv_4 3 + 3 \equiv_4 6 \equiv_4 2, 3 \cdot 3 \equiv_4 2 + 3 \equiv_4 5 \equiv_4 1, 4 \cdot 3 = 1 + 3 \equiv_4 4 \equiv_4 0.$ So, $|3| = \mathbf{4}$.

2. List the elements of U_{11}, U_{15}, and U_{20}.

Solutions: $U_{11} = \{1, 2, 3, 4, 5, 6, 7, 8, 9, 10\}$

$U_{15} = \{1, 2, 4, 7, 8, 11, 13, 14\}$

$U_{20} = \{1, 3, 7, 9, 11, 13, 17, 19\}$

3. Find the inverse of each element of U_9.

Solution: $U_9 = \{1, 2, 4, 5, 7, 8\}$

Since $1 \cdot 1 = 1, \mathbf{1^{-1} = 1}$.

Since $2 \cdot 5 = 10 \equiv_9 1, \mathbf{2^{-1} = 5}$ and $\mathbf{5^{-1} = 2}$.

Since $4 \cdot 7 = 28 \equiv_9 1, \mathbf{4^{-1} = 7}$ and $\mathbf{7^{-1} = 4}$.

Since $8 \cdot 8 = 64 \equiv_9, \mathbf{8^{-1} = 8}$.

LEVEL 2

4. Find the order of 32 in $(\mathbb{Z}_{40}, +)$.

Solution: $2 \cdot 32 \equiv_{40} 64 \equiv_{40} 24, 3 \cdot 32 \equiv_{40} 24 + 32 \equiv_{40} 56 \equiv_{40} 16,$

$4 \cdot 32 \equiv_{40} 16 + 32 \equiv_{40} 48 \equiv_{40} 8, 5 \cdot 32 \equiv_{40} 8 + 32 \equiv_{40} 40 \equiv_{40} 0.$

So, $|32| = \mathbf{5}$.

5. Let $(H, +)$ be a subgroup of $(\mathbb{Z}, +)$. Prove that there is $n \in H$ such that $H = n\mathbb{Z}$.

Proof: If $H = \{0\}$, then $H = 0\mathbb{Z}$. If $H \neq \{0\}$, then since H is closed under additive inverses, H must contain a positive integer. Let n be the least positive integer in H. We will show that $H = n\mathbb{Z}$. If $x \in n\mathbb{Z}$, then there is a $k \in \mathbb{Z}$ such that $x = nk$. Since H is closed under addition , $x = nk \in H$. So, $n\mathbb{Z} \subseteq H$. Conversely, let $x \in H$ and let $d = \gcd(x, n)$. By Theorem 8.18, there are integers a and b such that $ax + bn = d$. Since $n\mathbb{Z}$ is closed under addition, $d \in n\mathbb{Z}$. Since $d \leq n$, we must have $d = n$. It follows that x is a multiple of n, and so, $x \in n\mathbb{Z}$. So, $H \subseteq n\mathbb{Z}$. Since $n\mathbb{Z} \subseteq H$ and $H \subseteq n\mathbb{Z}$, we have $H = n\mathbb{Z}$, as desired. $\square$

6. Draw the multiplication table for U_{28}.

Solution: $U_{28} = \{1, 3, 5, 9, 11, 13, 15, 17, 19, 23, 25, 27\}$

·	1	3	5	9	11	13	15	17	19	23	25	27
1	1	3	5	9	11	13	15	17	19	23	25	27
3	3	9	15	27	5	11	17	23	1	13	19	25
5	5	15	25	17	27	9	19	1	11	3	13	23
9	9	27	17	25	15	5	23	13	3	11	1	19
11	11	5	27	15	9	3	25	19	13	1	23	17
13	13	11	9	5	3	1	27	25	23	19	17	15
15	15	17	19	23	25	27	1	3	5	9	11	13
17	17	23	1	13	19	25	3	9	15	27	5	11
19	19	1	11	3	13	23	5	15	25	17	27	9
23	23	13	3	11	1	19	9	27	17	25	15	5
25	25	19	13	1	23	17	11	5	27	15	9	3
27	27	25	23	19	17	15	13	11	9	5	3	1

7. Compute 128^{129} modulo 17.

Solution: By Fermat's Little Theorem, $128^{17} \equiv_{17} 128$, or equivalently, $128^{16} \equiv_{17} 1$. So, we have $128^{129} = 128^{128} \cdot 128 = (128^{16})^8 \cdot 128 \equiv_{17} 1^8 \cdot 128 \equiv_{17} 128 \equiv_{17} \mathbf{9}$.

8. Provide a counterexample for the following statement: For each $n \in \mathbb{Z}^+$, U_n is a cyclic group.

Solution: $U_{15} = \{1, 2, 4, 7, 8, 11, 13, 14\}$ is not cyclic. Observe that $11^2 \equiv_{15} 121 \equiv_{15} 1$. So, $\langle 11 \rangle$ is a subgroup of U_{15} of order 2. Similarly, $14^2 \equiv_{15} 196 \equiv_{15} 1$. So, $\langle 14 \rangle$ is also a subgroup of U_{15} of order 2. However, by Theorem 9.6, a cyclic group of order 8 has **exactly one** subgroup of order 2. Therefore, U_{15} **cannot** be cyclic.

Note: An alternative proof that U_{15} is not cyclic would be to just compute the order of each element and observe that no element has order 8.

LEVEL 3

9. Find the order of $(123)(45)(6789)$ in S_{10}.

Solution: $(123)^2 = (123)(123) = (132)$ and $(123)^3 = (132)(123) = (1)$. Therefore, $|(123)| = 3$. Similarly, $|(45)| = 2$ and $|(6789)| = 4$. So, $|(123)(45)(6789)| = \text{lcm}(3, 2, 4) = \mathbf{12}$.

Note: If you don't understand this solution, you can just compute the order directly by multiplying the given permutation by itself 12 times. While performing the computations, try to understand why this solution works.

10. Find all subgroups of $(\mathbb{Z}_{30}, +)$.

Solution: Since $(\mathbb{Z}_{30}, +)$ is cyclic, by Theorems 9.6 and 9.8, for each divisor d of 30, there is exactly one subgroup of order d and there are no other subgroups. The divisors of 30 are $1, 2, 3, 5, 6, 10, 15,$ and 30. The corresponding subgroups are as follows:

$$\langle 0 \rangle = \{0\}$$
$$\langle 15 \rangle = \{0, 15\}$$
$$\langle 10 \rangle = \{0, 10, 20\}$$
$$\langle 6 \rangle = \{0, 6, 12, 18, 24\}$$
$$\langle 5 \rangle = \{0, 5, 10, 15, 20, 25\}$$
$$\langle 3 \rangle = \{0, 3, 6, 9, 12, 15, 18, 21, 24, 27\}$$
$$\langle 2 \rangle = \{0, 2, 4, 6, 8, 10, 12, 14, 16, 18, 20, 22, 24, 26, 28\}$$
$$\langle 1 \rangle = \mathbb{Z}_{30}$$

11. Find all generators of $(\mathbb{Z}_{75}, +)$.

Solution: The generators of $\mathbb{Z}_{75}$ are the positive integers less than 75 that are relatively prime with 75. Here is a list:

$$1, 2, 4, 7, 8, 11, 13, 14, 16, 17, 19, 22, 23, 26, 28, 29, 31, 32, 34, 37, 38, 41,$$
$$43, 44, 46, 47, 49, 52, 53, 56, 58, 59, 61, 62, 64, 67, 68, 71, 73, 74$$

12. Let G be a group and let $a \in G$. Prove each of the following:

    (i) $|a^{-1}| = |a|$.

    (ii) $|a| = 1$ if and only if $a = e$.

    (iii) The order of any conjugate of a is equal to the order of a.

    (iv) If p is prime, $a \neq e$, and $a^p = e$, then $|a| = p$.

Proofs:

    (i)   If $a^n = e$, then $(a^{-1})^n = (a^n)^{-1} = e^{-1} = e$.

          Conversely, if $(a^{-1})^n = e$, then $a^n = ((a^{-1})^{-1})^n = ((a^{-1})^n)^{-1} = e^{-1} = e$.

          It follows that $|a^{-1}| = |a|$.   □

    (ii)   If $a = e$, then $a^1 = e$. So, $|a| = 1$.

          Conversely, suppose that $|a| = 1$. Then $a = a^1 = e$.   □

    (iii) We first prove by induction on $n \in \mathbb{N}$ that $(xax^{-1})^n = xa^nx^{-1}$. For the base case $(k = 0)$, we have $(xax^{-1})^0 = e$ by definition and $xa^0x^{-1} = xex^{-1} = xx^{-1} = e$. Assuming that $k \in \mathbb{N}$ and $(xax^{-1})^k = xa^kx^{-1}$, we get

$$(xax^{-1})^{k+1} = (xax^{-1})^k(xax^{-1}) = (xa^kx^{-1})(xax^{-1}) = xa^k(x^{-1}x)ax^{-1}$$
$$= xa^keax^{-1} = xa^kax^{-1} = xa^{k+1}x^{-1}$$

By the Principle of Mathematical Induction, for all $n \in \mathbb{N}$, $(xax^{-1})^n = xa^nx^{-1}$.

It follows that $(xax^{-1})^n = e$ if and only if $xa^nx^{-1} = e$ if and only if

$$a^n = ea^ne = (x^{-1}x)a^n(x^{-1}x) = x^{-1}(xa^nx^{-1})x = x^{-1}ex = x^{-1}x = e.$$

So, $|xax^{-1}| = |a|$, as desired. $\qquad\square$

(iv)   Since $a^p = e$, $|a| \leq p$. If $n \leq p$ and $a^n = e$, then $n \mid p$. Since p is prime, $n = p$. It follows that p is the least positive integer such that $a^p = e$. So, $|a| = p$. $\qquad\square$

13. Prove the Chinese Remainder Theorem.

Proof: We will prove the theorem by induction on $n \geq 1$. The base case of $k = 1$ is trivial. Assuming that the theorem holds for any system of k linear congruences satisfying the given conditions, assume that $n_1, n_2, \dots, n_k, n_{k+1}$ be pairwise relatively prime integers, let $c_1, c_2, \dots, c_k, c_{k+1} \in \mathbb{Z}$, and consider the following system of linear congruences:

$$x \equiv_{n_1} c_1,$$

$$x \equiv_{n_2} c_2,$$

$$\vdots \quad \vdots \quad \vdots$$

$$x \equiv_{n_k} c_k,$$

$$x \equiv_{n_{k+1}} c_{k+1},$$

By induction, we can let $x \equiv_{n_1 \cdot n_2 \cdots n_k} d$ be a unique solution of the first n linear congruences. Consider the following system of linear congruences:

$$x \equiv_{n_1 \cdot n_2 \cdots n_k} d,$$

$$x \equiv_{n_{k+1}} c_{k+1}.$$

Since $\gcd(n_1 \cdot n_2 \cdots n_k, n_{k+1}) = 1$, by Theorem 9.33, this system has a unique solution, up to congruence modulo $n_1 \cdot n_2 \cdots n_k \cdot n_{k+1}$. This is a unique solution of the original system, up to congruence modulo $n_1 \cdot n_2 \cdots n_k \cdot n_{k+1}$.

By the Principle of Mathematical Induction, the Chinese Remainder Theorem holds. $\qquad\square$

LEVEL 4

14. Let G be a group and let $a, b \in G$. Prove that $|ab| = |ba|$.

Proof: Let $m, n \in \mathbb{Z}^+$ and assume that $|ab| = m$ and $|ba| = n$. Then $(ab)^m = e$ and $(ba)^n = e$. Since $(ab)^m = e$, we have

$$(a^{-1}a)(ba)^m = (a^{-1}a)b(ab)^{m-1}a = a^{-1}(ab)(ab)^{m-1}a = a^{-1}(ab)^m a = a^{-1}ea = a^{-1}a = e.$$

It follows that $n = |ba| \leq m$.

A symmetrical argument shows that $m = |ab| \leq n$. So, $|ab| = m = n = |ba|$.

Now, assume that $|ba|$ is infinite. If $(ab)^m = e$ for some $m \in \mathbb{Z}^+$, then the previous argument shows that $|ba| \le m$, contradicting our assumption that $|ba|$ is infinite. So, $|ab|$ is infinite.

A symmetrical argument shows that if $|ab|$ is infinite, then $|ba|$ is infinite. $\qquad \square$

15. Find all subgroups of $\mathbb{Z}_5 \times \mathbb{Z}_3$.

Solution: $\mathbb{Z}_5 \times \mathbb{Z}_3$ is cyclic with generator $(1,1)$. Since $|\mathbb{Z}_5 \times \mathbb{Z}_3| = |\mathbb{Z}_5| \cdot |\mathbb{Z}_3| = 5 \cdot 3 = 15$, by Theorems 9.6 and 9.8, for each divisor d of 15, there is exactly one subgroup of order d and there are no other subgroups. The divisors of 15 are $1, 3, 5,$ and 15. The corresponding subgroups are as follows:

$$\langle 0 \rangle = \{0\}$$
$$\langle (0,1) \rangle = \{(0,0), (0,1), (0,2)\}$$
$$\langle (1,0) \rangle = \{(0,0), (1,0), (2,0), (3,0), (4,0)\}$$
$$\langle (1,1) \rangle = \mathbb{Z}_5 \times \mathbb{Z}_3$$

16. Let p be a prime number, let $n \in \mathbb{Z}^+$, and let Φ be Euler's totient function. Prove that $\Phi(p^n) = p^n - p^{n-1}$. Use this result to compute $\Phi(1024)$ and $\Phi(625)$.

Proof: The nonnegative integers less than p^n that have a common divisor with p^n are all the multiples of p. Since every pth integer is a multiple of p, we see that there are $\dfrac{p^n}{p} = p^{n-1}$ nonnegative multiples of p less than p^n. So, there are p^{n-1} nonnegative integers less than p^n that are **not** relatively prime with p^n. It follows that the number of positive integers less than p^n that are relatively prime with p^n is $p^n - p^{n-1}$. So, $\Phi(p^n) = p^n - p^{n-1}$. $\qquad \square$

$\Phi(1024) = \Phi(2^{10}) = 2^{10} - 2^9 = 1024 - 512 = \mathbf{512}$.

$\Phi(625) = \Phi(5^4) = 5^4 - 5^3 = 625 - 125 = \mathbf{500}$.

17. Let $n \in \mathbb{Z}^+$ and $[a]_n \in U_n$. Prove that $[a]_n^{\Phi(n)} \equiv_n [1]_n$, where Φ is Euler's totient function.

Proof: Since U_n is a group of order $\Phi(n)$, we can write $U_n = \left\{ [a_1]_n, [a_2]_n, \ldots, [a_{\Phi(n)}]_n \right\}$. If we multiply each element in U_n by $[a]_n$, we get the same group: $U_n = \left\{ [a_1 \cdot a]_n, [a_2 \cdot a]_n, \ldots, [a_{\Phi(n)} \cdot a]_n \right\}$. So, we have $[a_1]_n \cdot [a_2]_n \cdots [a_{\Phi(n)}]_n = [a_1 \cdot a]_n, [a_2 \cdot a]_n \cdots [a_{\Phi(n)} \cdot a]_n$, or equivalently,

$$\left[a_1 \cdot a_2 \cdots a_{\Phi(n)} \right]_n = \left[a_1 \cdot a \cdot a_2 \cdot a \cdots a_{\Phi(n)} \cdot a \right]_n$$
$$= \left[(a_1 \cdot a_2 \cdots a_{\Phi(n)}) a^{\Phi(n)} \right]_n = \left[a_1 \cdot a_2 \cdots a_{\Phi(n)} \right]_n \cdot \left[a^{\Phi(n)} \right]_n$$

So, we have $\left[a_1 \cdot a_2 \cdots a_{\Phi(n)} \right]_n \cdot [1]_n = \left[a_1 \cdot a_2 \cdots a_{\Phi(n)} \right]_n = \left[a_1 \cdot a_2 \cdots a_{\Phi(n)} \right]_n \cdot \left[a^{\Phi(n)} \right]_n$. Since U_n is a group, the left cancellation law holds, and so, $[1]_n = \left[a^{\Phi(n)} \right]_n = [a]_n^{\Phi(n)}$. $\qquad \square$

18. Let $a, b \in \mathbb{Z}$, let $n \in \mathbb{Z}^+$, let $d = \gcd(a, n)$ and suppose that $d \mid b$. Prove that the linear congruence $ax \equiv_n b$ has exactly d solutions, up to congruence modulo n.

Proof: We know by Theorem 9.23 that the linear congruence $ax \equiv_n b$ has a solution. Let's call this solution c. Since $\gcd(a, n)$ is a divisor of both a and n, there are integers s and t such that $a = \gcd(a, n) \cdot s$ and $n = \gcd(a, n) \cdot t$. We will show that for each $i = 1, 2, \ldots, d - 1$, $c + it$ is a solution of $ax \equiv_n b$.

Since $a = \gcd(a, n) \cdot s$ and $n = \gcd(a, n) \cdot t$, we have $at = \gcd(a, n) \cdot st = sn$. Therefore, we have $a(c + it) = ac + ait = ac + sni \equiv_n ac \equiv_n b$, as desired.

Next, let's show that if $0 \le i < j < \gcd(a, n) - 1$, then $c + it \not\equiv_n c + jt$. Suppose toward contradiction that $c + it \equiv_n c + jt$. Then $it \equiv_n jt$, and so, $n \mid (j - i)t$. Therefore, $(j - i)t = nr$ for some $r \in \mathbb{Z}$. So, we have $(j - i)n = (j - i)\gcd(a, n) \cdot t = \gcd(a, n) \cdot nr$. So, $j - i = \gcd(a, n) \cdot r$. Therefore, $\gcd(a, n) \le j - i < \gcd(a, n) - 1 - i < \gcd(a, n)$, a contradiction. $\square$

19. Let $a, b \in \mathbb{Z}^+$ with $\gcd(a, b) = 1$. Prove each of the following:

   (i) $(\mathbb{Z}_{ab}, +, \cdot) \cong (\mathbb{Z}_a, +, \cdot) \times (\mathbb{Z}_b, +, \cdot)$.

   (ii) $U_{ab} \cong U_a \times U_b$.

   (iii) If $n \in \mathbb{Z}^+$ and $n = p_1^{m_1} \cdot p_2^{m_2} \cdots p_k^{m_k}$ is the prime factorization of n and Φ is Euler's totient function, then $\Phi(n) = \left(p_1^{m_1} - p_1^{m_1 - 1}\right)\left(p_1^{m_2} - p_1^{m_2 - 1}\right) \cdots \left(p_1^{m_k} - p_1^{m_k - 1}\right)$.

   (iv) Compute $\Phi(1{,}047{,}816) = 299{,}376$.

Proofs:

   (i)   We define a function $f : \mathbb{Z}_{ab} \to \mathbb{Z}_a \times \mathbb{Z}_b$ by $f([k]_{ab}) = ([k]_a, [k]_b)$. We first show that f is well-defined. Suppose that $[k_1]_{ab} = [k_2]_{ab}$. Then $ab \mid k_2 - k_1$. So, there is an integer j such that $k_2 - k_1 = abj$. This equation shows that $a \mid k_2 - k_1$ and $b \mid k_2 - k_1$. So, $[k_1]_a = [k_2]_a$ and $[k_1]_b = [k_2]_b$. Therefore, $([k_1]_a, [k_1]_b) = ([k_2]_a, [k_2]_b)$.

   Next, we show that f is a homomorphism. We have

$$f([k_1]_{ab} + [k_2]_{ab}) = f([k_1 + k_2]_{ab}) = ([k_1 + k_2]_a, [k_1 + k_2]_b)$$
$$= ([k_1]_a + [k_2]_a, [k_1]_b + [k_2]_b) = ([k_1]_a, [k_1]_b) + ([k_2]_a, [k_2]_b)$$
$$= f([k_1]_{ab}) + f([k_2]_{ab}).$$
$$f([k_1]_{ab} \cdot [k_2]_{ab}) = f([k_1 \cdot k_2]_{ab}) = ([k_1 \cdot k_2]_a, [k_1 \cdot k_2]_b)$$
$$= ([k_1]_a \cdot [k_2]_a, [k_1]_b \cdot [k_2]_b) = ([k_1]_a, [k_1]_b) \cdot ([k_2]_a, [k_2]_b) = f([k_1]_{ab}) \cdot f([k_2]_{ab}).$$

   To see that f is injective, let $f([k_1]_{ab}) = f([k_2]_{ab})$. So, $([k_1]_a, [k_1]_b) = ([k_2]_a, [k_2]_b)$. It follows that $[k_1]_a = [k_2]_a$ and $[k_1]_b = [k_2]_b$. So, $a \mid k_2 - k_1$ and $b \mid k_2 - k_1$. Since $\gcd(a, b) = 1$, by Theorem 8.26, $\operatorname{lcm}(a, b) = ab$. So, by Problem 19 from Problem Set 8, $ab \mid k_2 - k_1$. Therefore, $[k_1]_{ab} = [k_2]_{ab}$.

Since f is an injection between two finite sets with the same number of elements, f is surjective. $\qquad\square$

(ii) We define $g: U_{ab} \to U_a \times U_b$ by $g(x) = f(x)$, where f is the function given in part (i) above. We need only show that $x \in U_{ab}$ if and only if $(x, x) \in U_a \times U_b$. Well, $x \in U_{ab}$ if and only if $\gcd(x, ab) = 1$ if and only if $\gcd(x, a) = 1$ and $\gcd(x, b) = 1$ if and only if $x \in U_a$ and $x \in U_b$. $\qquad\square$

(iii) It is easy to show by induction that $U_n \cong U_{p_1^{m_1}} \times U_{p_2^{m_2}} \times \cdots \times U_{p_k^{m_k}}$. Also, by Problem 16 above, we have $\left|U_{p_i^{m_i}}\right| = \Phi\left(U_{p_i^{m_i}}\right) = p_i^{m_i} - p_i^{m_i-1}$. It follows that

$$\Phi(n) = |U_n| = \left|U_{p_1^{m_1}} \times U_{p_2^{m_2}} \times \cdots \times U_{p_k^{m_k}}\right|$$

$$= \left|U_{p_1^{m_1}}\right| \cdot \left|U_{p_2^{m_2}}\right| \cdots \left|U_{p_k^{m_k}}\right| = (p_1^{m_1} - p_1^{m_1-1})(p_1^{m_2} - p_1^{m_2-1}) \cdots (p_1^{m_k} - p_1^{m_k-1}) \qquad\square$$

(iv) The prime factorization of $1,047,816$ is $2^3 \cdot 3^5 \cdot 7^2 \cdot 11$. It follows from part (iii) above that

$$\Phi(1,047,816) = \Phi(2^3 \cdot 3^5 \cdot 7^2 \cdot 11) = (2^3 - 2^2)(3^5 - 3^4)(7^2 - 7)(11)$$

$$= 4 \cdot 162 \cdot 42 \cdot 11 = \mathbf{299,376}. \qquad\square$$

20. Let G be a group, let $m, n \in \mathbb{Z}^+$, and let $a \in G$ with $|a| = n$. Prove that $\gcd(m, n) = 1$ if and only if $|a^m| = n$.

Proof: Assume that $\gcd(m, n) = 1$. By Theorem 8.18, there are $s, t \in \mathbb{Z}$ such that $sm + tn = 1$. Then $a = a^1 = a^{sm+tn} = a^{sm}a^{tn} = (a^m)^s(a^n)^t = (a^m)^s e^t = (a^m)^s e = (a^m)^s$. Let $x \in \langle a \rangle$ be arbitrary. Then there is $k \in \mathbb{Z}$ such that $x = a^k$. So, $x = a^k = ((a^m)^s)^k = (a^m)^{sk} \in \langle a^m \rangle$. It follows that a^m is a generator for $\langle a \rangle$, and so $|a^m| = |\langle a^m \rangle| = |\langle a \rangle| = |a| = n$.

Conversely, assume that $|a^m| = n$. Then $G = \langle a^m \rangle$, and so, $a \in \langle a^m \rangle$. Therefore, there is an integer k such that $a^1 = a = (a^m)^k = a^{mk}$. By Theorem 9.4, $mk \equiv_n 1$. So, m has a multiplicative inverse in $\mathbb{Z}_n$. Therefore, $m \in U_n$, and so, $\gcd(m, n) = 1$. $\qquad\square$

21. Let G be a group, let $m, n \in \mathbb{Z}^+$, and let $a \in G$ with $|a| = n$. Prove that $m \cdot |a^m| = \mathrm{lcm}(m, n)$.

Proof: Since $n | \mathrm{lcm}(m, n)$, by the Note following Theorem 9.4, $a^{\mathrm{lcm}(m,n)} = e$. It follows that

$$(a^m)^{\frac{\mathrm{lcm}(m,n)}{m}} = a^{\mathrm{lcm}(m,n)} = e.$$

So, $|a^m| \leq \frac{\mathrm{lcm}(m,n)}{m}$, or equivalently, $m \cdot |a^m| \leq \mathrm{lcm}(m, n)$.

Let $t < n$ and assume that $(a^m)^t = e$. Then $a^{mt} = e$. By the Note following Theorem 9.4, $n | mt$. Since $m | mt$ as well, mt is a common multiple of m and n. Therefore, $\mathrm{lcm}(m, n) \leq mt$, or equivalently, $\frac{\mathrm{lcm}(m,n)}{m} \leq t$. So, If $t < \frac{\mathrm{lcm}(m,n)}{m}$, then $(a^m)^t \neq e$. Thus, $|a^m| \geq \frac{\mathrm{lcm}(m,n)}{m}$, or equivalently, we have $m \cdot |a^m| \geq \mathrm{lcm}(m, n)$.

Since $m \cdot |a^m| \leq \mathrm{lcm}(m, n)$ and $m \cdot |a^m| \geq \mathrm{lcm}(m, n)$, we have $m \cdot |a^m| = \mathrm{lcm}(m, n)$. $\qquad\square$

Problem Set 10

LEVEL 1

1. Let $n \in \mathbb{Z}$. Compute $[\mathbb{Z}: n\mathbb{Z}]$.

Solution: $\mathbb{Z}/n\mathbb{Z} = \{\mathbb{Z}, 1 + \mathbb{Z}, 2 + \mathbb{Z}, \ldots, (n - 1) + \mathbb{Z}\}$. So, $[\mathbb{Z}: n\mathbb{Z}] = \boldsymbol{n}$.

2. Let G and H be groups such that $|G| = 14$ and $|H| = 45$. Compute $|G \cap H|$.

Solution: Since $G \cap H \leq G$, $|G \cap H| \,|\, 14$. Since $G \cap H \leq H$, $|G \cap H| \,|\, 45$. So, $|G \cap H| \,|\, \gcd(14, 45) = 1$. Therefore, $|G \cap H| = \boldsymbol{1}$.

LEVEL 2

3. Let G be a group of finite order and let H and K be subgroups of G with H a subgroup of K. Prove that $[G:H] = [G:K] \cdot [K:H]$.

Solution: By Langrange's Theorem, $[G:H] = \frac{|G|}{|H|} = \frac{|G|}{|K|} \cdot \frac{|K|}{|H|} = [G:K] \cdot [K:H]$.

4. Consider $\mathbb{R}^* = \mathbb{R} \setminus \{0\}$ as a group under multiplication. Find a subgroup H of $\mathbb{R}^*$ such that $[\mathbb{R}^*: H] = 2$.

Solution: Let $H = \mathbb{R}^+$ be the set of positive real numbers. Since 1 is a positive real number, the product of two positive real numbers is a positive real number, and the multiplicative inverse (reciprocal) of a positive real number is a positive real number, H is a subgroup of $\mathbb{R}^*$. The two cosets of H in $\mathbb{R}^*$ are H and $(-1)H$. Note that H is the set of positive real numbers and $(-1)H$ is the set of negative real numbers. It follows that $[\mathbb{R}^*: H] = 2$.

5. Let V be a vector space over a field F, let W be a subspace of V, and define $\pi: V \to V/W$ by $\pi(v) = v + W$. Prove that π is a linear transformation.

Proof: Let $v, w \in V$ and $a, b \in F$. Then we have
$$\pi(av + bw) = (av + bw) + W = (av + W) + (bw + W)$$
$$= a(v + W) + b(w + W) = a\pi(v) + b\pi(w).$$

Therefore, π is a linear transformation. $\qquad\qquad\qquad\qquad\qquad\qquad\qquad\square$

LEVEL 3

6. Consider the following subset of S_4:

$A_4 = \{(1), (123), (124), (134), (234), (132), (142), (143), (243), (12)(34), (13)(24), (14)(23)\}$.

Prove that A_4 is a subgroup of S_4 and that A_4 has no subgroup of order 6.

Proof: It can be checked that A_4 is a subgroup of S_4 by brute force. In other words, simply construct the multiplication table of A_4 and check that closure and the inverse property hold. Now, suppose toward contradiction that H is a subgroup of A_4 of order 6. Since $|A_4| = 12$ and $|H| = 6$, we have $[A_4 : H] = \frac{12}{6} = 2$. Let's show that for all $x \in A_4$, $x^2 \in H$. If $x \in H$, then $x^2 \in H$ because H is a group. Suppose toward contradiction that $x \in A_4 \setminus H$ and $x^2 \notin H$. Then $xH \neq H$ and $x^2 H \neq H$. Since $[A_4 : H] = 2$, we must have $xH = x^2 H$. It follows that $x = x^1 = x^{-1+2} = x^{-1} x^2 \in H$ (by Theorem 10.5), contradicting our assumption that $x \in A_4 \setminus H$. So, for all $x \in A_4$, $x^2 \in H$. For any 3-cycle (abc), we have $(abc) = (abc)^4 = ((abc)^2)^2$. So, every 3-cycle in A_4 is in H. But there are eight 3-cycles, contradicting our assumption that $|H| = 6$. Therefore, A_4 has no subgroup of order 6. $\qquad\square$

7. Let G be a group and let $H = \langle xyx^{-1}y^{-1} \mid x, y \in G \rangle$. Prove that H is a normal subgroup of G such that G/H is commutative. H is known as the **commutator subgroup** of G.

Proof: Let $h \in H$ and $g \in G$. There are $x, y \in G$ such that $h = xyx^{-1}y^{-1}$. Then we have

$$ghg^{-1} = g(xyx^{-1}y^{-1})g^{-1} = gx(g^{-1}g)y(g^{-1}g)x^{-1}(g^{-1}g)y^{-1}g^{-1}$$

$$= (gxg^{-1})(gyg^{-1})(gx^{-1}g^{-1})(gy^{-1}g^{-1}) = (gxg^{-1})(gyg^{-1})(gxg^{-1})^{-1}(gyg^{-1})^{-1} \in H.$$

So, $H \triangleleft G$.

Now, let $xH, yH \in G/H$. Then $x, y \in G$, and so, $(yx)^{-1}xy = x^{-1}y^{-1}xy \in H$. By Theorem 10.5, we have $yxH = xyH$. So, $(yH)(xH) = yxH = xyH = (xH)(yH)$. Since $xH, yH \in G/H$ were arbitrary, we see that G/H is commutative. $\qquad\square$

8. Let G be a group and let H be a subgroup of G such that $[G : H] = 2$. Prove that $H \triangleleft G$.

Proof: Suppose that $[G : H] = 2$. Then there are two left cosets of H in G, say H and xH and there are two right cosets of H in G, say H and Hy. Since the left cosets and right cosets each form a partition of G, we must have $xH = G \setminus H$ and $Hx = G \setminus H$. So, $xH = Hx$. By Theorem 10.15, $H \triangleleft G$. $\qquad\square$

9. Prove that every element of $\mathbb{Q}/\mathbb{Z}$ has finite order.

Proof: Let $\frac{a}{b} + \mathbb{Z} \in \mathbb{Q}/\mathbb{Z}$, where $a, b \in \mathbb{Z}$ and $b > 0$. Then $b\left(\frac{a}{b} + \mathbb{Z}\right) = a + \mathbb{Z} = \mathbb{Z}$ because $a \in \mathbb{Z}$. Therefore, $\left|\frac{a}{b} + \mathbb{Z}\right| \leq b$. $\qquad\square$

10. Let R be a ring, let I be an ideal of R such that $I \neq R$ and R/I is commutative. Is R necessarily commutative? If so, prove it. If not, provide a counterexample.

Solution: Let A and B be rings with A commutative and B not commutative. Then $A \times B$ is a noncommutative ring, where addition and multiplication are defined as follows:

$$(a, b) + (c, d) = (a + c, b + d) \text{ and } (a, b)(c, d) = (ac, bd)$$

in Let $I = \{(0, b)\mid b \in B\}$. Then I is an ideal of $A \times B$ and $A \times B / I \cong A$, which is commutative.

11. Describe a ring with exactly 2 maximal ideals.

Solution: Let F and K be fields. The only ideals of F are $\{0\}$ and F and the only ideals of K are $\{0\}$ and K. Let $R = F \times K$, let $I = \{(f, 0) \mid f \in F\}$ and let $J = \{(0, k) \mid k \in K\}$. Then I and J are the only two maximal ideals of R. As a specific example, $\mathbb{Q} \times \mathbb{Q}$ has exactly 2 maximal ideals.

LEVEL 4

12. Let G be a group and let $H \lhd G$ such that $|H|$ and $|G/H|$ are finite. Prove that $|G|$ is finite.

Proof: Suppose that $|H| = m$ and $|G/H| = n$. Let $x_1 H, x_2 H, \ldots, x_n H$ be the n cosets of H in G. By Theorem 10.4, $G = x_1 H \cup x_2 H \cup \cdots \cup x_n H$ and by Theorem 10.6, $|x_1 H| = |x_2 H| = \cdots = |x_n H| = |H|$. So, $|G| = |x_1 H \cup x_2 H \cup \cdots \cup x_n H| = |x_1 H| + |x_2 H| + \cdots + |x_n H| = n|H| = nm$. So, $|G|$ is finite. $\quad\square$

13. Let G be a group, let H be a subgroup of G, and let Y be a selector for the collection of cosets of H in G. For each $x \in Y$, let $f_x \colon xH \to H$ be a bijection and define $g \colon G \to H \times \{zH \mid z \in G\}$ by $g(y) = (f_x(y), xH)$, where $x \in Y$ and $y \in xH$. Prove that g is a bijection.

Proof: Let $y \in G$. By Theorem 10.4, there is exactly one coset xH such that $y \in xH$. So, $f_x(y)$ is an element of H, and so, $g(y) = (f_x(y), xH) \in H \times \{zH \mid z \in G\}$.

To see that g is injective, suppose that $g(y_1) = g(y_2)$. Then there are $x_1, x_2 \in Y$ with $y_1 \in x_1 H$, $y_2 \in x_2 H$, $f_{x_1}(y_1) = f_{x_2}(y_2)$, and $x_1 H = x_2 H$. Since $x_1, x_2 \in x_1 H$ and Y contains only one element from each coset, we must have $x_1 = x_2$. So, $f_{x_1}(y_1) = f_{x_1}(y_2)$. Since f_{x_1} is injective (because it is bijective), $y_1 = y_2$.

To see that g is surjective, let $(z, xH) \in H \times \{zH \mid z \in G\}$. Choose $w \in Y$ such that $xH = wH$. Let $y = f_w^{-1}(z)$. Then $y \in wH$, and so, $g(y) = (f_w(y), wH) = (z, xH)$. $\quad\square$

14. Let $\mathbb{Z}_n = \{[k]_n \mid k \in \mathbb{Z}\}$, where $[k]_n$ is the equivalence class of k under the equivalence $\equiv_n$ and consider the commutative ring $(\mathbb{Z}_n, +, \cdot)$, where addition and multiplication are defined by $[x]_n + [y]_n = [x + y]_n$ and $[xy]_n = [x]_n \cdot [y]_n$ (see Problem 10 from Problem Set 3). Prove that $\mathbb{Z}/n\mathbb{Z} \cong \mathbb{Z}_n$. Find the ideals of $\mathbb{Z}/15\mathbb{Z}$ and $\mathbb{Z}_{15}$ and show that there is a natural one-to-one correspondence between them.

Proof: Define $f \colon \mathbb{Z}/n\mathbb{Z} \to \mathbb{Z}_n$ by $f(x + n\mathbb{Z}) = [x]$. Suppose that $f(x + n\mathbb{Z}) = f(y + n\mathbb{Z})$, so that $[x] = [y]$. Then $x \equiv_n y$. So, $n \mid x - y$, and therefore, there is $k \in \mathbb{Z}$ such that $x - y = nk$. So, $x - y \in n\mathbb{Z}$, and so, $x + n\mathbb{Z} = y + n\mathbb{Z}$. Since $x + n\mathbb{Z}, y + n\mathbb{Z} \in \mathbb{Z}/n\mathbb{Z}$ were arbitrary, f is injective.

f is surjective because if $[x] \in \mathbb{Z}_n$, then $x \in \mathbb{Z}$ and $f(x + n\mathbb{Z}) = [x]$.

Now, we have

$$f\big((x + n\mathbb{Z}) + (y + n\mathbb{Z})\big) = f\big((x + y) + n\mathbb{Z}\big) = [x + y] = [x] + [y] = f(x + n\mathbb{Z}) + f(y + n\mathbb{Z}),$$

$$f\big((x + n\mathbb{Z})(y + n\mathbb{Z})\big) = f\big((xy) + n\mathbb{Z}\big) = [xy] = [x] \cdot [y] = f(x + n\mathbb{Z}) \cdot f(y + n\mathbb{Z}).$$

Therefore, $f \colon \mathbb{Z}/n\mathbb{Z} \cong \mathbb{Z}_n$.

$\mathbb{Z}/15\mathbb{Z} = \{15\mathbb{Z}, 1 + 15\mathbb{Z}, \ldots, 14 + 15\mathbb{Z}\}$ and $\mathbb{Z}_{15} = \{[0], [1], \ldots, [14]\}$.

The ideals of $\mathbb{Z}/15\mathbb{Z}$ are $\mathbb{Z}/15\mathbb{Z}$, $3\mathbb{Z}/15\mathbb{Z}$, $5\mathbb{Z}/15\mathbb{Z}$, $15\mathbb{Z}/15\mathbb{Z}$ and these correspond to the ideals of $\mathbb{Z}_{15}$, which are $\mathbb{Z}_{15}$, $\{[0],[3],[6],[9],[12]\}$, $\{[0],[5],[10]\}$, and $\{[0]\}$. □

15. Let G be a group such that $G/Z(G)$ is cyclic. Prove that G is commutative.

Proof: Since $G/Z(G)$ is cyclic, there is $a \in G$ such that $G/Z(G) = \langle aZ(G)\rangle$. Let $x, y \in G$. Then $xZ(G) = a^j Z(G)$ and $yZ(G) = a^k Z(G)$ for some integers j and k. So, there are $b, c, d, f \in Z(G)$ such that $xb = a^j c$ and $yd = a^k f$. Let $g = cb^{-1}$ and $h = fd^{-1}$. Since $Z(G)$ is a group, $g, h \in Z(G)$. Therefore,

$$xy = \left(a^j cb^{-1}\right)\left(a^k fd^{-1}\right) = \left(a^j g\right)(a^k h) = \left(ga^j\right)(a^k h) = ga^{j+k}h = ga^{k+j}h = \left(ga^k\right)\left(a^j h\right)$$

$$= (a^k g)(ha^j) = a^k(gh)a^j = a^k hga^j = (a^k h)\left(a^j g\right) = \left(a^k fd^{-1}\right)\left(a^j cb^{-1}\right) = yx.$$

Since $x, y \in G$ were arbitrary, G is commutative. □

16. Let H and K be finite subgroups of a group G and let $HK = \{hk \mid h \in H \wedge k \in K\}$. Prove that $|HK| \cdot |H \cap K| = |H| \cdot |K|$.

Proof: We will prove that $\frac{|H|}{|H\cap K|} = \frac{|HK|}{|K|}$ by showing that the number of cosets of $H \cap K$ in H is the same as the number of cosets of K in HK.

Since H is finite, there are finitely many cosets of $H \cap K$ in H, let's say $a_1(H \cap K), \ldots, a_m(H \cap K)$. Let $hk \in HK$. Then $h \in H$, and so, h is in some coset of $H \cap K$ in H, say $h \in a_i(H \cap K)$ for some $i \in \{1, 2, \ldots, m\}$. So, there is $a \in H \cap K$ with $h = a_i a$. Therefore, $hk = (a_i a)k = a_i(ak)$. Since $a \in H \cap K$, we have $a \in K$. Since $a \in K$, $k \in K$, and K is a group, $ak \in K$. So, $hk \in a_i K$.

Next, we see that $a_i K \cap a_j K \neq \emptyset \Rightarrow a_i K = a_j K \Rightarrow a_j^{-1} a_i \in K \Rightarrow a_j^{-1} a_i \in H \cap K \Rightarrow a_i = a_j \Rightarrow i = j$. So, if $i \neq j$, then $a_i K \cap a_j K = \emptyset$. That is, the cosets $a_i K$ are pairwise disjoint.

Thus, $\frac{|H|}{|H\cap K|} = \frac{|HK|}{|K|}$, and so, $|HK| \cdot |H \cap K| = |H| \cdot |K|$. □

17. Prove that there are exactly two groups of order 6, up to isomorphism.

Proof: $(\mathbb{Z}_6, +)$ is a commutative group of order 6 and $(S_3, \circ)$ is a noncommutative group of order 6. Therefore, there are at least two groups of order 6.

Let G be an arbitrary group of order 6. The order of each element must be 1, 2, 3, or 6. If G has an element of order 6, then G is cyclic and therefore, G is isomorphic to $\mathbb{Z}_6$.

Let G be a noncyclic group of order 6. We first show that G has an element of order 3. Suppose toward contradiction that G has no element of order 3. Then every nonidentity element has order 2. Let $a, b \in G$ be any two distinct nonidentity elements of G. Then $a^2 = e$, and so, $a = a^{-1}$. If $ab = e$, then $b = a^{-1} = a$. Therefore, ab cannot have order 1. So, ab has order 2. It follows that $ab = (ab)^{-1} = b^{-1}a^{-1} = ba$. So, $\{1, a, b, ab\}$ is a subgroup of G of order 4, contradicting Theorem 10.9. So, G must have an element of order 3.

Next, we show that G has an element of order 2. Suppose toward contradiction that G has no element of order 2. Then every nonidentity element has order 3. In other words, there are exactly 5 elements of order 3. If a is an element of order 3, then a is not equal to its own inverse. So, by pairing each nonidentity element with its inverse, we see that there must be an even number of nonidentity elements, contradicting that there are 5 such elements. So, G must have an element of order 2.

Let $a \in G$ have order 3 and let $b \in G$ have order 2. Then it is easy to see that the 6 distinct elements of G are e, a, a^2, b, ba, and ba^2.

It's easy to see that we cannot have $ab = e, a, a^2$, or b. So, $ab = ba$ or $ab = ba^2 = ba^{-1}$.

If $ab = ba$, then $(ba)^2 = baba = abba = ab^2a = aea = a^2$, $(ba)^3 = a^2ba = a^3b = b$, $(ba)^4 = bba = a$, $(ba)^5 = aba = ba^2$, and $(ba)^6 = ba^2ba = b^2a^3 = ee = e$. So, G is a cyclic group generated by ba, contradicting our assumption that G is not cyclic.

If $ab = ba^2$, then $G = \langle a, b \mid a^3 = e, b^2 = e, ab = ba^2 \rangle$. This group is isomorphic to S_3 (or D_3). $\qquad\square$

18. Let V be a vector space over a field F, let W be a subspace of V, and define $\pi\colon V \to V/W$ by $\pi(v) = v + W$. By Problem 5 above, π is a linear transformation. Suppose that U is a vector space over F and that $f\colon V \to U$ is a linear transformation such that $W \subseteq \ker(f)$. Prove that there is a unique linear transformation $g\colon V/W \to U$ such that $f = g \circ \pi$.

Proof: Define $g\colon V/W \to U$ by $g(v + W) = f(v)$. To see that g is well-defined, suppose that $v + W = w + W$. Then $v - w \in W$. Since $W \subseteq \ker(f)$, $f(v - w) = 0_U$. Since f is a linear transformation, $f(v) - f(w) = 0$, and so, $f(v) = f(w)$.

Now, we have

$$g\big((v + W) + (w + W)\big) = g\big((v + w) + W\big) = f(v + w)$$
$$= f(v) + f(w) = g(v + W) + g(w + W).$$
$$g\big(k(v + W)\big) = g(kv + W) = f(kv) = kf(v) = kg(v + W)$$

Therefore, g is a liner transformation.

Next, if $v \in V$, then $(g \circ \pi)(v) = g\big(\pi(v)\big) = g(v + W) = f(v)$. So, $f = g \circ \pi$.

Finally, we check uniqueness. Suppose that $h\colon V/W \to U$ satisfies $f = h \circ \pi$. Let $v + W \in V/W$. Since $\pi(v) = v + W$, we have

$$h(v + W) = h\big(\pi(v)\big) = (h \circ \pi)(v) = f(v) = (g \circ \pi)(v) = g\big(\pi(v)\big) = g(v + W).$$

So, $h = g$, as desired. $\qquad\square$

LEVEL 5

19. Let G be a group and let N be a normal subgroup of G such that N and G/N are finitely generated. Prove that G is finitely generated.

124

Proof: Let $N = \langle n_1, n_2, \ldots, n_j \rangle$ and let $G/N = \langle x_1 N, x_2 N, \ldots, x_k N \rangle$. We will show that G is generated by all products of the form $\prod \left(a_i \left(\prod b_j^i \right) \right)$, where each a_i is some x_t or its inverse for some t and each b_j^i is some n_i or its inverse.

Let $x \in G$. Then $xN = \prod a_i N$, where each a_i is some x_t or its inverse. So, $x = xe = \prod a_i y_i$, where each $y_i \in N$. For each i, $y_i = \prod b_j^i$, where each b_j^i is some n_i or its inverse. So, $x = \prod \left(a_i \left(\prod b_j^i \right) \right)$. $\square$

20. Let G be a group and let H be a subgroup of G such that H is the only subgroup of G with index $[G:H]$. Prove that H is normal in G.

Proof: First assume that G is finite. If $|K| = |H|$, by Lagrange's Theorem, $[G:K] = \frac{|G|}{|K|} = \frac{|G|}{|H|} = [G:H]$. Since H is the only subgroup of G with index $[G:H]$, $K = H$. Therefore, H is the only subgroup of G of order H.

Now, let $x \in G$. It is easily checked that $xHx^{-1} \leq H$. Define $f: H \to xHx^{-1}$ by $f(y) = xyx^{-1}$. It is easily checked that f is a bijection. So, $|H| = |xHx^{-1}|$. Therefore, $xHx^{-1} = H$. By Theorem 10.15, H is normal in G.

Next, assume that G is infinite and let $x \in G$. Define $f: G/H \to G/xHx^{-1}$ by $f(yH) = xyHx^{-1}$. Since $xyHx^{-1} = (xyx^{-1})xHx^{-1}$, $f(yH) = xyHx^{-1} \in G/xHx^{-1}$.

If $f(yH) = f(zH)$, then $xyHx^{-1} = xzHx^{-1}$, and so, $yH = zH$. So, f is injective.

If $yxHx^{-1} \in G/xHx^{-1}$, then $f(x^{-1}yxH) = xx^{-1}yxHx^{-1} = yxHx^{-1}$. So, f is surjective.

It follows that $[G:H] = \frac{|G|}{|H|} = \frac{|G|}{|xHx^{-1}|} = [G:xHx^{-1}]$. Since H is the only subgroup of G with index $[G:H]$, we have $xHx^{-1} = H$. By Theorem 10.15, H is normal in G. $\square$

21. Prove that there are exactly five groups of order 8, up to isomorphism.

Proof: $\mathbb{Z}_8$, $\mathbb{Z}_4 \times \mathbb{Z}_2$, and $\mathbb{Z}_2 \times \mathbb{Z}_2 \times \mathbb{Z}_2$ are commutative groups of order 8. $\mathbb{Z}_2 \times \mathbb{Z}_2 \times \mathbb{Z}_2$ does not have any elements of order 4 or 8, and so, it is not isomorphic to the other two groups. $\mathbb{Z}_4 \times \mathbb{Z}_2$ does not have an element of order 8, and so, it is not isomorphic to $\mathbb{Z}_8$.

The Dihedral group $D_4 = \langle r, s \mid r^4 = e, s^2 = e, sr = r^3 s \rangle = \{e, r, r^2, r^3, s, rs, r^2 s, r^3 s\}$ is a group of order 8 that is **not** commutative, and so, it is not isomorphic to the previous three groups.

Let $Q = \{1, i, j, k, -1, -i, -j, -k\}$. We make Q into a group by letting 1 be the identity, and defining multiplication so that $(-1)^2 = 1$, $i^2 = j^2 = k^2 = -1$, $(-1)i = -i$, $(-1)j = -j$, $(-1)k = -k$, $ij = k$, $jk = i$, $ki = j$, $ji = -k$, $kj = -i$, and $ik = -j$. Q is also a group of order 8 that is **not** commutative, and so, it is not isomorphic to any of the three commutative groups above. To see that Q is not isomorphic D_4, observe that the only element of order 2 in Q is -1, whereas in D_4, s and r^2 are two distinct elements of order 2.

Now, let G be any group of order 8. The order of each element must be 1, 2, 4, or 8.

If G has an element of order 8, then G is cyclic and therefore, G is isomorphic to $\mathbb{Z}_8$.

Next, assume that every nonidentity element of G has order 2. Then every element is equal to its own inverse ($a \cdot a = a^2 = e$ implies that $a = a^{-1}$). So, if $a, b \in G$. Then $ab = (ab)^{-1} = b^{-1}a^{-1} = ba$. Therefore, G is commutative. So, we have $G = \{e, a, b, c, ab, ac, bc, abc\}$. We show that G is isomorphic to $\mathbb{Z}_2 \times \mathbb{Z}_2 \times \mathbb{Z}_2$. To see this, define $f: G \to \mathbb{Z}_2 \times \mathbb{Z}_2 \times \mathbb{Z}_2$ by $f(e) = (0, 0, 0)$, $f(a) = (1, 0, 0)$, $f(b) = (0, 1, 0)$, $f(c) = (0, 0, 1)$, $f(ab) = (1, 1, 0)$, $f(ac) = (1, 0, 1)$, $f(bc) = (0, 1, 1)$, and $f(a, b, c) = (1, 1, 1)$. Clearly f is bijective and it is easy to verify that f is a homomorphism. For example, $f(ab) = (1, 1, 0) = (1, 0, 0) + (0, 1, 0) = f(a) + f(b)$.

Assume that G has at least one element a of order 4. Let b be any element not in $\langle a \rangle$ (so, b is not equal to e, a, a^2, or a^3). Then $G = \{e, a, a^2, a^3, b, ba, ba^2, ba^3\}$. Since the left cancellation law holds in groups, we cannot have b^2 equal to b, ba, ba^2, or ba^3. Also, b^2 cannot be equal to a or a^3 because then b would have order 8, and so, G would be isomorphic to $\mathbb{Z}_8$. So, $b^2 = e$ or $b^2 = a^2$. Similarly, we must have $ab = ba$ or $ab = ba^3$ (note that $ab = ba^2 \Rightarrow b^{-1}ab = a^2 \Rightarrow (b^{-1}ab)^2 = (a^2)^2 \Rightarrow b^{-1}a^2b = e \Rightarrow a^2 = e$, which is not true).

Let's look at each of these four cases separately.

$b^2 = e$, $ab = ba$: In this case, it is easy to check that G is commutative and isomorphic to $\mathbb{Z}_4 \times \mathbb{Z}_2$.

$b^2 = e$, $ab = ba^3$: In this case, we have $ba = ba(bb^{-1}) = b(ab)b^{-1} = b(ba^3)b^{-1} = b^2a^3b = a^3b$. So, we get $G = \langle a, b \mid a^4 = e, b^2 = e, ba = a^3b \rangle$, which is isomorphic to D_4.

$b^2 = a^2$, $ab = ba$: In this case, once again, G is commutative, b has order 4, and a^2 has order 2. So, it is easy to check that G is isomorphic to $\mathbb{Z}_4 \times \mathbb{Z}_2$.

$b^2 = a^2$, $ab = ba^3$: In this case, we get a group isomorphic to Q. Define $f: G \to Q$ by $f(a) = i$, $f(a^2) = -1$, $f(a^3) = -i$, $f(b) = j$, $f(ba) = -k$, $f(ba^2) = -j$, and $f(ba^3) = k$. Clearly f is a bijection and it is easy to verify that f is also a homomorphism. So, G is isomorphic to Q. $\square$

22. Find all groups of order 10, up to isomorphism.

Solution: $\mathbb{Z}_{10}$ is a commutative group of order 10 and

$$D_5 = \langle r, s \mid r^5 = e, s^2 = e, sr = r^4s \rangle = \{e, r, r^2, r^3, , r^4s, rs, r^2s, r^3s, r^4s\}$$ is a group of order 10 that is **not** commutative, and so, it is not isomorphic to $\mathbb{Z}_{10}$.

We will now prove that these are the only two groups of order 10, up to isomorphism.

Let G be an arbitrary group of order 10. The order of each element must be 1, 2, 5, or 10. If G has an element of order 10, then G is cyclic and therefore, G is isomorphic to $\mathbb{Z}_{10}$.

Let G be a noncyclic group of order 10. G has an element of order 5 and an element of order 2 for the same reason that a group of order 6 has an element of order 3 and an element of order 2 (see Problem 17).

126

Let $a \in G$ have order 5 and let $b \in G$ have order 2. Then the 10 distinct elements of G are $e, a, a^2, a^3, a^4, b, ba, ba^2, ba^3$, and ba^4.

It is not too hard to verify that we cannot have $ab = e, a, a^2, a^3, a^4$ or b. So, $ab = ba, ba^2, ba^3$, or ba^4.

If $ab = ba$, then it can be checked that ba generates G, contradicting our assumption that G is not cyclic.

If $ab = ba^2$, then $a = ba^2b$ and so, $a^2 = (ba^2b)(ba^2b) = ba^4b$. Also, we have $a^2 = bab$. Therefore, $ba^4b = bab$, and so, $a^4 = a$, which is not true. So, ab cannot be equal to ba^2.

If $ab = ba^3$, then $a = ba^3b$ and so, $a^2 = (ba^3b)(ba^3b) = ba^6b = bab = bba^3 = a^3$, which is not true. So, ab cannot be equal to ba^3.

If $ab = ba^4$, then $G = \langle a, b \mid a^5 = e, b^2 = e, ab = ba^4 \rangle$. This group is isomorphic to D_5. $\qquad \square$

23. Let V be a finite-dimensional vector space over a field F and let W be a subspace of V. Prove that $\dim V/W = \dim V - \dim W$.

Proof: Suppose that $\dim V = n + k$ and $\dim W = k$. Let $\{w_1, \dots, w_k\}$ be a basis for W and extend this basis to a basis $\{w_1, \dots, w_k, v_1, \dots, v_n\}$ of V. We will show that $\{v_1 + W, \dots, v_n + W\}$ is a basis of V/W.

Suppose that $c_1(v_1 + W) + \cdots c_n(v_n + W) = W$. Then, $(c_1 v_1 + \cdots + c_n v_n) + W = W$, and therefore, $c_1 v_1 + \cdots c_n v_n \in W$. So, there are weights $b_1, \dots, b_k$ such that $c_1 v_1 + \cdots + c_n v_n = b_1 w_1 + \cdots + b_k w_k$, or equivalently, $c_1 v_1 + \cdots + c_n v_n - b_1 w_1 - \cdots - b_k w_k = 0$. Since $\{w_1, \dots, w_k, v_1, \dots, v_n\}$ is linearly independent, all weights are 0. In particular, $c_1 = \cdots c_n = 0$, and so, $\{v_1 + W, \dots, v_n + W\}$ is linearly independent.

Let $v + W \in V/W$. Since $\{w_1, \dots, w_k, v_1, \dots, v_n\}$ spans V, there are weights $b_1, \dots, b_k, c_1, \dots, c_n$ such that $v = b_1 w_1 + \cdots b_k w_k + c_1 v_1 + \cdots c_n v_n$. Then we have

$$v + W = (b_1 w_1 + \cdots b_k w_k + c_1 v_1 + \cdots c_n v_n) + W = (c_1 v_1 + \cdots c_n v_n) + (b_1 w_1 + \cdots b_k w_k) + W$$
$$= (c_1 v_1 + \cdots c_n v_n) + W = c_1(v_1 + W) + \cdots c_n(v_n + W).$$

So, $\{v_1 + W, \dots, v_n + W\}$ spans V/W.

Since $\{v_1 + W, \dots, v_n + W\}$ is linearly independent and spans V/W, $\{v_1 + W, \dots, v_n + W\}$ is a basis for V/W.

It follows that $\dim V/W = n$. So, $\dim V - \dim W = (n + k) - k = n = \dim V/W$. $\qquad \square$

Problem Set 11

LEVEL 1

1. Use the First Isomorphism Theorem for rings to prove each of the following:

   (i) $\mathbb{Z}_{15}/\{0,3,6,9,12\} \cong \mathbb{Z}_3$

   (ii) $(\mathbb{Z}_2 \times \mathbb{Z}_2)/\{(0,0),(0,1)\} \cong \mathbb{Z}_2$

Proofs:

(i) Define a function $f:\mathbb{Z}_{15} \to \mathbb{Z}_3$ by $f([k]_{15}) = [k]_3$. If $[k_1]_{15} = [k_2]_{15}$, then $k_1 \equiv_{15} k_2$. So, $15|k_2 - k_1$. Therefore, there is $n \in \mathbb{Z}$ such that $k_2 - k_1 = 15n = 3(5n)$. So, $3|k_2 - k_1$, and therefore, $k_1 \equiv_3 k_2$. Thus, $[k_1]_3 = [k_2]_3$. So, f is well-defined.

It is clear that f is surjective. To see that f is a homomorphism, observe that

$$f([k_1 + k_2]_{15}) = [k_1 + k_2]_3 = [k_1]_3 + [k_2]_3 = f([k_1]_{15}) + f([k_2]_{15})$$

$$f([k_1 k_2]_{15}) = [k_1 k_2]_3 = [k_1]_3 \cdot [k_2]_3 = f([k_1]_{15}) \cdot f([k_2]_{15})$$

$$f([1]_{15}) = [1]_3$$

Now, $[k]_{15} \in \ker(f)$ if and only if $f([k]_{15}) = [0]_3$ if and only if $[k]_3 = [0]_3$ if and only if $3|k$ if and only if $k \in \{0,3,6,9,12\}$. So, $\ker(f) = \{0,3,6,9,12\}$.

By the First Homomorphism Theorem, $\mathbb{Z}_{15}/\{0,3,6,9,12\} \cong \mathbb{Z}_3$. □

(ii) Define a function $f:\mathbb{Z}_2 \times \mathbb{Z}_2 \to \mathbb{Z}_2$ by $f(j,k) = j$. It is clear that f is a surjective homomorphism. Now, $(j,k) \in \ker(f)$ if and only if $f(j,k) = 0$ if and only if $j = 0$ if and only if $(j,k) \in \{(0,0),(0,1)\}$. So, $\ker(f) = \{(0,0),(0,1)\}$.

By the First Homomorphism Theorem, $(\mathbb{Z}_2 \times \mathbb{Z}_2)/\{(0,0),(0,1)\} \cong \mathbb{Z}_2$. □

2. Let G and H be groups. Prove that $(G \times H)/(G \times \{e_H\}) \cong H$.

Proof: Define a function $f:G \times H \to H$ by $f(x,y) = y$. It is clear that f is a surjective homomorphism. Now, $(x,y) \in \ker(f)$ if and only if $f(x,y) = e_H$ if and only if $y = \{e_H\}$ if and only if $(x,y) \in G \times \{e_H\}$. So, $\ker(f) = G \times \{e_H\}$. By the First Homomorphism Theorem, $(G \times H)/(G \times \{e_H\}) \cong H$. □

3. List all the commutative groups of the given order, up to isomorphism:

   (i)   31

   (ii) 91

Solutions:

(i) Since 31 is prime, the only commutative group of order 31, up to isomorphism, is $\mathbb{Z}_{31}$.

(ii) Since $91 = 7 \cdot 13$, the only commutative group of order 91, up to isomorphism, is $\mathbb{Z}_7 \times \mathbb{Z}_{13}$ or $\mathbb{Z}_{91}$.

4. Let G be a commutative group. Prove that $G/\{x \in G \mid x^2 = e\} \cong \{x^2 \mid x \in G\}$.

Proof: Define a function $f: G \to \{x^2 \mid x \in G\}$ by $f(x) = x^2$. It is clear that f is surjective. To see that f is a homomorphism, observe that

$$f(xy) = (xy)^2 = xyxy = xxyy = x^2y^2 = f(x)f(y).$$

Now, $x \in \ker(f)$ if and only if $f(x) = e$ if and only if $x^2 = e$ if and only if $x \in \{x \in G \mid x^2 = e\}$. So, $\ker(f) = \{x \in G \mid x^2 = e\}$.

By the First Homomorphism Theorem, $G/\{x \in G \mid x^2 = e\} \cong \{x^2 \mid x \in G\}$. $\qquad\qquad \square$

5. List all the commutative groups of the given order, up to isomorphism:

    (i)   210

    (ii)   625

    (iii) 8575

Solutions:

(i) Since $210 = 2 \cdot 3 \cdot 5 \cdot 7$, the only commutative group of order 210, up to isomorphism, is $\mathbb{Z}_2 \times \mathbb{Z}_3 \times \mathbb{Z}_5 \times \mathbb{Z}_7$ or $\mathbb{Z}_{10}$.

(ii) Since $625 = 5^4$, the commutative groups of order 625, up to isomorphism, are

$$\mathbb{Z}_5 \times \mathbb{Z}_5 \times \mathbb{Z}_5 \times \mathbb{Z}_5, \mathbb{Z}_{25} \times \mathbb{Z}_5 \times \mathbb{Z}_5, \mathbb{Z}_{25} \times \mathbb{Z}_{25}, \mathbb{Z}_{125} \times \mathbb{Z}_5, \text{ and } \mathbb{Z}_{625}.$$

(iii) Since $8575 = 5^2 \cdot 7^3$, the commutative groups of order 8575, up to isomorphism, are

$$\mathbb{Z}_5 \times \mathbb{Z}_5 \times \mathbb{Z}_7 \times \mathbb{Z}_7 \times \mathbb{Z}_7, \mathbb{Z}_{25} \times \mathbb{Z}_7 \times \mathbb{Z}_7 \times \mathbb{Z}_7, \mathbb{Z}_5 \times \mathbb{Z}_5 \times \mathbb{Z}_{49} \times \mathbb{Z}_7, \mathbb{Z}_{25} \times \mathbb{Z}_{49} \times \mathbb{Z}_7$$

$$\mathbb{Z}_5 \times \mathbb{Z}_5 \times \mathbb{Z}_{343}, \text{ and } \mathbb{Z}_{25} \times \mathbb{Z}_{343}.$$

Note: We can also write the groups in part (iii) above as follows:

$$\mathbb{Z}_{35} \times \mathbb{Z}_{35} \times \mathbb{Z}_7, \mathbb{Z}_{175} \times \mathbb{Z}_7 \times \mathbb{Z}_7, \mathbb{Z}_{245} \times \mathbb{Z}_{35}, \mathbb{Z}_{1225} \times \mathbb{Z}_7$$

$$\mathbb{Z}_{1715} \times \mathbb{Z}_5, \text{ and } \mathbb{Z}_{8575}.$$

6. Let R be a ring, let I be an ideal of R, and let S be a subring of R with $I \subseteq S \subseteq R$. Prove that S/I is a subring of R/I. Furthermore, prove that if S is an ideal of R, then S/I is an ideal of R/I.

Proof: Assume that I is an ideal of R and S is a subring of R with $I \subseteq S \subseteq R$.

By Note 1 following Theorem 11.8, I is an ideal of S. Therefore, S/I is a ring.

Now, if $x + I \in S/I$, then $x \in S$. Since S is a subset of R, $x \in R$. Therefore, we have $x + I \in R/I$. Since $x + I \in S/I$ was arbitrary, $S/I \subseteq R/I$. It follows that S/I is a subring of R/I.

Now, assume that S is an ideal of R. Let $y + I \in S/I$ and let $x + I \in R/I$. Then $y \in S$ and $x \in R$. So, $xy \in S$ and $yx \in S$. It follows that $(x + I)(y + I) = xy + I \in S/I$ and $(y + I)(x + I) = yx + I \in S/I$. Therefore, S/I is an ideal of R/I. $\qquad\square$

7. Let R be a ring and let I be an ideal of R. Prove that every subring of R/I is of the form S/I for some subring S of R with $I \subseteq S \subseteq R$. Furthermore, prove that every ideal of R/I is of the form S/I for some ideal S of R with $I \subseteq S \subseteq R$.

Proof: Assume that I is an ideal of R and let K be a subring of R/I. We define S as follows: $S = \{x \in R \mid x + I \in K\}$.

Let's show that S is a subring of R. Since K is a subring of R/I, $0 + I, 1 + I \in K$. Therefore, $0, 1 \in S$. Let $x, y \in S$. Then $x + I, y + I \in K$. Since K is a subring of R/I, by Problem 5 in Problem Set 6, we have $(y - x) + I = (y + I) - (x + I) \in K$. So, $y - x \in S$. Also, we have $xy + I = (x + I)(y + I) \in K$. So, $xy \in S$. Therefore, S is a subring of R.

Next, let's show that $I \subseteq S$. To see this, let $x \in I$. Then $x + I = I$. Since K is a subring of R/I and I is the identity of R/I, $x + I = I \in K$. Therefore, $x \in S$.

We now show that $S/I = K$. Let $x + I \in S/I$. Then $x \in S$. By the definition of S, $x + I \in K$. Therefore, $S/I \subseteq K$. Conversely, let $x + I \in K$. By the definition of S, $x \in S$. So, $x + I \in S/I$. Thus, $K \subseteq S/I$. Since $S/I \subseteq K$ and $K \subseteq S/I$, we have $S/I = K$.

Finally, assume that K is an ideal of R/I. Let $y \in S$ and $x \in R$. By the definition of S, $y + I \in K$. Since K is an ideal of R/I, $xy + I = (x + I)(y + I) \in K$ and $yx + I = (y + I)(x + I) \in K$. By the definition of S, $xy \in S$ and $yx \in S$. Thus, S is an ideal of R. $\qquad\square$

8. Let V be a vector space over a field F and let U and W be subspaces of V with $W \subseteq U \subseteq V$. Prove that U/W is a subspace of V/W.

Proof: Assume that U and W are subspaces of V with $W \subseteq U \subseteq V$.

Since W and U are both vector spaces with the same operations and $W \subseteq U$, W is a subspace of U. Therefore, U/W is a vector space.

Now, if $x + W \in U/W$, then $x \in U$. Since U is a subset of V, $x \in V$. Therefore, we have $x + W \in V/W$. Since $x + W \in U/W$ was arbitrary, $U/W \subseteq V/W$. It follows that U/W is a subspace of V/W. $\qquad\square$

9. Let V be a vector space over a field F and let W be a subspace of V. Prove that every subspace of V/W is of the form U/W for some subspace U of V with $W \subseteq U \subseteq V$.

Proof: Assume that W is a subspace of V and let K be a subspace of V/W. We define U as follows: $U = \{x \in V \mid x + W \in K\}$.

Let's show that U is a subspace of V. Since K is a subspace of V/W, $0 + W = W \in K$. Therefore, $0 \in U$. Let $x, y \in U$ and let $k \in F$ Then $x + W, y + W \in K$. Since K is a subspace of V/W, we have $(x + y) + W = (x + W) + (y + W) \in K$. So, $x + y \in U$. Again, since K is a subspace of V/W, we have $kx + W = k(x + W) \in K$. So, $kx \in U$. Therefore, U is a subspace of V.

Next, let's show that $W \subseteq U$. To see this, let $x \in W$. Then $x + W = W$. Since K is a subspace of V/W and W is the identity of V/W, $x + W = W \in K$. Therefore, $x \in U$.

We now show that $U/W = K$. Let $x + W \in U/W$. Then $x \in U$. By the definition of U, $x + W \in K$. Therefore, $U/W \subseteq K$. Conversely, let $x + W \in K$. By the definition of U, $x \in U$. So, $x + W \in U/W$. Thus, $K \subseteq U/W$. Since $U/W \subseteq K$ and $K \subseteq U/W$, we have $U/W = K$. $\qquad\square$

10. Prove the vector space and ring versions of the Fourth Isomorphism Theorem.

Fourth Isomorphism Theorem—Vector Space Version: Let V be a vector space over a field F, let W be a subspace of V, let $\mathcal{X}$ be the set of all subspaces of V that contain W, let $\mathcal{Y}$ be the set of subspaces of V/W, and define $f: \mathcal{X} \to \mathcal{Y}$ by $f(U) = U/W$. Then f is a bijection.

Proof: Let's first check that f is a function from $\mathcal{X}$ to $\mathcal{Y}$. Let $U \in \mathcal{X}$. Then U is a subspace of V containing W. By Theorem 11.17, U/W is a subspace of V/W. So, $f(U) = U/W \in \mathcal{Y}$, as desired.

Next, let's check that f is injective. Suppose that $f(U) = f(Z)$. Then $U/W = Z/W$. Let $x \in U$. Then $x + W \in U/W$. Since $U/W = Z/W$, $x + W \in Z/W$. Therefore, $x \in Z$. So, $U \subseteq Z$. A symmetrical argument shows that $Z \subseteq U$. Thus, $U = Z$.

To see that f is surjective, let $K \in \mathcal{Y}$. Then K is a subspace of V/W. By Theorem 11.17, $K = U/W$ for some subspace U of V with $W \subseteq U \subseteq V$. So, $U \in \mathcal{X}$ and $f(U) = U/W = K$. $\qquad\square$

Fourth Isomorphism Theorem—Ring Version: Let R be a ring, let I be an ideal of R, let $\mathcal{X}$ be the set of all subrings of R that contain I, let $\mathcal{Y}$ be the set of subrings of R/I, and define $f: \mathcal{X} \to \mathcal{Y}$ by $f(S) = S/I$. Then f is a bijection.

Proof: Let's first check that f is a function from $\mathcal{X}$ to $\mathcal{Y}$. Let $S \in \mathcal{X}$. Then S is a subring of R containing I. By Theorem 11.15, S/I is a subring of R/I. So, $f(S) = S/I \in \mathcal{Y}$, as desired.

Next, let's check that f is injective. Suppose that $f(S) = f(T)$. Then $S/I = T/I$. Let $x \in S$. Then $x + I \in S/I$. Since $S/I = T/I$, $x + I \in T/I$. Therefore, $x \in T$. So, $S \subseteq T$. A symmetrical argument shows that $T \subseteq S$. Thus, $S = T$.

To see that f is surjective, let $K \in \mathcal{Y}$. Then K is a subring of R/I. By Theorem 11.16, $K = S/I$ for some subring S of R with $I \subseteq S \subseteq R$. So, $S \in \mathcal{X}$ and $f(S) = S/I = K$. $\qquad\square$

LEVEL 4

11. Let G be a group and for each $x \in G$, define the function $\phi_x: G \to G$ by $\phi_x(y) = xyx^{-1}$. Let $\text{Inn}(G) = \{\phi_x \mid x \in G\}$. Prove that $G/Z(G) \cong \text{Inn}(G)$, where $Z(G)$ is the center of G.

Proof: Define a function $f: G \to \text{Inn}(G)$ by $f(x) = \phi_x$. It is clear that f is surjective. To see that f is a homomorphism, observe that

$$f(xy) = \phi_{xy} = \phi_x \phi_y = f(x)f(y).$$

Now, $x \in \ker(f)$ if and only if $f(x) = \phi_e$ if and only if for all $y \in G$, $\phi_x(y) = \phi_e(y)$ if and only if for all $y \in G$, $xyx^{-1} = eye^{-1} = y$ if and only if for all $y \in G$, $xy = yx$ if and only if $x \in Z(G)$.

By the First Homomorphism Theorem, $G/Z(G) \cong \text{Inn}(G)$. $\qquad\square$

12. Let G and H be groups, let $N \lhd G$, and let $K \lhd H$. Prove that $(G \times H)/(N \times K) \cong G/N \times H/K$.

Proof: Define a function $f: G \times H \to G/N \times H/K$ by $f(x, y) = (xN, yK)$. It is clear that f is surjective. To see that f is a homomorphism, observe that

$$f\big((x, y)(z, w)\big) = f(xz, yw) = (xzN, ywK) = \big((xN)(zN), (yK)(wK)\big)$$
$$= (xN, yK)(zN, wK) = f(x, y)f(z, w).$$

Now, $(x, y) \in \ker(f)$ if and only if $(xN, yK) = (N, K)$ if and only if $xN = N$ and $yK = K$ if and only if $x \in N$ and $y \in K$ if and only if $(x, y) \in N \times K$. So, $\ker(f) = N \times K$.

By the First Homomorphism Theorem, $(G \times H)/(N \times K) \cong G/N \times H/K$. $\qquad\square$

13. Let $m, n \in \mathbb{Z}^+$. Prove that $m\mathbb{Z} \cap n\mathbb{Z} = \text{lcm}(m, n)\mathbb{Z}$ and $m\mathbb{Z} + n\mathbb{Z} = \gcd(m, n)\mathbb{Z}$.

Proof: Let $k \in m\mathbb{Z} \cap n\mathbb{Z}$. Then $k \in m\mathbb{Z}$ and $k \in n\mathbb{Z}$. So, there are integers a and b such that $k = ma$ and $k = nb$. So, $m \mid k$ and $n \mid k$. By Problem 19 in Problem Set 8, $\text{lcm}(m, n) \mid k$. Thus, there is an integer c such that $k = \text{lcm}(m, n) \cdot c$. So, $k \in \text{lcm}(m, n)\mathbb{Z}$. Since $k \in m\mathbb{Z} \cap n\mathbb{Z}$ was arbitrary, we have $m\mathbb{Z} \cap n\mathbb{Z} \subseteq \text{lcm}(m, n)\mathbb{Z}$.

Next, let $k \in \text{lcm}(m, n)\mathbb{Z}$. Then there is an integer c such that $k = \text{lcm}(m, n) \cdot c$. Since $\text{lcm}(m, n)$ is a multiple of m, there is an integer a such that $\text{lcm}(m, n) = ma$. So, $k = (ma)c = m(ac)$. Since $a, c \in \mathbb{Z}$ and $\mathbb{Z}$ is closed under multiplication, $ac \in \mathbb{Z}$. So, $k \in m\mathbb{Z}$. A similar argument shows that $k \in n\mathbb{Z}$. Therefore, $k \in m\mathbb{Z} \cap n\mathbb{Z}$. Since $k \in \text{lcm}(m, n)\mathbb{Z}$ was arbitrary, $\text{lcm}(m, n)\mathbb{Z} \subseteq m\mathbb{Z} \cap n\mathbb{Z}$.

Since $m\mathbb{Z} \cap n\mathbb{Z} \subseteq \text{lcm}(m, n)\mathbb{Z}$ and $\text{lcm}(m, n)\mathbb{Z} \subseteq m\mathbb{Z} \cap n\mathbb{Z}$, we have $m\mathbb{Z} \cap n\mathbb{Z} = \text{lcm}(m, n)\mathbb{Z}$.

Let $k \in m\mathbb{Z} + n\mathbb{Z}$. Then there are integers a and b such that $k = ma + nb$. Since m and n are multiples of $\gcd(m, n)$, there are integers c and d such that $m = \gcd(m, n) \cdot c$ and $n = \gcd(m, n) \cdot d$. So, we have $k = \gcd(m, n) \cdot ac + \gcd(m, n) \cdot bd = \gcd(m, n)(ac + bd)$. Since $a, b, c, d \in \mathbb{Z}$ and $\mathbb{Z}$ is closed under addition and multiplication, $ac + bd \in \mathbb{Z}$. So, $k \in \gcd(m, n)\mathbb{Z}$. Since $k \in m\mathbb{Z} + n\mathbb{Z}$ was arbitrary, $m\mathbb{Z} + n\mathbb{Z} \subseteq \gcd(m, n)\mathbb{Z}$.

Next, let $k \in \gcd(m, n)\mathbb{Z}$. Then there is an integer c such that $k = \gcd(m, n) \cdot c$. By Theorem 8.18, there are integers a and b such that $\gcd(m, n) = am + bn$. So, $k = (am + bn)c = m(ac) + n(bc)$. Since $a, b, c \in \mathbb{Z}$ and $\mathbb{Z}$ is closed under multiplication, $ac, bd \in \mathbb{Z}$. So, $k \in m\mathbb{Z} + n\mathbb{Z}$. Since $k \in \gcd(m, n)\mathbb{Z}$ was arbitrary, $\gcd(m, n)\mathbb{Z} \subseteq m\mathbb{Z} + n\mathbb{Z}$.

Since $m\mathbb{Z} + n\mathbb{Z} \subseteq \gcd(m,n)\,\mathbb{Z}$ and $\gcd(m,n)\,\mathbb{Z} \subseteq m\mathbb{Z} + n\mathbb{Z}$, we have $m\mathbb{Z} + n\mathbb{Z} = \gcd(m,n)\,\mathbb{Z}$. $\quad\square$

14. Let $a, b \in \mathbb{Z}^+$ with $\gcd(a,b) = 1$. Prove that the groups $(\mathbb{Z} \times \mathbb{Z})/\langle(a,b)\rangle$ and $\mathbb{Z}$ are isomorphic.

Proof: Define a function $f: \mathbb{Z} \times \mathbb{Z} \to \mathbb{Z}$ by $f(j,k) = jb - ka$. To see that f is a homomorphism, observe that

$$f\big((j,k) + (m,n)\big) = f(j + m, k + n) = (j + m)b - (k + n)a$$
$$= (jb - ka) + (mb - na) = f(j,k) + f(m,n).$$

To see that f is surjective, let $x \in \mathbb{Z}$. Since $\gcd(a,b) = 1$, by Theorem 8.18, there are integers m and n such that $1 = ma + nb$. So, $x = x(ma + nb) = (xn)b - (-xm)a$. It follows that $f(xn, -xm) = x$.

Now, $(j,k) \in \ker(f)$ if and only if $f(j,k) = 0$ if and only if $jb - ka = 0$ if and only if $jb = ka$ if and only if there is an integer n such that $j = na$ and $k = nb$ if and only if there is an integer n such that $(j,k) = (na, nb)$ if and only if $(j,k) \in \langle(a,b)\rangle$. So, $\ker(f) = \langle(a,b)\rangle$.

By the First Homomorphism Theorem, $(\mathbb{Z} \times \mathbb{Z})/\langle(a,b)\rangle \cong \mathbb{Z}$. $\quad\square$

15. Let $f: \mathcal{X} \to \mathcal{Y}$ be the bijection defined in the Fourth Isomorphism Theorem and let $A, B \in \mathcal{X}$. Prove each of the following:

    (i) $A \leq B$ if and only if $f(A) \leq f(B)$.

    (ii) If $A \subseteq B$, then $[B:A] = [f(B):f(A)]$.

Proofs: I prove the group versions below. $\mathcal{X}$ is the set of all subgroups of G that contain N, $\mathcal{Y}$ is the set of subgroups of G/N, and $f: \mathcal{X} \to \mathcal{Y}$ is the bijection defined by $f(H) = H/N$.

  (i) Suppose that $A \leq B$. Then $f(A) = A/N$ and $f(B) = B/N$. Let $x + N \in A/N$. Then $x \in A$. Since $A \leq B$, $x \in B$. So, $x + N \in B/N$. Since $x + N \in A/N$ was arbitrary, $A/N \leq B/N$. In other words, $f(A) \leq f(B)$.

    Now, suppose that $f(A) \leq f(B)$, so that $A/N \leq B/N$. Let $x \in A$. Then $x + N \in A/N$. Since $A/N \leq B/N$, $x + N \in B/N$. So, $x \in B$. Since $x \in A$ was arbitrary, $A \leq B$. $\quad\square$

  (ii) $[f(B):f(A)] = [B/N:A/N] = \dfrac{|B/N|}{|A/N|} = |B/A| = [B:A].$ $\quad\square$

16. Let $f: \mathcal{X} \to \mathcal{Y}$ be the bijection defined in the group version of the Fourth Isomorphism Theorem. Let $H \in \mathcal{X}$. Prove that $H \lhd G$ if and only if $f(H) \lhd G/N$. State and prove the analogous result for the ring version of the Fourth Isomorphism Theorem.

Proof: Recall that $\mathcal{X}$ is the set of all subgroups of G that contain N, $\mathcal{Y}$ is the set of subgroups of G/N, and $f: \mathcal{X} \to \mathcal{Y}$ is the bijection defined by $f(H) = H/N$.

Suppose that $H \lhd G$. By Theorem 11.13, $f(H) = H/N \lhd G/N$. Conversely, suppose that $f(H) \lhd G/N$. So, $H/N \lhd G/N$. By Theorem 11.14, $H \lhd G$. $\quad\square$

Ring version: Let $f: \mathcal{X} \to \mathcal{Y}$ be the bijection defined in the ring version of the Fourth Isomorphism Theorem. Let $S \in \mathcal{X}$. Prove that $S \lhd R$ if and only if $f(S) \lhd R/I$.

Proof of ring version: Recall that $\mathcal{X}$ is the set of all subrings of R that contain I, $\mathcal{Y}$ is the set of subrings of R/I, and $f: \mathcal{X} \to \mathcal{Y}$ is the bijection defined by $f(S) = S/I$.

Suppose that $S \lhd R$. By Theorem 11.15, $f(S) = S/I \lhd R/I$. Conversely, suppose that $f(S) \lhd R/I$. So, $S/I \lhd R/I$. By Theorem 11.16, $S \lhd R$. $\qquad\qquad\square$

LEVEL 5

17. $G = \{1, 4, 11, 14, 16, 19, 26, 29, 31, 34, 41, 44\}$ is a group under multiplication modulo 45. Express G as both an external and internal direct product of cyclic groups.

Solution: Since $|G| = 12 = 2^2 \cdot 3$, G is isomorphic to $\mathbb{Z}_2 \times \mathbb{Z}_2 \times \mathbb{Z}_3 \cong \mathbb{Z}_6 \times \mathbb{Z}_2$ or $\mathbb{Z}_4 \times \mathbb{Z}_3 \cong \mathbb{Z}_{12}$.

We have the following:

$$\langle 1 \rangle = \{1\}$$
$$\langle 4 \rangle = \{1, 4, 16, 19, 31, 34\}$$
$$\langle 11 \rangle = \{1, 11, 31, 26, 16, 41\}$$
$$\langle 14 \rangle = \{1, 14, 16, 44, 31, 29 \}$$
$$\langle 16 \rangle = \{1, 16, 31\}$$
$$\langle 19 \rangle = \{1, 19\}$$
$$\langle 26 \rangle = \{1, 26\}$$
$$\langle 29 \rangle = \{1, 29, 31, 44, 16, 14\}$$
$$\langle 31 \rangle = \{1, 31, 16\}$$
$$\langle 34 \rangle = \{1, 34, 31, 19, 16, 4\}$$
$$\langle 41 \rangle = \{1, 41, 16, 26, 31, 11\}$$
$$\langle 44 \rangle = \{1, 44\}$$

So, the order diagram of G is $\{(1, 1), (2, 3), (3, 2), (6, 6)\}$. Since this matches the order diagram of $\mathbb{Z}_6 \times \mathbb{Z}_2$, we see that as an external direct product of cyclic groups, we have $G \cong \mathbb{Z}_6 \times \mathbb{Z}_2$, or equivalently, $G \cong \mathbb{Z}_2 \times \mathbb{Z}_2 \times \mathbb{Z}_3$.

As an internal direct product of cyclic groups, we have $G \cong \langle 4 \rangle \times \langle 26 \rangle$. This works because 4 is an element of maximal order (the order of 4 is 6), and 26 is an element of order $\frac{|G|}{|\langle 4 \rangle|} = \frac{12}{6} = 2$ and $26 \notin \langle 4 \rangle$.

18. Prove that isomorphic finite groups have the same order diagram, where the order diagram of G is $d(G) = \{(n, x_n) \mid n \in \mathbb{Z}^+ \wedge x_n = |\{x \in G \mid |x| = n\}| > 0\}$.

Proof: Let G and H be isomorphic finite groups and let $f: G \to H$ be an isomorphism. Let $x \in G$. We show that $|x| = |f(x)|$. To see this, suppose that $x^n = e_G$. By part (ii) of Problem 13 from Problem Set 7, $(f(x))^n = f(x^n) = f(e_G) = e_H$. So, $|f(x)| \le |x|$. Similarly, if $(f(x))^n = e_H$, then we have $x^n = f^{-1}(f(x^n)) = f^{-1}((f(x))^n) = f^{-1}(e_H) = e_G$. So, $|x| \le |f(x)|$.

Since $|f(x)| \leq |x|$ and $|x| \leq |f(x)|$, we have $|x| = |f(x)|$.

Now, suppose that $(n, x_n) \in d(G)$. Then there are n distinct elements in G of order n. For each element $x \in G$ of order n, the element $f(x) \in H$ also has order n. Since f is a bijection, there is a one-to-one correspondence between the elements of order n in G and the elements of order n in H. So, $(n, x_n) \in d(H)$. Since $(n, x_n) \in d(G)$ was arbitrary, $d(G) \subseteq d(H)$. A symmetrical argument shows that $d(H) \subseteq d(G)$. Therefore $d(G) = d(H)$, as desired. $\qquad\square$

19. List all the commutative groups of order 183,495,637, up to isomorphism.

Solution: Since $183{,}495{,}637 = 13^3 17^4$, the commutative groups of order 183,495,637, up to isomorphism, are

$$\mathbb{Z}_{13} \times \mathbb{Z}_{13} \times \mathbb{Z}_{13} \times \mathbb{Z}_{17} \times \mathbb{Z}_{17} \times \mathbb{Z}_{17} \times \mathbb{Z}_{17}$$

$$\mathbb{Z}_{169} \times \mathbb{Z}_{13} \times \mathbb{Z}_{17} \times \mathbb{Z}_{17} \times \mathbb{Z}_{17} \times \mathbb{Z}_{17}$$

$$\mathbb{Z}_{2197} \times \mathbb{Z}_{17} \times \mathbb{Z}_{17} \times \mathbb{Z}_{17} \times \mathbb{Z}_{17}$$

$$\mathbb{Z}_{13} \times \mathbb{Z}_{13} \times \mathbb{Z}_{13} \times \mathbb{Z}_{289} \times \mathbb{Z}_{17} \times \mathbb{Z}_{17}$$

$$\mathbb{Z}_{169} \times \mathbb{Z}_{13} \times \mathbb{Z}_{17} \times \mathbb{Z}_{289} \times \mathbb{Z}_{17} \times \mathbb{Z}_{17}$$

$$\mathbb{Z}_{2197} \times \mathbb{Z}_{17} \times \mathbb{Z}_{289} \times \mathbb{Z}_{17} \times \mathbb{Z}_{17}$$

$$\mathbb{Z}_{13} \times \mathbb{Z}_{13} \times \mathbb{Z}_{13} \times \mathbb{Z}_{289} \times \mathbb{Z}_{289}$$

$$\mathbb{Z}_{169} \times \mathbb{Z}_{13} \times \mathbb{Z}_{289} \times \mathbb{Z}_{289}$$

$$\mathbb{Z}_{2197} \times \mathbb{Z}_{289} \times \mathbb{Z}_{289}$$

$$\mathbb{Z}_{13} \times \mathbb{Z}_{13} \times \mathbb{Z}_{13} \times \mathbb{Z}_{4913} \times \mathbb{Z}_{17}$$

$$\mathbb{Z}_{169} \times \mathbb{Z}_{13} \times \mathbb{Z}_{4913} \times \mathbb{Z}_{17}$$

$$\mathbb{Z}_{2197} \times \mathbb{Z}_{4913} \times \mathbb{Z}_{17}$$

$$\mathbb{Z}_{13} \times \mathbb{Z}_{13} \times \mathbb{Z}_{13} \times \mathbb{Z}_{83{,}521}$$

$$\mathbb{Z}_{169} \times \mathbb{Z}_{13} \times \mathbb{Z}_{83{,}521}$$

$$\mathbb{Z}_{2197} \times \mathbb{Z}_{83{,}521}$$

20. Let G be a finite commutative group and let $k \in \mathbb{Z}^+$ such that k divides $|G|$. Prove that G has a subgroup of order k.

Proof: We prove this by induction on $m = |G|$.

Base case ($m = 0$): If $|G| = 1$, then $G = \{e\}$. The only positive divisor of 1 is $k = 1$ and $G = \{e\}$ is a subgroup of G of order 1.

Inductive step: Assume that for any group H of order $j < m$ and $k \in \mathbb{Z}^+$ dividing j, there is a subgroup of H of order k. Let G be a group of order m, suppose that $k > 1$ divides m, and let p be a prime factor of k. By the Fundamental Theorem of Commutative Groups, G has a cyclic subgroup K of order p^t for some $t \in \mathbb{Z}^+$. By Theorem 9.6, K has a subgroup L of order p, and L is also a subgroup of G. Now, G/L is a commutative group of order $\frac{m}{p}$. Since $\frac{k}{p}$ divides $\frac{m}{p}$, by the inductive hypothesis, there is a subgroup M/L of H/L, where M is a subgroup of G and $|M/L| = \frac{k}{p}$. We have $|M| = \left(\frac{|M|}{|L|}\right) \cdot |L| = \frac{k}{p} \cdot p = k$.

By the Principle of Mathematical Induction, for all $k \in \mathbb{Z}^+$ with k dividing the order of G, there is a subgroup of G of order k. $\qquad\square$

LEVEL 1

1. Compute the order of each permutation.

    (i)   (12345)

    (ii) (12)(345)(6789)

Solutions:

(i) $(12345)^2 = (13524)$

   $(12345)^3 = (13524)(12345) = (14253)$

   $(12345)^4 = (14253)(12345) = (15432)$

   $(12345)^5 = (15432)(12345) = (1)$

   So, $|(12345)| = \mathbf{5}$.

   Alternatively, the order of a cycle is simply the length of the cycle. So, $|(12345)| = \mathbf{5}$.

(ii) $|(12)(345)(6789)| = \text{lcm}(2, 3, 4) = \mathbf{12}$.

2. Express each permutation as a product of transpositions.

    (i)   (123456)

    (ii) (123)(4567)

    (iii) (123)(345)(25)(1576)

Solutions:

(i) $(123456) = \mathbf{(16)(15)(14)(13)(12)}$

(ii) $(123)(4567) = \mathbf{(13)(12)(47)(46)(45)}$

(iii) $(123)(345)(25)(1576) = \mathbf{(13)(12)(35)(34)(25)(16)(17)(15)}$

3. Determine if each permutation is even or odd.

    (i)   (1837942)

    (ii) (123)(34)(4567)

Solutions:

(i) Since the length of (1837942) is 7, which is odd, (183794) is **even**.

(ii) (123) is even, (34) is odd, and (4567) is odd. Therefore, (123) can be expressed as a product of an even number of transpositions and (34) and (4567) can each be expressed as a product of an odd number of transpositions. Since the sum of an even integer and two odd integers is even, $(123)(34)(4567)$ can be expressed as a product of an even number of transpositions. Therefore, $(123)(34)(4567)$ is **even**.

LEVEL 2

4. Prove each of the following:

    (i)   The product of two even permutations is even.

    (ii)   The product of two odd permutations is even.

    (iii) The product of an even permutation and an odd permutation is odd.

Proofs:

(i) Let π and σ be even permutations. Then $\pi = \pi_1 \pi_2 \cdots \pi_{2j}$ and $\sigma = \sigma_1 \sigma_2 \cdots \sigma_{2k}$, where $j, k \in \mathbb{Z}^+$, π_i is a transposition for each $i = 1, 2, \ldots, 2j$ and σ_i is a transposition for each $i = 1, 2, \ldots, 2k$. Then $\pi\sigma = \pi_1 \pi_2 \cdots \pi_{2j} \sigma_1 \sigma_2 \cdots \sigma_{2k}$, which is a product of $2j + 2k = 2(j + k)$ transpositions. So, $\pi\sigma$ is even. $\square$

(ii) Let π and σ be odd permutations. Then $\pi = \pi_1 \pi_2 \cdots \pi_{2j+1}$ and $\sigma = \sigma_1 \sigma_2 \cdots \sigma_{2k+1}$, where $j, k \in \mathbb{Z}^+$, π_i is a transposition for each $i = 1, 2, \ldots, 2j + 1$ and σ_i is a transposition for each $i = 1, 2, \ldots, 2k + 1$. Then $\pi\sigma = \pi_1 \pi_2 \cdots \pi_{2j+1} \sigma_1 \sigma_2 \cdots \sigma_{2k+1}$, which is a product of $(2j + 1) + (2k + 1) = 2j + 2k + 2 = 2(j + k + 1)$ transpositions. So, $\pi\sigma$ is even. $\square$

(iii) Let π be an even permutation and let σ be an odd permutation. Then $\pi = \pi_1 \pi_2 \cdots \pi_{2j}$ and $\sigma = \sigma_1 \sigma_2 \cdots \sigma_{2k+1}$, where $j, k \in \mathbb{Z}^+$, π_i is a transposition for each $i = 1, 2, \ldots, 2j$ and σ_i is a transposition for each $i = 1, 2, \ldots, 2k + 1$. Then $\pi\sigma = \pi_1 \pi_2 \cdots \pi_{2j} \sigma_1 \sigma_2 \cdots \sigma_{2k+1}$, which is a product of $2j + (2k + 1) = 2(j + k) + 1$ transpositions. So, $\pi\sigma$ is odd.

Similarly, $\sigma\pi$ is odd. $\square$

5. Prove that for $n > 1$, the function $\Delta_n \colon S_n \to \{-1, 1\}$ is a surjective homomorphism, where Δ_n is defined by $\Delta_n(\pi) = \begin{cases} -1 & \text{if } \pi \text{ is odd.} \\ 1 & \text{if } \pi \text{ is even.} \end{cases}$

Proof: If π and σ are both even, then by part (i) of Problem 4 above, $\pi\sigma$ is even. So,

$$\Delta_n(\pi\sigma) = 1 = 1 \cdot 1 = \Delta_n(\pi) \cdot \Delta_n(\sigma).$$

If π and σ are both odd, then by part (ii) of Problem 4 above, $\pi\sigma$ is even. So,

$$\Delta_n(\pi\sigma) = 1 = (-1) \cdot (-1) = \Delta_n(\pi) \cdot \Delta_n(\sigma).$$

If π is even and σ is odd, then by part (iii) of Problem 4 above, $\pi\sigma$ is odd. So,

$$\Delta_n(\pi\sigma) = -1 = 1 \cdot (-1) = \Delta_n(\pi) \cdot \Delta_n(\sigma).$$

If π is odd and σ is even, then by part (iii) of Problem 4 above, $\pi\sigma$ is odd. So,

$$\Delta_n(\pi\sigma) = -1 = (-1) \cdot 1 = \Delta_n(\pi) \cdot \Delta_n(\sigma).$$

To see that Δ_n is surjective, simply observe that (1) is even and (12) is odd, so that $\Delta_n\big((1)\big) = 1$ and $\Delta_n\big((12)\big) = -1$. $\square$

6. Prove that $GL_2(\mathbb{Z}_2)$ is isomorphic to S_3.

138

Proof: $GL_2(\mathbb{Z}_2)$ consists of all 2×2 matrices with each entry equal to 0 or 1 and nonzero determinant. It is easy enough to write down this set explicitly:

$$GL_2(\mathbb{Z}_2) = \left\{ \begin{bmatrix} 1 & 0 \\ 0 & 1 \end{bmatrix}, \begin{bmatrix} 1 & 0 \\ 1 & 1 \end{bmatrix}, \begin{bmatrix} 0 & 1 \\ 1 & 0 \end{bmatrix}, \begin{bmatrix} 0 & 1 \\ 1 & 1 \end{bmatrix}, \begin{bmatrix} 1 & 1 \\ 1 & 0 \end{bmatrix}, \begin{bmatrix} 1 & 1 \\ 0 & 1 \end{bmatrix} \right\}.$$

By Problem 17 in Problem Set 10 (and its proof), the only noncommutative group of order 6, up to isomorphism, is S_3. So, it suffices to prove that $GL_2(\mathbb{Z}_2)$ is not commutative.

$$\begin{bmatrix} 0 & 1 \\ 1 & 0 \end{bmatrix}\begin{bmatrix} 1 & 1 \\ 1 & 0 \end{bmatrix} = \begin{bmatrix} 1 & 0 \\ 1 & 1 \end{bmatrix} \qquad\qquad \begin{bmatrix} 1 & 1 \\ 1 & 0 \end{bmatrix}\begin{bmatrix} 0 & 1 \\ 1 & 0 \end{bmatrix} = \begin{bmatrix} 1 & 1 \\ 0 & 1 \end{bmatrix}$$

Since $\begin{bmatrix} 0 & 1 \\ 1 & 0 \end{bmatrix}$ and $\begin{bmatrix} 1 & 1 \\ 1 & 0 \end{bmatrix}$ do not commute, $GL_2(\mathbb{Z}_2)$ is a noncommutative group of order 6, and therefore, must be isomorphic to S_3. □

7. Let $U_2 = \{A \in GL_2(F) \mid A \text{ is upper triangular}\}$, $L_2 = \{A \in GL_2(F) \mid A \text{ is lower triangular}\}$, and $D_2 = \{A \in GL_2(F) \mid A \text{ is diagonal}\}$. Prove that U_2, L_2, and D_2 are matrix groups.

Proof: Let $U_2 = \{A \in GL_2(F) \mid A \text{ is upper triangular}\}$. To see that U_2 is a matrix group, first observe that $U_2 \subseteq GL_2(F)$ and $I = \begin{bmatrix} 1 & 0 \\ 0 & 1 \end{bmatrix}$ is upper triangular. Let $A, B \in U_2$, say $A = \begin{bmatrix} a_{11} & a_{12} \\ 0 & a_{22} \end{bmatrix}$ and $B = \begin{bmatrix} b_{11} & b_{12} \\ 0 & b_{22} \end{bmatrix}$. By Theorem 12.23, B is invertible and by the proof of Theorem 12.23, $B^{-1} = \frac{1}{\det B}\begin{bmatrix} b_{22} & -b_{12} \\ 0 & b_{11} \end{bmatrix}$. Therefore,

$$AB^{-1} = \begin{bmatrix} a_{11} & a_{12} \\ 0 & a_{22} \end{bmatrix} \cdot \frac{1}{\det B}\begin{bmatrix} b_{22} & -b_{12} \\ 0 & b_{11} \end{bmatrix} = \frac{1}{\det B}\begin{bmatrix} a_{11}b_{22} & -a_{11}b_{12} + a_{12}b_{11} \\ 0 & a_{22}b_{11} \end{bmatrix},$$

which is upper triangular. By Problem 5 in Problem Set 6, we have $U_2 \le GL_2(F)$.

Next, let $L_2 = \{A \in GL_2(F) \mid A \text{ is lower triangular}\}$. To see that L_2 is a matrix group, first observe that $L_2 \subseteq GL_2(F)$ and $I = \begin{bmatrix} 1 & 0 \\ 0 & 1 \end{bmatrix}$ is lower triangular. Let $A, B \in L_2$, say $A = \begin{bmatrix} a_{11} & 0 \\ a_{21} & a_{22} \end{bmatrix}$ and $B = \begin{bmatrix} b_{11} & 0 \\ b_{21} & b_{22} \end{bmatrix}$. By Theorem 12.23, B is invertible and by the proof of Theorem 12.23, $B^{-1} = \frac{1}{\det B}\begin{bmatrix} b_{22} & 0 \\ -b_{21} & b_{11} \end{bmatrix}$. Therefore,

$$AB^{-1} = \begin{bmatrix} a_{11} & 0 \\ a_{21} & a_{22} \end{bmatrix} \cdot \frac{1}{\det B}\begin{bmatrix} b_{22} & 0 \\ -b_{21} & b_{11} \end{bmatrix} = \frac{1}{\det B}\begin{bmatrix} a_{11}b_{22} & 0 \\ a_{21}b_{22} - a_{22}b_{21} & a_{22}b_{11} \end{bmatrix},$$

which is lower triangular. By Problem 5 in Problem Set 6, we have $L_2 \le GL_2(F)$.

Finally, let $D_2 = \{A \in GL_2(F) \mid A \text{ is diagonal}\}$. To see that D_2 is a matrix group, first observe that $D_2 \subseteq GL_2(F)$ and $I = \begin{bmatrix} 1 & 0 \\ 0 & 1 \end{bmatrix}$ is diagonal. Let $A, B \in D_2$, say $A = \begin{bmatrix} a_{11} & 0 \\ 0 & a_{22} \end{bmatrix}$ and $B = \begin{bmatrix} b_{11} & 0 \\ 0 & b_{22} \end{bmatrix}$. Then B is invertible and $B^{-1} = \begin{bmatrix} \frac{1}{b_{11}} & 0 \\ 0 & \frac{1}{b_{22}} \end{bmatrix}$. Therefore, $AB^{-1} = \begin{bmatrix} a_{11} & 0 \\ 0 & a_{22} \end{bmatrix}\begin{bmatrix} \frac{1}{b_{11}} & 0 \\ 0 & \frac{1}{b_{22}} \end{bmatrix} = \begin{bmatrix} \frac{a_{11}}{b_{11}} & 0 \\ 0 & \frac{a_{22}}{b_{22}} \end{bmatrix},$

139

which is diagonal. By Problem 5 in Problem Set 6, we have $D_2 \leq GL_2(F)$. $\qquad \square$

LEVEL 3

8. Let π and σ be disjoint permutations. Prove that for each $n \in \mathbb{Z}^+$, $(\pi\sigma)^n = \pi^n\sigma^n$.

Proof: We first prove that for each $n \in \mathbb{Z}^+$, $\pi\sigma^n = \sigma^n\pi$. We prove this by induction on $n \in \mathbb{Z}^+$.

Base case ($k = 1$): By Theorem 12.6, $\pi\sigma^1 = \pi\sigma = \sigma\pi = \sigma^1\pi$.

Inductive step: Assume that $k \in \mathbb{Z}^+$ and $\pi\sigma^k = \sigma^k\pi$. Then we have

$$\pi\sigma^{k+1} = \pi(\sigma^k\sigma) = (\pi\sigma^k)\sigma = (\sigma^k\pi)\sigma = \sigma^k(\pi\sigma) = \sigma^k(\sigma\pi) = (\sigma^k\sigma)\pi = \sigma^{k+1}\pi.$$

By the Principle of Mathematical Induction, for all $n \in \mathbb{Z}^+$, $\pi\sigma^n = \sigma^n\pi$.

Now, we prove that for each $n \in \mathbb{Z}^+$, $(\pi\sigma)^n = \pi^n\sigma^n$. We prove this by induction on $n \in \mathbb{Z}^+$.

Base case ($k = 1$): $(\pi\sigma)^1 = \pi\sigma = \pi^1\sigma^1$.

Inductive step: Assume that $k \in \mathbb{Z}^+$ and $(\pi\sigma)^k = \pi^k\sigma^k$. Then we have

$$(\pi\sigma)^{k+1} = (\pi\sigma)^k(\pi\sigma) = (\pi^k\sigma^k)(\pi\sigma) = \pi^k(\sigma^k\pi)\sigma = \pi^k(\pi\sigma^k)\sigma = (\pi^k\pi)(\sigma^k\sigma) = \pi^{k+1}\sigma^{k+1}.$$

By the Principle of Mathematical Induction, for all $n \in \mathbb{Z}^+$, $(\pi\sigma)^n = \pi^n\sigma^n$. $\qquad \square$

9. Let $n \geq 3$ and let $s, t \in \{1, 2, \dots, n\}$ with $s \neq t$. Prove that $A_n = \langle (stu) | 1 \leq u \leq n \wedge u \neq s, t \rangle$.

Proof: $A_3 = \{(1), (123), (132)\}$, and so, the result is clear for $n = 3$. Let $n \geq 3$. If $a, b, c, d \in \{1, \dots, n\}$ are distinct, then $(ab)(cd) = (acb)(acd)$. If $a, b, c \in \{1, \dots, n\}$ are distinct, then $(ab)(ac) = (acb)$. Since every element of A_n can be written as a product of elements of the form $(ab)(cd)$ and $(ab)(ac)$, we see that A_n is generated by all 3-cycles. Now, any 3-cycle has one of the forms (stu), (sut), (suv), (tuv), or (uvw), where u, v, w are distinct and $u, v, w \neq s, t$. We have $(sut) = (stu)^2$, $(suv) = (stv)(stu)^2$, $(tuv) = (stv)^2(stu)$, and $(uvw) = (stu)^2(stw)(stv)^2(stu)$. Therefore, $A_n = \langle (stu) | 1 \leq u \leq n \wedge u \neq s, t \rangle$. $\qquad \square$

10. Write down a formula for the determinant of a 4×4 matrix in terms of the entries of the matrix.

Permutation	Even or Odd	Term
(1)	Even	$a_{11}a_{22}a_{33}a_{44}$
(123)	Even	$a_{12}a_{23}a_{31}a_{44}$
(132)	Even	$a_{13}a_{21}a_{32}a_{44}$
(124)	Even	$a_{12}a_{24}a_{33}a_{41}$
(142)	Even	$a_{14}a_{21}a_{33}a_{42}$
(134)	Even	$a_{13}a_{22}a_{34}a_{41}$
(143)	Even	$a_{14}a_{22}a_{31}a_{43}$
(234)	Even	$a_{11}a_{23}a_{34}a_{42}$
(243)	Even	$a_{11}a_{24}a_{32}a_{43}$
(12)(34)	Even	$a_{12}a_{21}a_{34}a_{43}$
(13)(24)	Even	$a_{13}a_{24}a_{31}a_{42}$
(23)(14)	Even	$a_{14}a_{23}a_{32}a_{41}$
(12)	Odd	$-a_{12}a_{21}a_{33}a_{44}$
(13)	Odd	$-a_{13}a_{22}a_{31}a_{44}$
(14)	Odd	$-a_{14}a_{22}a_{33}a_{41}$
(23)	Odd	$-a_{11}a_{23}a_{32}a_{44}$
(24)	Odd	$-a_{11}a_{24}a_{33}a_{42}$
(34)	Odd	$-a_{11}a_{22}a_{34}a_{43}$
(1234)	Odd	$-a_{12}a_{23}a_{34}a_{41}$
(1243)	Odd	$-a_{12}a_{24}a_{31}a_{43}$
(1324)	Odd	$-a_{13}a_{24}a_{32}a_{41}$
(1342)	Odd	$-a_{13}a_{21}a_{34}a_{42}$
(1423)	Odd	$-a_{14}a_{23}a_{31}a_{42}$
(1432)	Odd	$-a_{14}a_{21}a_{32}a_{43}$

So, if A is a 4×4 matrix, then det A is the following:

$$a_{11}a_{22}a_{33}a_{44} + a_{12}a_{23}a_{31}a_{44} + a_{13}a_{21}a_{32}a_{44} + a_{12}a_{24}a_{33}a_{41} + a_{14}a_{21}a_{33}a_{42} + a_{13}a_{22}a_{34}a_{41}$$
$$+ a_{14}a_{22}a_{31}a_{43} + a_{11}a_{23}a_{34}a_{42} + a_{11}a_{24}a_{32}a_{43} + a_{12}a_{21}a_{34}a_{43} + a_{13}a_{24}a_{31}a_{42} + a_{14}a_{23}a_{32}a_{41}$$
$$- a_{12}a_{21}a_{33}a_{44} - a_{13}a_{22}a_{31}a_{44} - a_{14}a_{22}a_{33}a_{41} - a_{11}a_{23}a_{32}a_{44} - a_{11}a_{24}a_{33}a_{42} - a_{11}a_{22}a_{34}a_{43}$$
$$- a_{12}a_{23}a_{34}a_{41} - a_{12}a_{24}a_{31}a_{43} - a_{13}a_{24}a_{32}a_{41} - a_{13}a_{21}a_{34}a_{42} - a_{14}a_{23}a_{31}a_{42} - a_{14}a_{21}a_{32}a_{43}$$

11. Let π be a product of k disjoint cycles of lengths $n_1, n_2, .., n_k$, respectively. Prove that the order of π is $\text{lcm}(n_1, n_2, \ldots, n_k)$.

Proof: First note that the order of an m-cycle is m. Let $\pi = \pi_1 \pi_2 \cdots \pi_k$ be a product of k disjoint cycles of lengths $n_1, n_2, \ldots, n_k$, respectively. Let $t = \text{lcm}(n_1, n_2, \ldots, n_k)$. By Problem 8 above, we have

$$\pi^t = \pi_1^t \pi_2^t \cdots \pi_k^t = (1)(1) \cdots (1) = (1).$$

So, $|\pi|$ divides t.

If $\pi^u = (1)$, then since the cycles are disjoint, we have $\pi_1^u = (1), \pi_2^u = (1), \ldots, \pi_k^u = (1)$. Therefore, for each $i = 1, 2, \ldots, k$, n_i divides u. Therefore, t divides u.

Thus, $|\pi| = t$. $\qquad\qquad\square$

12. Prove that two cycles in S_n have the same length if and only if they are conjugates of each other.

Proof: Let π be the k-cycle $(a_1 a_2 \cdots a_k)$. Then $\sigma \pi \sigma^{-1}$ is the k-cycle $(\sigma(a_1) \sigma(a_2) \cdots \sigma(a_k))$. To see this, observe that for each $i = 1, 2, \ldots, k - 1$, $\sigma \pi \sigma^{-1}(\sigma(a_i)) = \sigma \pi(a_i) = \sigma(a_{i+1})$ and for $i = k$, $\sigma \pi \sigma^{-1}(\sigma(a_k)) = \sigma \pi(a_k) = \sigma(a_1)$. Since $\sigma: \{1, 2, \ldots, n\} \to \{1, 2, \ldots, n\}$ is a bijection, π and $\sigma \pi \sigma^{-1}$ both have length k.

Conversely, suppose that $\pi = (a_1 a_2 \cdots a_k)$ and $\sigma = (b_1 b_2 \cdots b_k)$. Define $\tau: \{1, 2, \ldots, n\} \to \{1, 2, \ldots, n\}$ by $\tau(a_i) = b_i$. Then $\tau \pi \tau^{-1}$ is the k-cycle $(\tau(a_1) \tau(a_2) \cdots \tau(a_k)) = (b_1 b_2 \cdots b_k)$. So, $\tau \pi \tau^{-1} = \sigma$. $\qquad\square$

13. Prove that $|S_n| = n!$

Proof: We prove this by induction on $n \in \mathbb{Z}^+$.

Base case ($k = 1$): Clearly there is just 1 bijection from $\{1\}$ to $\{1\}$.

Inductive step: Assume that $k \in \mathbb{Z}^+$ and $|S_k| = k!$.

Let $H \leq S_{k+1}$ consist of the permutations π such that $\pi(k + 1) = k + 1$. Then $|H| = |S_k|$. By Lagrange's theorem, $|S_{k+1}| = |H|[S_{k+1}:H] = (k!)[S_{k+1}:H]$. So, it suffices to show that there are $k + 1$ cosets of H in S_{k+1}. For each $i = 1, 2, \ldots, k$, let π_i be the transposition $(i, k + 1)$ (in other words, $\pi_i(i) = k + 1, \pi_i(k + 1) = i$, and $\pi_i(j) = j$ for $j \neq i, k + 1$). Also, let $\pi_{k+1} = (1)$. We will show that $X = \{\pi_i H \mid i = 1, 2 \ldots, k + 1\}$ is the set of cosets of H in S_{k+1}.

First, let $\sigma \in S_{k+1}$ and assume that $\sigma(k + 1) = i$. Then $\pi_i^{-1} \sigma(k + 1) = \pi_i^{-1}(i) = k + 1$. Therefore, $\pi_i^{-1} \sigma \in H$. So, $\sigma \in \pi_i H$. This shows that every permutation in S_{k+1} is in a coset in X.

Next, suppose that $i, j \in \{0, 1, \ldots, k + 1\}$ with $i \neq j$. Then $\sigma_j^{-1} \sigma_i(k + 1) = \sigma_j^{-1}(i) \neq k + 1$. Therefore, $\sigma_j^{-1} \sigma_i \notin H$. So, $\sigma_i H \neq \sigma_j H$. This shows that the cosets in X are distinct.

It follows that $[S_{k+1}:H] = |X| = k + 1$, and so, $|S_{k+1}| = (k!)[S_{k+1}:H] = (k!)(k + 1) = (k + 1)!$. $\qquad\square$

14. Let $n \geq 3$ and let N be a normal subgroup of A_n containing a 3-cycle. Prove that $N = A_n$.

Proof: Let $(stu) \in N$ and let $a \in \{1, 2, \ldots, n\}$ with $a \neq s, t, u$. Then we have

$$(sta) = (st)(ua)(stu)^2(ua)(st) = \big((st)(ua)\big)(stu)^2\big((st)(ua)\big)^{-1}.$$

Therefore, $(sta) \in N$. By Problem 9 above, $N = A_n$. □

15. Prove that the determinant of an $n \times n$ upper triangular matrix A is the product of the entries of A that lie on the main diagonal of A. Is the same result true for a lower triangular matrix A.

Proof: We prove this by induction on $n \in \mathbb{Z}^+$.

Base case ($k = 1$): The determinant of the 1×1 matrix $[a]$ is a (note that every 1×1 matrix is upper triangular).

Inductive step: Assume that for $k \in \mathbb{Z}^+$, the determinant of a $k \times k$ upper triangular matrix is the product of the entries on the main diagonal of the matrix.

Let A be a $(k + 1) \times (k + 1)$ matrix. We have

$$\det A = \sum_{\pi \in S_{k+1}} \Delta_k(\pi) a_{1,\pi(1)} a_{2,\pi(2)} \cdots a_{k+1,\pi(k+1)}$$

Now, if $\pi(k + 1) \neq k + 1$, then $\pi(k + 1) < k + 1$, and so, $a_{k+1,\pi(k+1)} = 0$. Therefore, if $\pi(k + 1) \neq k + 1$, then $\Delta_k(\pi) a_{1,\pi(1)} a_{2,\pi(2)} \cdots a_{k+1,\pi(k+1)} = 0$. So,

$$\det A = a_{k+1,k+1} \sum_{\pi \in S_k} \Delta_k(\pi) a_{1,\pi(1)} a_{2,\pi(2)} \cdots a_{k,\pi(k)} = a_{k+1,k+1} \det B,$$

where B is the $k \times k$ matrix that we get from removing the $(k + 1)^{\text{st}}$ row and column of A. By the inductive hypothesis, $\det B = a_{11} a_{22} \cdots a_{kk}$. Therefore, $\det A = a_{1,1} a_{2,2} \cdots a_{k,k} a_{k+1,k+1}$, as desired.

The same result is true for a lower triangular matrix A. The proof is similar. □

LEVEL 5

16. Let $(1) \in S_n$ be the identity and suppose that $(1) = \pi_1 \pi_2 \cdots \pi_k$, where for each $i = 1, 2, \ldots, k$, π_i is a transposition. Prove that k is even. (This is Lemma 12.11.)

Proof: First note that if $a, b \in \{1, 2, \ldots, n\}$ with $a \neq b$, then $(1) \neq (ab)$.

Suppose that $(1) = \pi_1 \pi_2 \cdots \pi_k$, where for each $i = 1, 2, \ldots, k$, π_i is a transposition. By the note above, $k \geq 2$. We will now show that (1) can be written as a product of $k - 2$ transpositions.

Choose $a \in \{1, 2, \ldots, n\}$ and the greatest $i \geq 2$ such that $\pi_i = (ab)$ moves a.

Case 1: If $\pi_{i-1} = (ab)$, then $\pi_{i-1}\pi_i = (ab)(ab) = (1)$, and so, $(1) = \pi_1 \pi_2 \cdots \pi_{i-2}\pi_{i+1} \cdots \pi_k$. In this case, we have succeeded in writing (1) as a product of $k - 2$ transpositions.

Case 2: If $\pi_{i-1} = (ac)$, where $c \neq a, b$, then $\pi_{i-1}\pi_i = (ac)(ab) = (abc) = (ab)(bc)$. Replace π_{i-1} by (ab) and π_i by (bc). Now $i-1$ is the greatest positive integer such that a is moved by π_{i-1}.

Case 3: If $\pi_{i-1} = (bc)$, where $c \neq a, b$, then $\pi_{i-1}\pi_i = (bc)(ab) = (acb) = (ac)(bc)$. Replace π_{i-1} by (ac) and π_i by (bc). Now $i-1$ is the greatest positive integer such that a is moved by π_{i-1}.

Case 4: If $\pi_{i-1} = (cd)$, where $c, d \neq a, b$, then $\pi_{i-1}\pi_i = (cd)(ab) = (ab)(cd)$. Replace π_{i-1} by (ab) and π_i by (cd). Now $i-1$ is the greatest positive integer such that a is moved by π_{i-1}.

If Case 2, 3, or 4 occurs, we continue to repeat the procedure with the same positive integer a until Case 1 occurs. Case 1 must eventually occur. Otherwise, we eventually wind up with $\pi_1 = (ab)$ with $a \neq b$, and π_j fixes a for all $j > i$. But then (1) moves a to b, which of course we know it does not.

So, we showed that if (1) can be written as a product of k transpositions, then it can be written as a product of $k-2$ transpositions. If k were odd, then by repeating this process, we can eventually write (1) as a single transposition (xy). But then (1) moves x to y, which once again, we know it does not.

Therefore, k must be even. $\qquad\square$

17. Prove that $S_n = \langle (12), (12 \cdots n) \rangle$.

Proof: Let $\pi = (12)$ and $\sigma = (12 \cdots n)$.

By the proof of Problem 12 above, $\sigma\pi\sigma^{-1} = (\sigma(1)\sigma(2)) = (23)$. We can then use induction to show that for each $k = 1, 2, \ldots, n-2$, $\sigma^k\pi\sigma^{-k} = (k+1\ k+2)$. So, $\langle (12), (12 \cdots n) \rangle$ contains all the transpositions $(12), (23), \ldots, (n-1\ n)$. By part 3 of Example 12.10, all that we need to show is that $(1n) \in \langle (12), (23), \ldots, (n-1\ n) \rangle$. But $(1n) = (n-1\ n)\cdots(34)(23)(12)(23)(34)\cdots(n-1\ n)$. $\quad\square$

18. Prove that if H is a subgroup of S_n such that $[S_n : H] = 2$, then $H = A_n$.

Proof: Let H be a subgroup of S_n such that $[S_n : H] = 2$. Then there are exactly 2 cosets of H in S_n, namely H and $S_n \setminus H$. If $\pi \in S_n \setminus H$, then $\pi^2 \in H$. To see this, assume towards contradiction that $\pi^2 \notin H$. Then $\pi^2 \in \pi H$ (this is the only other coset of H in S_n), and so, $\pi^2 H = \pi H$. But then $\pi H = H$, and so, $\pi \in H$, contradicting our assumption that $\pi \in S_n \setminus H$. So, given $s, t, u \in \{1, 2, \ldots, n\}$, we have $(stu) = (sut)^2 \in H$. Therefore, H contains all 3-cycles, and so, by Problem 9 above, $H = A_n$. $\quad\square$

19. Prove that for $n \geq 5$, A_n has no proper normal subgroups.

Proof: Let N be a normal subgroup of A_n. There are five cases to consider.

Case 1: If N contains a 3-cycle, then by Problem 14 above, $N = A_n$.

Case 2: Suppose that N contains an element of the form $\pi = (a_1 a_2 \cdots a_k)\sigma$, where $k \geq 4$, σ and $(a_1 a_2 \cdots a_k)$ are disjoint, and σ is a product of disjoint cycles. Let $\tau = (a_1 a_2 a_3)$. Since N is normal in A_n, $\tau\pi\tau^{-1} \in N$. Since N is a subgroup of A_n, $\pi^{-1}\tau\pi\tau^{-1} \in N$. We have

$$\pi^{-1}\tau\pi\tau^{-1} = \sigma^{-1}(a_1 a_k a_{k-1} \cdots a_2)(a_1 a_2 a_3)(a_1 a_2 \cdots a_{k-1} a_k)\sigma(a_1 a_3 a_2) = (a_1 a_3 a_k).$$

144

By Problem 14 above, $N = A_n$.

Case 3: Suppose that N contains an element of the form $\pi = (a_1 a_2 a_3)(a_4 a_5 a_6)\sigma$, where σ and $(a_1 a_2 a_3)(a_4 a_5 a_6)$ are disjoint and σ is a product of disjoint cycles. Let $\tau = (a_1 a_2 a_4)$. Since N is normal in A_n, $\tau\pi\tau^{-1} \in N$. Since N is a subgroup of A_n, $\pi^{-1}\tau\pi\tau^{-1} \in N$. We have

$$\pi^{-1}\tau\pi\tau^{-1} = \sigma^{-1}(a_4 a_6 a_5)(a_1 a_3 a_2)(a_1 a_2 a_4)(a_1 a_2 a_3)(a_4 a_5 a_6)\sigma(a_1 a_4 a_2) = (a_1 a_4 a_2 a_6 a_3).$$

By Case 2, $N = A_n$.

Case 4: Suppose that N contains an element of the form $\pi = (a_1 a_2 a_3)\sigma$, where σ and $(a_1 a_2 a_3)$ are disjoint and σ is a product of disjoint transpositions. Then $\pi^2 \in N$ and we have

$$\pi^2 = (a_1 a_2 a_3)\sigma(a_1 a_2 a_3)\sigma = (a_1 a_2 a_3)^2 \sigma^2 = (a_1 a_2 a_3)^2 = (a_1 a_3 a_2).$$

By Problem 14 above, $N = A_n$.

Case 5: Suppose that every element of N is a disjoint product of transpositions. Since $N \subseteq A_n$, each element of N must be a disjoint product of an even number of transpositions. Let $\pi \in N$ with $\pi = (a_1 a_2)(a_3 a_4)\sigma$, where σ and $(a_1 a_2)(a_3 a_4)$ are disjoint. Let $\tau = (a_1 a_2 a_3)$. Then N contains

$$\pi^{-1}\tau\pi\tau^{-1} = \sigma^{-1}(a_3 a_4)(a_1 a_2)(a_1 a_2 a_3)(a_1 a_2)(a_3 a_4)\sigma(a_1 a_3 a_2) = (a_1 a_3)(a_2 a_4).$$

Since $n \geq 5$, there is $c \in \{1, 2, \ldots, n\}$ such that $c \neq a_1, a_2, a_3, a_4$. Let $\delta = (a_1 a_3)(a_2 a_4)$ and let $\rho = (a_1 a_3 c)$. We have $\delta \in N$ and $\rho \in A_n$. So, $\delta\rho\delta\rho^{-1} \in N$. Now,

$$\delta\rho\delta\rho^{-1} = (a_1 a_3)(a_2 a_4)(a_1 a_3 c)(a_1 a_3)(a_2 a_4)(a_1 c a_3) = (a_1 a_3 c).$$

By Problem 14 above, $N = A_n$. $\qquad\square$

20. Prove that for each $n \in \mathbb{Z}^+$, the set of $n \times n$ permutation matrices forms a group under matrix multiplication that is isomorphic to S_n.

Proof: Let P_n be the set of permutation matrices. Define a function $f: S_n \to P_n$ by $f(\pi) = A_\pi$, where
$$(A_\pi)_{ij} = f(\pi)_{ij} = \begin{cases} 1 & \text{if } \pi(j) = i. \\ 0 & \text{if } \pi(j) \neq i. \end{cases}$$

To see that f is surjective, let $A \in P_n$ and define $\pi: \{1, 2, \ldots, n\} \to \{1, 2, \ldots, n\}$ by $\pi(j) = i$ if and only if $a_{ij} = 1$. Since 1 appears exactly once in each row and column of A, $\pi \in S_n$. Clearly $f(\pi) = A$.

To see that f is injective, suppose that $f(\pi) = f(\sigma)$. Then $\pi(j) = i$ if and only if $f(\pi)_{ij} = 1$ if and only if $f(\sigma)_{ij} = 1$ if and only if $\sigma(j) = i$. So, $\pi = \sigma$.

To see that f is a homomorphism, let $\pi, \sigma \in S_n$. Then

$$\left(f(\pi)f(\sigma)\right)_{ij} = \sum_{k=1}^{n} f(\pi)_{ik} f(\sigma)_{kj} = \begin{cases} 1 & \text{if } \pi(t) = i \text{ and } \sigma(j) = t \text{ for some } t \\ 0 & \text{otherwise} \end{cases} = f(\pi\sigma)_{ij}$$

So, $f(\pi)f(\sigma) = f(\pi\sigma)$. $\qquad\square$

Problem Set 13

LEVEL 1

1. Describe the 5 conjugacy classes of S_4.

Solution:

$$[(1)]_C = \{1\}$$
$$[(12)]_C = \{(12), (13), (14), (23), (24), (34)\}$$
$$[(123)]_C = \{(123), (132), (124), (142), (134), (143), (234), (243)\}$$
$$[(1234)]_C = \{(1234), (1243), (1324), (1342), (1423), (1432)\}$$
$$[(12)(34)]_C = \{(12)(34), (13)(24), (14)(23)\}$$

2. Let G be a group of order 40. Prove that G has a normal subgroup of order 5.

Proof: We have $40 = 2^3 \cdot 5$. By the Second Sylow Theorem, the number of Sylow 5-subgroups (of order 5) must be one of the following: $1, 6, 11, 16, 21, 26, 31, 36, \ldots$. By the Fourth Sylow Theorem, the number of Sylow 5-subgroups must be one of the following: $1, 2, 4, 5, 8, 10, 20, 40$. So, there must be exactly one Sylow 5-subgroup. By part 2 of Example 13.17, this subgroup is normal in G. $\qquad\square$

3. Let G be a group and let H and K be subgroups of G. Prove that if H is a normal subgroup of K, then K is a subgroup of $N_H(G)$.

Proof: Let $x \in K$. Since H is a normal subgroup of K, by Theorem 10.15 ($1 \to 4$), $xHx^{-1} = H$. So, $x \in N_H(G)$. Since $x \in K$ was arbitrary, $K \leq N_H(G)$. $\qquad\square$

LEVEL 2

4. Let G be a group and define a relation $\sim$ on G by $h \sim k$ if and only if k is a conjugate of h. Prove that $\sim$ is an equivalence relation on G. Then generalize this result to an arbitrary group action.

Proof: $h = ehe^{-1}$, and so, $h \sim h$. Therefore, $\sim$ is reflexive.

If $h \sim k$, then there is $g \in G$ such that $k = ghg^{-1}$. $h = g^{-1}kg = g^{-1}k(g^{-1})^{-1}$, and so, $k \sim h$. Therefore, $\sim$ is symmetric.

Finally, suppose that $h \sim k$ and $k \sim j$. Then there are $g_1, g_2 \in G$ such that $k = g_1hg_1^{-1}$ and $j = g_2kg_2^{-1}$. So, $j = g_2(g_1hg_1^{-1})g_2^{-1} = (g_2g_1)h(g_2g_1)^{-1}$. So, $h \sim j$, and therefore, $\sim$ is transitive.

Since $\sim$ is reflexive, symmetric, and transitive, $\sim$ is an equivalence relation.

Now, suppose that the group G acts on a set A. Define a relation $\sim$ on A by $a \sim b$ if and only if there is a $g \in G$ with $b = g \cdot a$.

We have $a = e \cdot a$, and so, $a \sim a$. Therefore, $\sim$ is reflexive.

If $a \sim b$, then there is $g \in G$ such that $b = g \cdot a$. So, $a = e \cdot a = (g^{-1}g) \cdot a = g^{-1} \cdot (g \cdot a) = g^{-1} \cdot b$. It follows that $b \sim a$. Therefore, $\sim$ *is symmetric*.

Finally, suppose that $a \sim b$ and $b \sim c$. Then there are $g_1, g_2 \in G$ such that $b = g_1 \cdot a$ and $c = g_2 \cdot b$. So, $c = g_2 \cdot b = g_2 \cdot (g_1 \cdot a) = (g_2 g_1) \cdot a$ So, $a \sim c$, and therefore, $\sim$ is transitive.

Since $\sim$ is reflexive, symmetric, and transitive, $\sim$ is an equivalence relation. $\quad\square$

5. Let G be a group and let $h, k \in G$ be conjugates of each other. Prove that for each $j \in \mathbb{Z}$, $|h^j| = |k^j|$.

Proof: Since h and k are conjugates of each other, there is $g \in G$ such that $k = ghg^{-1}$. If $(h^j)^n = e$, then $(k^j)^n = ((ghg^{-1})^j)^n = (gh^j g^{-1})^n = g(h^j)^n g^{-1} = geg^{-1} = gg^{-1} = e$. A symmetric argument shows that if $(k^j)^n = e$, then $(h^j)^n = e$. Therefore, $|h^j| = |k^j|$. $\quad\square$

6. Determine if the following statement is true or false. If it is true, prove it. If it is false, provide a counterexample. "If G is a group and $h, k \in G$ have the same order, then h and k are in the same conjugacy class."

Solution: The statement is false. For example, in S_4, (12) and $(12)(34)$ have the same order, but they are in different conjugacy classes.

7. Let G be a group, let p be prime, and let H be a p-subgroup of G such that p does **not** divide $[G : H]$. Prove that H is a Sylow p-subgroup of G.

Proof: Since H is a p-subgroup of G, there is a positive integer k such that $|H| = p^k$. By Lagrange's Theorem, $|G| = |H| \cdot [G : H] = p^k \cdot [G : H]$. So, p^k divides $|G|$. If p^{k+1} were to divide $|G|$, then we would have $|G| = p^{k+1}a$ for some integer a. So, $p^{k+1}a = p^k \cdot [G : H]$, and therefore, $[G : H] = pa$. But this shows that p divides $[G : H]$, contrary to the given assumption. Therefore, p^{k+1} does **not** divide $|G|$, and so, H is a Sylow p-subgroup of G. $\quad\square$

LEVEL 3

8. Let G be a finite group, let p be prime, let H be a Sylow p-subgroup of G, and let N be a normal subgroup of G. Prove that $H \cap N$ is a Sylow p-subgroup of N.

Proof: By Lagrange's Theorem, $|G| = |H|[G : H]$. Since H is a p-Sylow subgroup, it follows that $[G : H]$ is **not** divisible by p.

By Theorem 11.6, $HN = \{xy \mid x \in H \text{ and } y \in N\}$ is a subgroup of G. Also, $H \cap N$ is a subgroup of H, and so, the order of $H \cap N$ is a power of p.

By Problem 7 above, it suffices to show that p does **not** divide $[N: H \cap N]$. By Problem 16 in Problem Set 10, we have $|HN| \cdot |H \cap N| = |H| \cdot |N|$, so that $\frac{|HN|}{|H|} = \frac{|N|}{|H \cap N|}$, or equivalently, $[HN: H] = [N: H \cap N]$. By Problem 3 in Problem Set 10, we have $[G: H] = [G: HN][HN: H]$, so that $[HN: H]$ divides $[G: H]$. Since $[HN: H] = [N: H \cap N]$, we have $[N: H \cap N]$ divides $[G: H]$. Since p does not divide $[G: H]$, p does not divide $[N: H \cap N]$, as desired. $\qquad \square$

9. Let G be a finite group, let p be prime, let H be a Sylow p-subgroup of G, and let N be a normal subgroup of G. Prove that HN/N is a Sylow p-subgroup of G/N.

Proof: By the Second Isomorphism Theorem, $HN/N \cong N/(H \cap N)$. So, HN/N is a p-subgroup of G/N. By Problem 3 in Problem Set 10, we have $[G: H] = [G: HN] \cdot [HN: H]$. So, $[G: HN]$ divides $[G: H]$. Since p does not divide $[G: H]$, p does not divide $[G: HN]$. Since $[G/N: HN/N] = [G: HN]$, p does not divide $[G/N: HN/N]$. Therefore, by Problem 7 above, HN/N is a Sylow p-subgroup of G/N. $\qquad \square$

10. Let p, q be prime with $q > p$. Prove that a group of order pq has a normal Sylow q-subgroup.

Proof: Let G be a group of order pq. By the Second Sylow Theorem, the number of subgroups of G of order q must be one of the following: $1, q + 1, 2q + 1, \dots$ By the Fourth Sylow Theorem, the number of subgroups of G of order q must be $1, p, q,$ or pq.

Since q and pq are divisible by q, the number of subgroups cannot be q or pq. Since $p < q$, the number of subgroups cannot be p. So there is exactly one subgroup of G of order q. By part 2 of Example 13.17, this subgroup is normal in G. $\qquad \square$

11. Let G be a group acting on a set A. The group action is said to be **faithful** if for all $x \in G$ with $x \neq e$, there is $a \in A$ such that $x \cdot a \neq a$. Provide an example of a group action that is **not** faithful.

Solution: Let G be a commutative group, let $S = \{H \mid H \leq G\}$ be the set of subgroups of G, and let G act on S by conjugation. This action is **not** faithful. To see this, let $x \in G$ with $x \neq e$ and let $H \in S$. Then $x \cdot H = H$ if and only if $xHx^{-1} = H$ if and only if $xH = Hx$. Since G is commutative, $xH = Hx$ is always true. Therefore, there is no $H \in S$ such that $x \cdot H \neq H$. It follows that this action is **not** faithful.

LEVEL 4

12. Let G be a group of order 12. Prove that G has either a normal Sylow 2-subgroup or a normal Sylow 3-subgroup.

Proof: Let G be a group of order $12 = 2^2 \cdot 3$. By the First Sylow Theorem, G has a Sylow 3-subgroup, which has order 3. By the Second Sylow Thoerem, the number of Sylow 3-subgroups of G is one of the following: $1, 4, 7, 10, \dots$ By the Fourth Sylow Theorem, the number of Sylow 3-subgroups of G is $1, 2, 3, 4, 6,$ or 12. So, the number of Sylow 3-subgroups of G is 1 or 4. If there is just 1 Sylow 3-subgroup, then by part 2 of Example 13.17, this subgroup is normal in G.

So, assume that there are 4 Sylow 3-subgroups of G. Since the intersection of any two of these subgroups is $\{e\}$, G has $4 \cdot 2 = 8$ elements of order 3. So, there is 1 element of order 1 and 8 elements of order 3, leaving us with 3 additional elements. By the First Sylow Theorem, there must be a Sylow 2-subgroup, which has order 4. This Sylow 2-subgroup must consist of the last 3 elements, together with the identity. Thus, there is exactly 1 Sylow 2-subgroup. By part 2 of Example 13.17, this subgroup is normal in G. □

13. Prove that a group of order 105 has a subgroup of order 35.

Proof: Let G be a group of order $105 = 3 \cdot 5 \cdot 7$. By the Second Sylow Thoerem, the number of Sylow 7-subgroups of G is one of the following: $1, 8, 15, 22, \ldots$ By the Fourth Sylow Theorem, the number of Sylow 7-subgroups of G is $1, 3, 5, 7, 15, 21, 35,$ or 105. So, the number of Sylow 7-subgroups of G is 1 or 15.

Similarly, the number of Sylow 5-subgroups of G is 1 or 21.

Suppose toward contradiction that there are 15 Sylow 7-subgroups and 21 Sylow 5-subgroups. Then G has $15 \cdot 6 = 90$ elements of order 7 and $21 \cdot 4 = 84$ elements of order 5. Since G has only 105, elements, we see that this is impossible.

So either the number of Sylow 7-subgroups is 1 or the number of Sylow 5-subgroups is 1.

Let H be a Sylow 7-subgroup and let K be a Sylow 5-subgroup. Let $HK = \{xy \mid x \in H, y \in K\}$. Then $|HK| = 7 \cdot 5 = 35$. Since one of H or K is normal, by Theorem 11.6, HK is a subgroup of G. □

14. Prove that there are exactly two groups of order 99, up to isomorphism.

Proof: Let G be a group of order $99 = 3^2 \cdot 11$. By the Second Sylow Thoerem, the number of Sylow 3-subgroups of G is one of the following: $1, 4, 7, 10, 13, \ldots$ By the Fourth Sylow Theorem, the number of Sylow 3-subgroups of G is $1, 3, 9, 11, 33,$ or 99. So, the number of Sylow 3-subgroups of G is 1.

Similarly, the number of Sylow 11-subgroups of G is 1.

Let H be the unique Sylow 3-subgroup of G and let K be the unique Sylow 5-subgroup of G. Let $HK = \{xy \mid x \in H, y \in K\}$. Then $G = HK$ and $H \cap K = \{e\}$. Therefore, $G \cong H \times K$. Since K has prime order, K is cyclic, and therefore, commutative. By Theorem 13.8, H is commutative. Since the direct product of commutative groups is commutative, G is commutative. By the Fundamental Theorem of Commutative Groups, $G \cong \mathbb{Z}_3 \times \mathbb{Z}_3 \times \mathbb{Z}_{11}$ or $G \cong \mathbb{Z}_9 \times \mathbb{Z}_{11}$. □

15. Prove that Lagrange's Theorem follows from the Orbit-Stabilizer Theorem by defining an appropriate group action.

Proof: Let G be a group and define an action of G on $\mathcal{P}(G)$ by left multiplication. In other words, if $g \in G$ and $X \in \mathcal{P}(G)$, then $g \cdot X = gX$. Now, if $H \leq G$, then $\text{orb}(H) = \{gH \mid g \in G\} = G/H$ is the set of left cosets of H in G. Also, $G_H = \{g \in G \mid gH = H\} = H$ (because H is a subgroup of G). It follows from the Orbit-Stabilizer Theorem that $\frac{|G|}{|H|} = |G/H| = |\text{orb}(H)| = [G:G_H] = [G:H]$. Therefore, we have $|G| = |H|[G:H]$, as desired. □

16. Let p be an odd prime. Prove that there are exactly 2 groups of order $2p$, up to isomorphism.

Proof: Let G be a group of order $2p$, where p is an odd prime. By the Second Sylow Thoerem, the number of Sylow p-subgroups of G is one of the following: $1, p + 1, 2p + 1, 3p + 1, \ldots$ By the Fourth Sylow Theorem, the number of Sylow p-subgroups of G is $1, 2, p$, or $2p$. So, the number of Sylow p-subgroups of G is 1.

Let P be the unique Sylow p-subgroup of G. By part 2 of Example 13.17, P is normal in G. Since the order of P is prime, P is cyclic. So, there is $x \in G$ such that $P = \langle x \rangle$.

By the First Sylow Theorem, G has at least 1 Sylow 2-subgroup. In particular, there is $y \in G$ such that the order of y is 2. So, $G = \{e, x, x^2, \ldots, x^{p-1}, y, yx, yx^2, \ldots, yx^{p-1}\}$.

Since P is a normal subgroup of G, $yxy^{-1} \in P = \langle x \rangle$. So, there is $k \in \{0, 1, 2, \ldots, p - 1\}$ such that $yxy^{-1} = x^k$.

If $k = p - 1$, then $yxy^{-1} = x^{p-1}$, or equivalently, $yx = x^{p-1}y$, and so, G is isomorphic to the Dihedral group D_p.

Suppose that $k < p - 1$. Since $y^2 = e$, we have $(yx)^2 = yxyx = yxy^{-1}x = x^k x = x^{k+1}$. So, the even powers of yx are powers of x, while the odd powers of x have the form yx^j for some integer j. Since the order of yx divides $2p$, the order of yx is $1, 2, p$, or $2p$.

If yx has order 1, then $yx = e$, and so, $x = y^{-1} = y$, which is impossible because x and y have different orders.

If yx has order 2, then $(yx)^2 = e$, and so, $x^{k+1} = e$. But $0 \leq k < p - 1$, and so, $0 < k + 1 \leq p - 1$. Since x has order p, we cannot have $x^{k+1} = e$.

If yx has order p, then $(yx)^p = e$, and so, $yx^j = e$ for some integer j. So, $x^j = y^{-1} = y$. But x^j has order 1 or p, whereas y has order 2. So, once again, this is impossible.

It follows that yx has order $2p$. Therefore, G is cyclic.

So, we have shown that G is isomorphic to either D_p or $\mathbb{Z}_{2p}$. □

17. Prove that there are exactly 2 groups of order 21, up to isomorphism.

Proof: Let G be a group of order $21 = 3 \cdot 7$. By Problem 10 above, G has a normal Sylow 7-subgroup N. Since the order of P is prime, P is cyclic. So, there is $x \in G$ such that $P = \langle x \rangle$.

By the First Sylow Theorem, G has at least 1 Sylow 3-subgroup. In particular, there is $y \in G$ such that the order of y is 3.

Since P is a normal subgroup of G, $yxy^{-1} \in P = \langle x \rangle$. So, there is $k \in \{0, 1, 2, 3, 4, 5, 6\}$ such that $yxy^{-1} = x^k$.

Since $y^3 = e$, we have

$$x = y^3 x y^{-3} = y^2 (yxy^{-1}) y^{-2} = y^2 x^k y^{-2} = (y^2 x y^{-2})^k = (yyxy^{-1}y^{-1})^k = (yx^k y^{-1})^k$$
$$= ((yxy^{-1})^k)^k = (yxy^{-1})^{k^2} = (x^k)^{k^2} = x^{k^3}.$$

By Theorem 9.4, $k^3 \equiv_7 1$, and so, $7 | k^3 - 1$. Therefore, $k \equiv_7 1, 2$, or 4.

If $k = 1$, then $yxy^{-1} = x^1 = x$, and so, $yx = xy$. Then $(xy)^3 = x^3 y^3 = x^3$ and $(xy)^7 = x^7 y^7 = y$. It follows that the order of xy is 21, and so G is cyclic. So, G is isomorphic to $\mathbb{Z}_{21}$.

If $k = 2$, then $yxy^{-1} = x^2$. So, we have

$$y^2 x y^{-2} = y(yxy^{-1})y^{-1} = yx^2 y^{-1} = (yxy^{-1})(yxy^{-1}) = x^2 x^2 = x^4.$$

We get the group with generators and relations $\langle x, y \mid x^7 = e, y^3 = e, yx = x^2 y \rangle$.

The matrices $\begin{bmatrix} 1 & 1 \\ 0 & 1 \end{bmatrix}$ and $\begin{bmatrix} 4 & 0 \\ 0 & 2 \end{bmatrix}$ with entries in $\mathbb{Z}_7$ generate such a group.

If $k = 4$, then $yxy^{-1} = x^4$. So, we have

$$y^2 x y^{-2} = y(yxy^{-1})y^{-1} = yx^4 y^{-1} = (yxy^{-1})^4 = (x^4)^4 = x^{16} = x^2.$$

Therefore, we get the same group that we get for $k = 2$. $\qquad\square$

Problem Set 14

LEVEL 1

1. Prove that if $(R, +, \cdot)$ is a ring, but **not** an integral domain, then $(R[x], +, \cdot)$ is **not** an integral domain.

Proof: Since R is not an integral domain, there are $a, b \in R$ with $a, b \neq 0$ and $ab = 0$. Then the constant polynomials $a, b \in R[x]$ are nonzero and satisfy $ab = 0$. Therefore, $R[x]$ is not an integral domain. $\qquad\square$

2. Let R be an integral domain and define a relation $\sim$ on R by $a \sim b$ if and only if a and b are associates. Prove that $\sim$ is an equivalence relation on R.

Proof: Since $a = a \cdot 1$ and $1 \in R$ is invertible, $a \sim a$, and so, R is reflexive.

Suppose that $a \sim b$. Then there is an invertible $u \in R$ such that $a = bu$. Then $b = au^{-1}$. Since u^{-1} is invertible, $b \sim a$, and so, R is symmetric.

Suppose that $a \sim b$ and $b \sim c$. Then there are invertible $u, v \in R$ such that $a = bu$ and $b = cv$. It follows that $a = bu = (cv)u = c(vu)$. Since the product of invertible elements is invertible, vu is invertible. Therefore, $a \sim c$, and so, $\sim$ is transitive.

Since $\sim$ is reflexive, symmetric, and transitive, $\sim$ is an equivalence relation. $\qquad\square$

3. Prove that every field is a Euclidean domain.

Proof: Let F be a field and define $f : F \setminus \{0\} \to \mathbb{N}$ by $f(x) = 0$ for all $x \in F \setminus \{0\}$. Let $a, b \in F$ with $b \neq 0$, let $k = b^{-1}a$, and let $r = 0$. Then $a = bk + r$, as desired. $\qquad\square$

LEVEL 2

4. Let F be a field and let $p(x) \in F[x]$ be an irreducible polynomial. Prove that $\langle p(x) \rangle$ is a maximal ideal of $F[x]$.

Proof: Let J be an ideal of $F[x]$ with $\langle p(x) \rangle \subseteq J \subseteq F[x]$. Since $F[x]$ is a PID, there is $q(x) \in F[x]$ such that $J = \langle q(x) \rangle$. Since $p(x) \in \langle p(x) \rangle$ and $\langle p(x) \rangle \subseteq \langle q(x) \rangle$, we have $p(x) \in \langle q(x) \rangle$. So, there is $r(x) \in F[x]$ such that $p(x) = q(x)r(x)$. Since $p(x)$ is irreducible, we have either $q(x) \in F \setminus \{0\}$ or $r(x) \in F \setminus \{0\}$. If $q(x) \in F \setminus \{0\}$, say $q(x) = a \in F$, then $1 = aa^{-1} = q(x)a^{-1} \in \langle q(x) \rangle$, and so, $\langle q(x) \rangle = F[x]$. If $r(x) \in F \setminus \{0\}$, say $r(x) = b \in F$, then $p(x) = q(x) \cdot b$, or equivalently, $q(x) = p(x) \cdot b^{-1}$, and so, $q(x) \in \langle p(x) \rangle$. So, $\langle q(x) \rangle \subseteq \langle p(x) \rangle$, and thus, $\langle q(x) \rangle = \langle p(x) \rangle$. $\qquad\square$

5. Let $p(x) \in \mathbb{Q}[x]$. Prove that there is $q(x) \in \mathbb{Z}[x]$ such that $q(x)$ has the same roots as $p(x)$.

Proof: Let $p(x) \in \mathbb{Q}[x]$, say $p(x) = \frac{a_0}{b_0} + \frac{a_1}{b_1}x + \cdots + \frac{a_n}{b_n}x^n$, with $a_0, b_0, a_1, b_1, \ldots, a_n, b_n \in \mathbb{Z}$. Then we have $p(x) = \frac{1}{b_0 b_1 \cdots b_n}(a_0 b_1 b_2 \cdots b_n + a_1 b_0 b_2 \cdots b_n x + \cdots + a_n b_0 b_1 \cdots b_{n-1} x^n)$.

Let $q(x) = a_0 b_1 b_2 \cdots b_n + a_1 b_0 b_2 \cdots b_n x + \cdots + a_n b_0 b_1 \cdots b_{n-1} x^n$. Then $q(x) \in \mathbb{Z}[x]$ and $q(x)$ has the same roots as $p(x)$. $\square$

6. Prove that every Euclidean domain is a PID.

Proof: Let R be a Euclidean domain with Euclidean function $f: R \setminus \{0\} \to \mathbb{N}$. So, if $a, b \in R$ and $b \neq 0$, then there exist $k, r \in R$ such that $a = bk + r$ and either $r = 0$ or $f(r) < f(b)$. Let I be an ideal of R and let $x \in I$ be such that $f(x) \leq f(y)$ for all $y \in I$.

We will now show that $I = \langle x \rangle$. Since $x \in I$, it is clear that $\langle x \rangle \subseteq I$. For the reverse inclusion, let $y \in I$. Then there are $k, r \in R$ such that $y = xk + r$ and either $r = 0$ or $f(r) < f(x)$. Since $x \in I$ and I is an ideal of R, $xk \in I$. Since $y, xk \in I$ and $(I, +)$ is a subgroup of $(R, +)$, $r = y - xk \in I$. Therefore, we cannot have $f(r) < f(x)$. So, $r = 0$. Therefore, $y = xk \in \langle x \rangle$. So, $\langle x \rangle \subseteq I$.

Since $\langle x \rangle \subseteq I$ and $I \subseteq \langle x \rangle$, we have $I = \langle x \rangle$. So, R is a PID. $\square$

LEVEL 3

7. Prove that $\mathbb{Z}[x]$ is **not** a PID.

Proof: We will prove that the ideal $\langle 2, x \rangle$ is not a principal ideal in $\mathbb{Z}[x]$. Suppose toward contradiction that there is a polynomial $p(x) \in \mathbb{Z}[x]$ such that $\langle 2, x \rangle = \langle p(x) \rangle$. Since $2 \in \langle p(x) \rangle$, there is a polynomial $q(x) \in \mathbb{Z}[x]$ such that $2 = p(x)q(x)$. Since $\mathbb{Z}$ is an integral domain, we have

$$\text{degree}\left(p(x)q(x)\right) = \text{degree } p(x) + \text{degree } q(x).$$

So, $p(x)$ and $q(x)$ must both be constant polynomials. So, $p(x)$ is equal to $1, -1, 2,$ or -2.

If $p(x) = 1$ or -1, then $\langle p(x) \rangle = \mathbb{Z}[x]$. But $x + 1 \notin \langle 2, x \rangle$. If $p(x) = 2$ or -2, then we have $x + 2 \in \langle 2, x \rangle$, but $x + 2 \notin \langle p(x) \rangle$. It follows that $\langle 2, x \rangle$ is not a principal ideal in $\mathbb{Z}[x]$. $\square$

8. Let F be a field, let $a(x), b(x) \in F[x]$, and let $I = \{c(x)a(x) + d(x)b(x) \mid c(x), d(x) \in F[x]\}$. Prove that I is an ideal of $F[x]$.

Proof: $0 = 0 \cdot a(x) + 0 \cdot b(x) \in I$. So, $I \neq \emptyset$.

Let $c_1(x)a(x) + d_1(x)b(x), c_2(x)a(x) + d_2(x)b(x) \in I$. Then

$$\left(c_1(x)a(x) + d_1(x)b(x)\right) - \left(c_2(x)a(x) + d_2(x)b(x)\right)$$
$$= \left(c_1(x) - c_2(x)\right)a(x) + \left(d_1(x) - d_2(x)\right)b(x) \in I.$$

So, $(I, +)$ is a subgroup of $(F[x], +)$.

Since $(F[x], +)$ is commutative, so is $(I, +)$.

Let $c(x)a(x) + d(x)b(x) \in I$ and $p(x) \in F[x]$. Then

$$\left(c(x)a(x) + d(x)b(x)\right)p(x) = \left(c(x)p(x)\right)a(x) + \left(d(x)p(x)\right)b(x) \in I.$$

So, I absorbs $F[x]$.

Since $(I, +)$ is a subgroup of $(F[x], +)$ and I absorbs $F[x]$, I is an ideal of $F[x]$. □

9. Let F be a field, let $a(x), b(x), c(x) \in F[x]$ with $a(x)$ and $b(x)$ relatively prime, and suppose that $a(x)|b(x)c(x)$. Prove that $a(x)|c(x)$.

Proof: Let $a(x), b(x), c(x) \in F[x]$ with $a(x)$ and $b(x)$ relatively prime and let $a(x)|b(x)c(x)$. Since $\gcd(a(x), b(x)) = 1$, by Theorem 14.20, there are polynomials $p(x)$ and $q(x)$ such that $1 = p(x)a(x) + q(x)b(x)$. Since $a(x)|b(x)c(x)$, there is a polynomial $k(x)$ such that $b(x)c(x) = a(x)k(x)$. Multiplying each side of the equation $1 = p(x)a(x) + q(x)b(x)$ by $c(x)$ and using the distributive property (as well as associativity and commutativity of multiplication),

$$c(x) = c(x)\big(p(x)a(x) + q(x)b(x)\big) = c(x)p(x)a(x) + c(x)q(x)b(x)$$

$$= c(x)p(x)a(x) + q(x)b(x)c(x) = c(x)p(x)a(x) + q(x)a(x)k(x)$$

$$= a(x)\big(c(x)p(x) + q(x)k(x)\big).$$

Therefore, $a(x)|c(x)$. □

10. Let F be a field, let $p(x) \in F[x]$ be irreducible, and let $a_1(x), a_2(x), \dots, a_n(x) \in F[x]$. Suppose that $p(x)|\, a_1(x)a_2(x)\cdots a_n(x)$. Prove that there is an integer j with $1 \le j \le n$ such that $p(x)|a_j(x)$.

Proof: We will prove this by induction on $n \ge 1$.

Base Case ($n = 1$): We are given that $p(x)$ is irreducible, $a_1(x) \in F[x]$, and $p(x)|a_1(x)$. So, the result holds for $n = 1$.

Inductive Step: Let $k \in \mathbb{N}$ and assume that the result holds for $n = k$.

Let $p(x)$ be irreducible and let $a_1(x), a_2(x), \dots a_k(x), a_{k+1}(x)$ be polynomials such that $p(x)|a_1(x)a_2(x)\cdots a_k(x)a_{k+1}(x)$. Since $p(x)$ is irreducible, its only monic factors are 1 and $p(x)$. Therefore, $\gcd\big(p(x), a_1(x)a_2(x)\cdots a_k(x)\big)$ is either 1 or $p(x)$.

If $\gcd\big(p(x), a_1(x)a_2(x)\cdots a_k(x)\big) = 1$, then by Problem 9 above, $p(x)|a_{k+1}(x)$.

If $\gcd\big(p(x), a_1(x)a_2(x)\cdots a_k(x)\big) = p(x)$, then $p(x)|a_1(x)a_2(x)\cdots a_k(x)$, and by our inductive assumption, there is an integer j with $1 \le j \le k$ such that $p(x)|a_j(x)$.

Therefore, the result holds for $n = k + 1$.

By the Principle of Mathematical Induction, the result holds for all $n \in \mathbb{N}$ with $n \ge 1$. □

11. Prove that every nonconstant polynomial $a(x)$ over a field F can be factored **uniquely** as a product $kp_1(x)p_2(x)\cdots p_n(x)$, where k is a constant and for each $i = 1, 2, \dots, n$, $p_i(x)$ is a monic irreducible polynomial, up to the order in which the factors are written.

154

Proof: By Theorem 14.12, $a(x)$ can be written as a product of irreducible factors, say

$$a(x) = a_1(x)a_2(x) \cdots a_n(x).$$

For each $i = 1, 2, \ldots, n$, write $a_i(x) = k_i p_i(x)$, where k_i is the leading coefficient of a_i. Also, let $k = k_1 k_2 \cdots k_n$. Then $a(x) = k p_1(x) p_2(x) \cdots p_n(x)$ has the desired form.

We need to show that any two such prime factorizations are equal. Assume toward contradiction that $a(x)$ can be written in the following two different ways:

$$a(x) = k p_1(x) p_2(x) \cdots p_n(x) = t q_1(x) q_2(x) \cdots q_m(x),$$

where $p_1(x), p_2(x), \ldots, p_n(x), q_1(x), q_2(x), \ldots, q_m(x)$ are monic irreducible polynomials and k, t are constants. By cancelling common factors on the left with common factors on the right, we may assume that for all $i \leq n$ and $j \leq m$, $p_i \neq q_j$. Suppose $1 \leq i \leq n$. Then $p_i(x) | k p_1(x) p_2(x) \cdots p_n(x)$. Since $k p_1(x) p_2(x) \cdots p_n(x) = t q_1(x) q_2(x) \cdots q_m(x)$, we have $p_i(x) | t q_1(x) q_2(x) \cdots q_m(x)$. By Problem 10 above, together with the fact that $p_i(x)$ does not divide t, there is j with $1 \leq j \leq m$ such that $p_i(x) | q_j(x)$. Since $q_j(x)$ is irreducible, $p_i(x)$ and $q_j(x)$ must be associates. However, $p_i(x)$ and $q_j(x)$ are both monic, and therefore, they are equal. This is a contradiction. $\square$

12. Let $a(x) \in \mathbb{R}[x]$. Prove that if a complex number z is a root of $a(x)$, then the conjugate of z is also a root of $a(x)$.

Proof: Let $a(x) \in \mathbb{R}[x]$, say $a(x) = a_0 + a_1 x + \cdots + a_n x^n$ and suppose that z is a root of $a(x)$. Then we have the following:

$$a(\bar{z}) = a_0 + a_1 \bar{z} + \cdots + a_n \bar{z}^n.$$

Since $a_0, a_1, \ldots, a_n \in \mathbb{R}$, $\bar{a}_0 = a_0, \bar{a}_1 = a_1, \ldots, \bar{a}_n = a_n$. Therefore, $a(\bar{z}) = \bar{a}_0 + \bar{a}_1 \bar{z} + \cdots + \bar{a}_n \bar{z}^n$. By Problem 5 in Problem Set 7, we then have $a(\bar{z}) = \overline{a_0 + a_1 x + \cdots + a_n x^n} = \bar{0} = 0$. So, $\bar{z}$ is a root of $a(x)$. $\square$

LEVEL 4

13. Prove that $x^2 + 1$ is irreducible over $\mathbb{R}$.

Proof: If $x^2 + 1 = (ax + b)(cx + d)$, then we have $x^2 + 1 = acx^2 + (ad + bc)x + bd$. So, $ac = 1$, $ad + bc = 0$, and $bd = 1$. We then have that $0 = cd(ad + bc) = (ac)d^2 + (bd)c^2 = d^2 + c^2$. So, $c = d = 0$. It follows that $x^2 + 1 = (ax + b)(0x + 0) = (ax + b) \cdot 0 = 0$, which is impossible. It follows that $x^2 + 1$ is irreducible over $\mathbb{R}$. $\square$

14. Prove that the ring of Gaussian integers, $\mathbb{Z}[i] = \{a + bi \mid a, b \in \mathbb{Z}\}$, is a PID.

Proof: We first prove that $\mathbb{Z}[i]$ is an integral domain. We already know that $\mathbb{Z}[i]$ is a ring from Problem 7 in Problem Set 6. To see that multiplication is commutative in $\mathbb{Z}[i]$, let $a + bi, c + di \in \mathbb{Z}[i]$. Since multiplication and addition are commutative in $\mathbb{Z}$, we have

$$(a + bi)(c + di) = (ac - bd) + (ad + bc)i = (ca - db) + (cb + da)i = (c + di)(a + bi).$$

155

Now, suppose that $(a + bi)(c + di) = 0$ and $a + bi \neq 0$. Then $ac - bd = 0$ and $ad + bc = 0$. Also, either $a \neq 0$ or $b \neq 0$. If $a = 0$, then $bd = 0$ and $bc = 0$. Since $b \neq 0$, $d = 0$ and $c = 0$, and so, $c + di = 0$. If $b = 0$, then $ac = 0$ and $ad = 0$. Since $a \neq 0$, $c = 0$ and $d = 0$, and so, $c + di = 0$. So, now assume that both $a \neq 0$ and $b \neq 0$. Multiplying the equation $ac - bd = 0$ by $-d$ and the equation $ad + bc = 0$ by c gives $-acd + bd^2 = 0$ and $acd + bc^2 = 0$. Adding these two equation gives us the equation $bc^2 + bd^2 = 0$. So, $b(c^2 + d^2) = 0$. Since $b \neq 0$, we have $c^2 + d^2 = 0$. Thus, $c = d = 0$, and so, $c + di = 0$. It follows that $\mathbb{Z}[i]$ has no zero divisors, and therefore, $\mathbb{Z}[i]$ is an integral domain.

We will now prove that $\mathbb{Z}[i]$ is a Euclidean Domain. It will then follow from Problem 6 above that $\mathbb{Z}[i]$ is a PID.

We define a function $f \colon \mathbb{Z}[i] \setminus \{0\} \to \mathbb{N}$ by $f(a + bi) = a^2 + b^2$. Let $a + bi, c + di \in \mathbb{Z}[i]$ with $c + di \neq 0$. There exist $e, f \in \mathbb{Q}$ such that $\frac{a+bi}{c+di} = e + fi$. Let g and h be the closest integers to e and f, respectively (so that $|g - e| \leq \frac{1}{2}$ and $|h - f| \leq \frac{1}{2}$). Let $k = g + hi$, $u = e - g$, $v = f - h$, and $r = (c + di)(u + vi)$. Observe that $k, r \in \mathbb{Z}[i]$ (you should check that $r \in \mathbb{Z}[i]$). Then we have

$$a + bi = (c + di)(e + fi) = (c + di)(u + g + vi + hi)$$
$$= (c + di)(g + hi) + (c + di)(u + vi) = (c + di)k + r.$$

If $r = 0$, then $a + bi = (c + di)k$. If $r \neq 0$, we have

$$f(r) = (c^2 + d^2)(u^2 + v^2) \leq (c^2 + d^2)\left(\frac{1}{4} + \frac{1}{4}\right) = \frac{1}{2}(c^2 + d^2) < c^2 + d^2 = f(c + di).$$

This proves that $\mathbb{Z}[i]$ is a Euclidean Domain. $\qquad\square$

15. Let $a(x) = a_0 + a_1 x + \cdots + a_n x^n \in \mathbb{Z}[x]$ and let $\frac{m}{k} \in \mathbb{Q}$ with $\gcd(m, k) = 1$. Suppose that $\frac{m}{k}$ is a root of $a(x)$. Prove that $m | a_0$ and $k | a_n$.

Proof: Suppose that $\frac{m}{k}$ is a root of $a(x)$. Then we have $a\left(\frac{m}{k}\right) = 0$, or equivalently,

$$a_0 + a_1 \left(\frac{m}{k}\right) + \cdots + a_n \left(\frac{m}{k}\right)^n = 0.$$

Multiplying each side of this equation by k^n gives us

$$a_0 k^n + a_1 m k^{n-1} + \cdots + a_n m^n = 0.$$

Using the distributive property, we have

$$a_0 k^n + m(a_1 k^{n-1} + \cdots + a_n m^{n-1}) = 0.$$

Subtracting $a_0 k^n$ from each side of this equation gives us

$$m(a_1 k^{n-1} + \cdots + a_n m^{n-1}) = -a_0 k^n.$$

So, $m | a_0 k^n$. Since $\gcd(m, k) = 1$, by Euclid's Principle (Theorem 8.19), $m | a_0$.

Now, let's go back to this equation:

$$a_0 k^n + a_1 m k^{n-1} + \cdots + a_n m^n = 0.$$

Using the distributive property in a different way, we have

$$k(a_0 k^{n-1} + a_1 m k^{n-2} + \cdots + a_{n-1} m^{n-1}) + a_n m^n = 0.$$

Subtracting $a_n m^n$ from each side of this equation gives us

$$k(a_0 k^{n-1} + a_1 m k^{n-2} + \cdots + a_{n-1} m^{n-1}) = -a_n m^n.$$

So, $k \mid a_n m^n$. Since $\gcd(m, k) = 1$, by Euclid's Principle again, $k \mid a_n$. $\quad\square$

LEVEL 5

16. Let $(R, +, \cdot)$ be a ring. Prove that $(R[x], +, \cdot)$ is a left R-algebra. Then prove that $(R[x], +, \cdot)$ is commutative if and only if R is commutative.

Proof: Addition in $(R[x], +, \cdot)$ is defined by

$$(a_k x^k + a_{k-1} x^{k\ 1} + \cdots + a_1 x + a_0) + (b_k x^k + b_{k-1} x^{k-1} + \cdots + b_1 x + b_0)$$
$$= (a_k + b_k) x^k + (a_{k-1} + b_{k-1}) x^{k-1} + \cdots + (a_1 + b_1) x + (a_0 + b_0).$$

Since R is closed under addition, $a_k + b_k, a_{k-1} + b_{k-1}, \ldots, a_1 + b_1, a_0 + b_0 \in R$. Therefore, $R[x]$ is closed under addition.

Simple computations show that addition is associative in $R[x]$, $0 = 0x^k + 0x^{k-1} + \cdots + 0x + 0$ is an additive identity in $R[x]$, and the additive inverse of $a_k x^k + a_{k-1} x^{k-1} + \cdots + a_1 x + a_0$ is $-a_k x^k - a_{k-1} x^{k-1} - \cdots - a_1 x - a_0$. One more simple computation can be used to verify that addition is commutative.

The computations showing that $(R[x], +, \cdot)$ is a left R-module are also very straightforward.

Here comes the hard part... Multiplication in $(R[x], +, \cdot)$ is defined by

$$(a_k x^k + a_{k-1} x^{k-1} + \cdots + a_1 x + a_0)(b_k x^k + b_{k-1} x^{k-1} + \cdots + b_1 x + b_0)$$
$$= c_{2k} x^{2k} + c_{2k-1} 2 x^{k-1} + \cdots + c_1 x + c_0,$$

where $c_i = a_i b_0 + a_{i-1} b_1 + \cdots + a_1 b_{i-1} + a_0 b_i$ for each $i = 0, 1, \ldots, 2k$.

Since R is closed under addition and multiplication, $c_i = a_i b_0 + a_{i-1} b_1 + \cdots + a_1 b_{i-1} + a_0 b_i \in \mathbb{Z}$ for each $i = 0, 1, \ldots, 2k$. Therefore, $R[x]$ is closed under multiplication.

We show that 1 is a multiplicative identity for $R[x]$. We have

$$1 \cdot (a_k x^k + a_{k-1} x^{k-1} + \cdots + a_1 x + a_0) = c_k x^k + c_{k-1} x^{k-1} + c_1 x + c_0,$$

where $c_i = 0a_0 + 0a_1 + \cdots + 0a_{i-1} + 1a_i = a_i$. So,

$$1 \cdot (a_k x^k + a_{k-1} x^{k-1} + \cdots + a_1 x + a_0) = a_k x^k + a_{k-1} x^{k-1} + \cdots + a_1 x + a_0.$$

Similarly, $(a_k x^k + a_{k-1} x^{k-1} + \cdots + a_1 x + a_0) \cdot 1 = c_k x^k + c_{k-1} x^{k-1} + c_1 x + c_0,$

where $c_i = a_i \cdot 1 + a_{i-1} \cdot 0 + \cdots + a_1 \cdot 0 + a_0 \cdot 0 = a_i$. So,

$$(a_k x^k + a_{k-1} x^{k-1} + \cdots + a_1 x + a_0) \cdot 1 = a_k x^k + a_{k-1} x^{k-1} + \cdots + a_1 x + a_0.$$

Now, we check associativity. Let $A, B, D \in R[x]$, where $A = a_k x^k + a_{k-1} x^{k-1} + \cdots + a_1 x + a_0$, $B = b_k x^k + b_{k-1} x^{k-1} + \cdots + b_1 x + b_0$, and $D = d_k x^k + d_{k-1} x^{k-1} + \cdots + d_1 x + d_0$.

Then $AB = C$, where $C = c_k x^k + c_{k-1} x^{k-1} + \cdots + c_1 x + c_0$ with

$$c_i = a_i b_0 + a_{i-1} b_1 + \cdots + a_1 b_{i-1} + a_0 b_i \text{ for each } i = 0, 1, \ldots, 2k.$$

So, $(AB)D = E$, where $E = e_k x^k + e_{k-1} x^{k-1} + \cdots + e_1 x + e_0$ such that for each $i = 0, 1, \ldots, 2k$,

$$e_i = c_i d_0 + c_{i-1} d_1 + \cdots + c_1 d_{i-1} + c_0 d_i$$
$$= (a_i b_0 + a_{i-1} b_1 + \cdot + a_0 b_i) d_0 + (a_{i-1} b_0 + a_{i-2} b_1 + \cdot + a_0 b_{i-1}) d_1 + \cdots + (a_0 b_0) d_i.$$

Now, $BD = F$, where $F = f_k x^k + f_{k-1} x^{k-1} + \cdots + f_1 x + f_0$ with

$$f_i = b_i d_0 + b_{i-1} d_1 + \cdots + b_1 d_{i-1} + b_0 d_i \text{ for each } i = 0, 1, \ldots, 2k.$$

So, $A(BD) = G$, where $G = g_k x^k + g_{k-1} x^{k-1} + \cdots + g_1 x + g_0$ such that for each $i = 0, 1, \ldots, 2k$,

$$g_i = a_i f_0 + a_{i-1} f_1 + \cdots + a_1 f_{i-1} + a_0 f_i$$
$$= a_i (b_0 d_0) + a_{i-1} (b_1 d_0 + b_0 d_1) + \cdots + a_0 (b_i d_0 + b_{i-1} d_1 + \cdots + b_1 d_{i-1} + b_0 d_i).$$

Since $(AB)D = E$ and $A(BD) = G$, the proof is complete once we verify that $E = G$, or equivalently, for each $i = 0, 1, \ldots, 2k$,

$$(a_i b_0 + a_{i-1} b_1 + \cdot + a_0 b_i) d_0 + (a_{i-1} b_0 + a_{i-2} b_1 + \cdot + a_0 b_{i-1}) d_1 + \cdots + (a_0 b_0) d_i$$

$$= a_i (b_0 d_0) + a_{i-1} (b_1 d_0 + b_0 d_1) + \cdots + a_0 (b_i d_0 + b_{i-1} d_1 + \cdots + b_1 d_{i-1} + b_0 d_i).$$

This equation can easily be verified by using the distributive property in R and rearranging the terms.

The proofs of left and right distributivity, as well as the compatibility of scalar and vector multiplication are similar (but not as tedious). $\square$

17. Prove that there is no rational number x such that $x^2 = 2$.

Proof: We first prove that every rational number can be written in the form $\frac{m}{n}$, where $m \in \mathbb{Z}$, $n \in \mathbb{Z}^*$, and at least one of m or n is **not** even.

To see this, let x be a rational number. Then there are $a \in \mathbb{Z}$ and $b \in \mathbb{Z}^*$ such that $x = \frac{a}{b}$. Let j be the largest integer such that 2^j divides a and let k be the largest integer such that 2^k divides b. Since, 2^j divides a, there is $c \in \mathbb{Z}$ such that $a = 2^j c$. Since, 2^k divides b, there is $d \in \mathbb{Z}$ such that $b = 2^k d$.

Observe that c is odd. Indeed, if c were even, then there would be an integer s such that $c = 2s$. But then $a = 2^j c = 2^j (2s) = (2^j \cdot 2)s = (2^j \cdot 2^1)s = 2^{j+1}s$. So, 2^{j+1} divides a, contradicting the maximality of j.

Similarly, d is odd.

So, we have $x = \dfrac{a}{b} = \dfrac{2^j c}{2^k d}$.

If $j \geq k$, then, $j - k \geq 0$ and $x = \dfrac{2^j c}{2^k d} = \dfrac{2^{j-k}c}{d}$. Let $m = 2^{j-k}c$ and $n = d$. Then $x = \dfrac{m}{n}$, $m \in \mathbb{Z}$ (because $\mathbb{Z}$ is closed under multiplication), $n \in \mathbb{Z}^*$ (if $n = 0$, then $b = 2^k d = 2^k n = 2^k \cdot 0 = 0$), and $n = d$ is odd.

If $j < k$, then $k - j > 0$ and $x = \dfrac{2^j c}{2^k d} = \dfrac{c}{2^{k-j}d}$. Let $m = c$ and $n = 2^{k-j}d$. Then $x = \dfrac{m}{n}$, $m = c \in \mathbb{Z}$, $n \in \mathbb{Z}^*$ (because $\mathbb{Z}$ is closed under multiplication, and if n were 0, then d would be 0, and then b would be 0), and $m = c$ is odd. $\qquad\square$

Now, assume toward contradiction that there is a rational number a such that $a^2 = 2$. Since a is a rational number, there are $m \in \mathbb{Z}$ and $n \in \mathbb{Z}^*$, **not both even**, so that $a = \dfrac{m}{n}$.

So, we have $\dfrac{m^2}{n^2} = \dfrac{m \cdot m}{n \cdot n} = \dfrac{m}{n} \cdot \dfrac{m}{n} = a \cdot a = a^2 = 2 = \dfrac{2}{1}$. Thus, $m^2 \cdot 1 = n^2 \cdot 2$. So, $m^2 = 2n^2$. Therefore, m^2 is even. If m were odd, then by Problem 15 in Problem Set 8, $m^2 = m \cdot m$ would be odd. So, **m is even**.

Since m is even, there is $k \in \mathbb{Z}$ such that $m = 2k$. Replacing m by $2k$ in the equation $m^2 = 2n^2$ gives us $2n^2 = m^2 = (2k)^2 = (2k)(2k) = 2\big(k(2k)\big)$. So, $n^2 = k(2k) = (k \cdot 2)k = (2k)k = 2(k \cdot k)$. So, we see that n^2 is even, and again by Problem 15 in Problem Set 8, **n is even**.

So, we have m even and n even, contrary to our original assumption that m and n are not both even. Therefore, there is no rational number a such that $a^2 = 2$. $\qquad\square$

18. A commutative ring R is called a **Noetherian ring** if whenever $I_1 \subseteq I_2 \subseteq \cdots$ is a chain of ideals, then there is $n \in \mathbb{Z}^+$ such that for all $k > n$, $I_k = I_n$. Prove that a PID is a Noetherian ring.

Proof: Let R be a PID and suppose that $I_1 \subseteq I_2 \subseteq \cdots$ is a chain of ideals. Since R is a PID, there is a list $a_1, a_2, \ldots$ such that for each $i \in \mathbb{Z}^+$, $I_i = \langle a_i \rangle$. So, we have

$$\langle a_1 \rangle \subseteq \langle a_2 \rangle \subseteq \langle a_3 \rangle \subseteq \cdots$$

It is easy to check that the union of these ideals is an ideal. Since R is a PID, this ideal must be a principal ideal $\langle b \rangle$. We must have $b \in \langle a_n \rangle$ for some n. Then $b \in \langle a_k \rangle$ for all $k \geq n$. It follows that for all $k \geq n$, $\langle b \rangle = \langle a_k \rangle$. But then for all $k > n$, $I_k = \langle a_k \rangle = \langle a_n \rangle = I_n$.

Therefore, R is a Noetherian ring. $\qquad\square$

19. Prove that every PID is a UFD.

Proof: Let R be a PID and let $c \in R$ with $c \neq 0$ and c noninvertible.

We first show that c has an irreducible factor. If c is not irreducible, then $c = a_1 b_1$ for some noninvertible $a_1, b_1 \in R$. So, $c \in \langle a_1 \rangle$, and so, $\langle c \rangle \subset \langle a_1 \rangle$. Note $\langle c \rangle$ cannot be equal to $\langle a_1 \rangle$ because if $\langle c \rangle = \langle a_1 \rangle$, then $a_1 = ck$ for some $k \in R$, and so, $c = (ck)b_1 = c(kb_1)$. Since R is a domain, the left cancellation law holds, and so, $1 = kb_1$, contradicting our assumption that b_1 is noninvertible.

Now, if a_1 is not irreducible, then $a_1 = a_2 b_2$ for some noninvertible $a_2, b_2 \in R$. So, $a_1 \in \langle a_2 \rangle$, and so, $\langle a_1 \rangle \subset \langle a_2 \rangle$ for the same reason as above. We continue this procedure to find $a_1, a_2, \ldots$ such that

$$\langle a_1 \rangle \subset \langle a_2 \rangle \subset \langle a_3 \rangle \subset \cdots$$

By Problem 18 above, there is $n \in \mathbb{Z}^+$ such that $\langle a_n \rangle = \langle a_{n+1} \rangle$, contradicting the fact that $\langle a_n \rangle$ is a **proper** subset of $\langle a_{n+1} \rangle$.

It follows that c has an irreducible factor.

We now show that c can be written as a finite product of irreducible elements of R and an invertible element of R. If c is irreducible, we are done. So, assume that c is not irreducible.

By the above result, $c = a_1 b_1$, where a_1 is irreducible and b_1 is noninvertible. The same argument in the second paragraph above shows that $\langle c \rangle \subset \langle a_1 \rangle$. If b_1 is irreducible, then we are done. Otherwise, we can write $b_1 = a_2 b_2$, where a_2 is irreducible and b_2 is noninvertible. Continuing in this fashion gives

$$\langle a_1 \rangle \subset \langle a_2 \rangle \subset \langle a_3 \rangle \subset \cdots$$

Once again, by Problem 18 above, there is $n \in \mathbb{Z}^+$ such that $\langle a_n \rangle = \langle a_{n+1} \rangle$, contradicting the fact that $\langle a_n \rangle$ is a **proper** subset of $\langle a_{n+1} \rangle$.

So, c can be written as a finite product of irreducible elements of R and an invertible element of R.

The proof of uniqueness is nearly identical to the proofs of Problems 9, 10, and 11 above. $\square$

Problem Set 15

LEVEL 1

1. Let E be a field. Prove that F is a subfield of E if and only if $F^* \neq \emptyset$, $F \subseteq E$, F is closed under subtraction and multiplication, and F^* is closed under taking multiplicative inverses.

Proof: First let F be a subfield of E. Since $1 \in F$ and $1 \neq 0$, $F^* \neq \emptyset$. By definition, $F \subseteq E$, F is closed under addition and F is closed under taking additive inverses. Therefore, if $x, y \in F$, then we have $x - y = x + (-y) \in F$. So, F is closed under subtraction. By Problem 14 from Problem Set 2, F is closed under multiplication. Finally, by definition, F^* is closed under taking multiplicative inverses.

Conversely, suppose that $F^* \neq \emptyset$, $F \subseteq E$, F is closed under subtraction and multiplication, and F^* is closed under taking multiplicative inverses. Since $F^* \neq \emptyset$ and $F^* \subseteq F$, it follows that $F \neq \emptyset$. Since F is closed under subtraction, by Problem 5 from Problem Set 6, $(F, +)$ is a group. Since commutativity is closed downwards, $+$ is commutative in F. So, $(F, +)$ is a commutative group. Let $x, y \in F^*$. Since F^* is closed under taking multiplicative inverses, $y^{-1} \in F^*$. Since F^* is closed under multiplication, $xy^{-1} \in F^*$. Once again, since commutativity is closed downwards, $\cdot$ is commutative in F^*. So, by Problem 5 from Problem Set 6, $(F^*, \cdot)$ is a commutative group. Both left and right distributivity are closed downwards, and so, multiplication is distributive over addition in F. Finally, it is easy to see that $0 \neq 1$ because these are the same elements in F as they are in E. So, F is a subfield of E. $\square$

2. Find the minimal polynomial of $\sqrt{11}$ over $\mathbb{Q}$.

Solution: The minimal polynomial cannot be linear because $\sqrt{11} \notin \mathbb{Q}$. Since $\left(\sqrt{11}\right)^2 - 11 = 0$, the minimal polynomial is $x^2 - 11$.

3. Prove that $\mathbb{Q}\left(\sqrt{2}, \sqrt{3}\right) = \mathbb{Q}\left(\sqrt{2} + \sqrt{3}\right)$.

Proof: We first show that $\mathbb{Q}\left(\sqrt{2}, \sqrt{3}\right) \subseteq \mathbb{Q}\left(\sqrt{2} + \sqrt{3}\right)$. Observe that

$$\left(\sqrt{2} + \sqrt{3}\right)^{-1} = \frac{1}{\sqrt{2} + \sqrt{3}} = \frac{\sqrt{2} - \sqrt{3}}{2 - 3} = \sqrt{3} - \sqrt{2}.$$

Since $\mathbb{Q}\left(\sqrt{2} + \sqrt{3}\right)$ is closed under taking multiplicative inverses, $\sqrt{3} - \sqrt{2} \in \mathbb{Q}\left(\sqrt{2} + \sqrt{3}\right)$. Since $\mathbb{Q}\left(\sqrt{2} + \sqrt{3}\right)$ is closed under addition, $2\sqrt{3} = \left(\sqrt{2} + \sqrt{3}\right) + \left(\sqrt{3} - \sqrt{2}\right) \in \mathbb{Q}\left(\sqrt{2} + \sqrt{3}\right)$. Therefore, $\sqrt{3} = \frac{1}{2}\left(2\sqrt{3}\right) \in \mathbb{Q}\left(\sqrt{2} + \sqrt{3}\right)$. Similarly, $\sqrt{2} = \frac{1}{2}\left[\left(\sqrt{2} + \sqrt{3}\right) - \left(\sqrt{3} - \sqrt{2}\right)\right] \in \mathbb{Q}\left(\sqrt{2} + \sqrt{3}\right)$. So, $\mathbb{Q}\left(\sqrt{2} + \sqrt{3}\right)$ is a field containing $\mathbb{Q}$, $\sqrt{2}$, and $\sqrt{3}$. Therefore, $\mathbb{Q}\left(\sqrt{2}, \sqrt{3}\right) \subseteq \mathbb{Q}\left(\sqrt{2} + \sqrt{3}\right)$.

Conversely, since $\sqrt{2}, \sqrt{3} \in \mathbb{Q}\left(\sqrt{2}, \sqrt{3}\right)$ and $\mathbb{Q}\left(\sqrt{2}, \sqrt{3}\right)$ is closed under addition, we have $\sqrt{2} + \sqrt{3} \in \mathbb{Q}\left(\sqrt{2}, \sqrt{3}\right)$. So, $\mathbb{Q}\left(\sqrt{2}, \sqrt{3}\right)$ is a field containing $\mathbb{Q}$ and $\sqrt{2} + \sqrt{3}$. Therefore, we have $\mathbb{Q}\left(\sqrt{2} + \sqrt{3}\right) \subseteq \mathbb{Q}\left(\sqrt{2}, \sqrt{3}\right)$. Since $\mathbb{Q}\left(\sqrt{2}, \sqrt{3}\right) \subseteq \mathbb{Q}\left(\sqrt{2} + \sqrt{3}\right)$ and $\mathbb{Q}\left(\sqrt{2} + \sqrt{3}\right) \subseteq \mathbb{Q}\left(\sqrt{2}, \sqrt{3}\right)$, it follows that $\mathbb{Q}\left(\sqrt{2}, \sqrt{3}\right) = \mathbb{Q}\left(\sqrt{2} + \sqrt{3}\right)$. $\square$

4. Prove that each of the following numbers is algebraic over the given field:

    (i) $2i$ over $\mathbb{Q}$

    (ii) $\sqrt{3} + \sqrt{5}$ over $\mathbb{Q}$

    (iii) $\sqrt{\pi}$ over $\mathbb{Q}(\pi)$

Proofs:

(i) $(2i)^2 + 4 = -4 + 4 = 0$. So, $2i$ is a root of the polynomial $x^2 + 4$. Note that the coefficients of this polynomial are 1 and 4, which are both in $\mathbb{Q}$.   □

(ii) $\left(\left(\sqrt{3} + \sqrt{5} \right)^2 - 8 \right)^2 - 60 = \left(\left(3 + 2\sqrt{15} + 5 \right) - 8 \right)^2 - 60 = \left(2\sqrt{15} \right)^2 - 60$

$$= 4 \cdot 15 - 60 = 60 - 60 = 0.$$

So, $\sqrt{3} + \sqrt{5}$ is a root of the polynomial $(x^2 - 8)^2 - 60 = x^4 - 16x^2 + 4$. Note that the coefficients of this polynomial are 1, -16, and 4, which are all in $\mathbb{Q}$.   □

(iii) $\left(\sqrt{\pi} \right)^2 - \pi = \pi - \pi = 0$. So, $\sqrt{\pi}$ is a root of the polynomial $x^2 - \pi$. Note that the coefficients of this polynomial are 1 and $-\pi$, which are both in $\mathbb{Q}(\pi)$.   □

LEVEL 2

5. Find the minimal polynomial of $\sqrt{2} + i$ over each of the following fields:

    (i) $\mathbb{Q}$

    (ii) $\mathbb{Q}(i)$

    (iii) $\mathbb{R}$

Solutions:

(i)   Since $\sqrt{2} + i \in \mathbb{Q}(i, \sqrt{2})$, the degree of the minimal polynomial is $[\mathbb{Q}(i, \sqrt{2}) : \mathbb{Q}]$. By Theorem 15.11, $[\mathbb{Q}(i, \sqrt{2}) : \mathbb{Q}] = [\mathbb{Q}(i, \sqrt{2}) : \mathbb{Q}(i)][\mathbb{Q}(i) : \mathbb{Q}] = 2 \cdot 2 = 4$.

$$\left(\left(\sqrt{2} + i \right)^2 - 1 \right)^2 + 8 = \left(\left(2 + 2i\sqrt{2} - 1 \right) - 1 \right)^2 + 8 = \left(2i\sqrt{2} \right)^2 + 8 = -8 + 8 = 0.$$

So, $\sqrt{2} + i$ is a root of the polynomial $(x^2 - 1)^2 + 8 = x^4 - 2x^2 + 9$. Note that the coefficients of this polynomial are 1, -2, and 9, which are in $\mathbb{Q}$. So, the minimal polynomial of $\sqrt{2} + i$ over $\mathbb{Q}$ is $x^4 - 2x^2 + 9$.

(ii) $\left(\sqrt{2} + i \right)^2 - 2i\left(\sqrt{2} + i \right) - 3 = \left(2 + 2i\sqrt{2} - 1 \right) - 2i\sqrt{2} + 2 - 3 = 0.$

So, $\sqrt{2} + i$ is a root of the polynomial $x^2 - 2ix - 3$. Note that the coefficients of this polynomial are 1, $-2i$, and -3, which are all in $\mathbb{Q}(i)$. So, the minimal polynomial of $\sqrt{2} + i$ over $\mathbb{Q}(i)$ is $x^2 - 2ix - 3$.

(iii) $\left(\sqrt{2} + i \right)^2 - 2\sqrt{2}\left(\sqrt{2} + i \right) + 3 = \left(2 + 2i\sqrt{2} - 1 \right) - 4 - 2i\sqrt{2} + 3 = 0.$

So, $\sqrt{2} + i$ is a root of the polynomial $x^2 - 2\sqrt{2}x + 3$. Note that the coefficients of this polynomial are 1, $-2\sqrt{2}$, and 3, which are all in $\mathbb{R}$. So, the minimal polynomial of $\sqrt{2} + i$ over $\mathbb{R}$ is $x^2 - 2\sqrt{2}x + 3$.

6. Find the splitting field for $x^4 + 1$ over both $\mathbb{Q}$ and $\mathbb{R}$.

Solution: The roots of $x^4 + 1$ are the solutions to the equation $x^4 = -1$. Here we have $r = 1$ and $\theta = \pi$. So, $x = \sqrt[4]{1}e^{i\left(\frac{\pi + 2k\pi i}{4}\right)} = e^{i\left(\frac{\pi + 2k\pi i}{4}\right)}$ for $k = 0, 1, 2, 3$. These are $x = e^{\frac{\pi}{4}i}, e^{\frac{3\pi}{4}i}, e^{\frac{5\pi}{4}i}, e^{\frac{7\pi}{4}i}$, or equivalently, $x = \frac{1}{\sqrt{2}}(1 + i), \frac{1}{\sqrt{2}}(-1 + i), \frac{1}{\sqrt{2}}(-1 - i), \frac{1}{\sqrt{2}}(1 - i)$. If we let $z = \frac{1}{\sqrt{2}}(1 + i)$, then we see that the splitting field for $x^4 + 1$ over $\mathbb{Q}$ is $\mathbb{Q}(z)$ (because each of the other roots is a power of z). We now show that $\mathbb{Q}(z) = \mathbb{Q}(\sqrt{2}, i)$.

Clearly $z \in \mathbb{Q}(\sqrt{2}, i)$, and so, $\mathbb{Q}(z) \subseteq \mathbb{Q}(\sqrt{2}, i)$. Conversely, we have

$$z^2 = \frac{1}{\sqrt{2}}(1 + i) \cdot \frac{1}{\sqrt{2}}(1 + i) = \frac{1}{2}(1 + 2i - 1) = \frac{1}{2} \cdot 2i = i.$$

So, $i \in \mathbb{Q}(z)$. Then, we have

$$\frac{1 + i}{z} = \frac{(1 + i)\sqrt{2}}{1 + i} = \sqrt{2}.$$

So, $\sqrt{2} \in \mathbb{Q}(z)$.

Since $i, \sqrt{2} \in \mathbb{Q}(z)$, we have $\mathbb{Q}(\sqrt{2}, i) \subseteq \mathbb{Q}(z)$.

Since $\mathbb{Q}(z) \subseteq \mathbb{Q}(\sqrt{2}, i)$ and $\mathbb{Q}(\sqrt{2}, i) \subseteq \mathbb{Q}(z)$, it follows that $\mathbb{Q}(z) = \mathbb{Q}(\sqrt{2}, i)$. So, the splitting field for $x^4 + 1$ over $\mathbb{Q}$ is $\mathbb{Q}(\sqrt{2}, i)$.

Since $\sqrt{2} \in \mathbb{R}$, the splitting field for $x^4 + 1$ over $\mathbb{R}$ is $\mathbb{Q}(i)$.

7. Let F be a field and let $a(x) = a_0 + a_1 x + a_2 x^2 + \cdots + a_n x^n \in F[x]$. The **derivative** of $a(x)$ is the polynomial in $F[x]$ defined by $a'(x) = a_1 + 2a_2 x + \cdots + na_n x^{n-1}$. Prove each of the following:

   (i)   If $a(x), b(x) \in F[x]$, then $(a + b)'(x) = a'(x) + b'(x)$.

   (ii)   If $a(x) \in F[x]$ and $k \in F$, then $(ka)'(x) = k(a'(x))$.

   (iii) If $a(x), b(x) \in F[x]$, then $(ab)'(x) = a(x)b'(x) + b(x)a'(x)$.

Proofs:

   (i) $(a + b)(x) = (a_0 + b_0) + (a_1 + b_1)x + (a_2 + b_2)x^2 + \cdots + (a_n + b_n)x^n$. Therefore,

$$(a + b)'(x) = (a_1 + b_1) + 2(a_2 + b_2)x + \cdots + n(a_n + b_n)x^{n-1}$$
$$= (a_1 + 2a_2 + \cdots + na_n x^{n-1}) + (b_1 + 2b_2 + \cdots + nb_n x^{n-1})$$
$$= a'(x) + b'(x). \qquad \square$$

(ii) $(ka)(x) = (ka_0) + (ka_1)x + (ka_2)x^2 + \cdots + (ka_n)x^n$. Therefore,

$$(ka)'(x) = ka_1 + 2(ka_2) + \cdots + n(ka_n)x^{n-1} = k(a_1 + 2a_2 + \cdots + na_n x^{n-1})$$
$$= k(a'(x)). \qquad \square$$

(iii) $(ab)(x) = a_0 b_0 + (a_0 b_1 + a_1 b_0)x + (a_0 b_2 + a_1 b_1 + a_2 b_0)x^2 + \cdots + (a_n b_n)x^{2n}$. So,

$$(ab)'(x) = (a_0 b_1 + a_1 b_0) + 2(a_0 b_2 + a_1 b_1 + a_2 b_0)x + \cdots + 2n(a_n b_n)x^{2n-1}$$

$$a(x)b'(x) = (a_0 + a_1 x + a_2 x^2 + \cdots + a_n x^n)(b_1 + 2b_2 x + \cdots + nb_n x^{n-1})$$
$$= a_0 b_1 + (2a_0 b_2 + a_1 b_1)x + \cdots + (na_n b_n)x^{2n-1}.$$

$$b(x)a'(x) = (b_0 + b_1 x + b_2 x^2 + \cdots + b_n x^n)(a_1 + 2a_2 x + \cdots + na_n x^{n-1})$$
$$= a_1 b_0 + (a_1 b_1 + 2a_2 b_0)x + \cdots + (na_n b_n)x^{2n-1}.$$

It's now easy to see that $(ab)'(x) = a(x)b'(x) + b(x)a'(x)$. $\qquad \square$

LEVEL 3

8. Compute $\left[\mathbb{Q}(\sqrt[3]{2}, \sqrt[4]{5}) : \mathbb{Q}\right]$.

Solution: The minimal polynomial of $\sqrt[3]{2}$ over $\mathbb{Q}$ is $x^3 - 2$. So, $\left[\mathbb{Q}(\sqrt[3]{2}) : \mathbb{Q}\right] = 3$. The minimal polynomial of $\sqrt[4]{5}$ over $\mathbb{Q}(\sqrt[3]{2})$ is $x^4 - 5$. So, $\left[\mathbb{Q}(\sqrt[3]{2}, \sqrt[4]{5}) : \mathbb{Q}(\sqrt[3]{2})\right] = 4$. By Theorem 15.11, we have

$$\left[\mathbb{Q}(\sqrt[3]{2}, \sqrt[4]{5}) : \mathbb{Q}\right] = \left[\mathbb{Q}(\sqrt[3]{2}, \sqrt[4]{5}) : \mathbb{Q}(\sqrt[3]{2})\right], \left[\mathbb{Q}(\sqrt[3]{2}) : \mathbb{Q}\right] = 3 \cdot 4 = \mathbf{12}.$$

9. Let F and E be fields with $F \leq E$ and let $A = \{x \in E \mid x \text{ is algebraic over } F\}$. Prove that $A \leq E$. A is called the **algebraic closure** of F in E.

Proof: If $c \in F$, then c is algebraic over F because it is a root of the polynomial $x - c \in F[x]$. So, $F \subseteq A$. Since $1 \in F$, 1 is algebraic over F. Therefore, $A^* \neq \emptyset$. Let $c, d \in A$, say c is a root of $a(x) \in F[x]$ and d is a root of $b(x) \in F[x]$. Then $c - d$ is a root of $(a - b)(x) = a(x) - b(x)$ and cd is a root of $(ab)(x) = a(x)b(x)$. So, $c - d, cd \in A$. Let $c \in A$ with $c \neq 0$. Since c is algebraic over F, $[F(c) : F]$ is finite (it is equal to the degree of the minimal polynomial of c over F). By part 2 of Example 15.12, $F(c)$ is an algebraic extension of F. Since $c^{-1} \in F(c)$, c^{-1} is algebraic over F. By Problem 1 above, $A \leq E$. $\qquad \square$

10. Let F be a field and let $a(x) \in F[x]$ be a nonconstant polynomial. Prove that there exists a splitting field for $a(x)$ over F.

Proof: We prove this by induction on the degree of $a(x)$.

Base case (degree $a(x) = 1$): In this case, $a(x)$ is linear and the splitting field for $a(x)$ over F is F.

Inductive step: Assume that for any field E and any polynomial $b(x)$ of degree less than that of $a(x)$, a splitting field for $b(x)$ over E exists.

By the Fundamental Theorem of Field Extensions (Theorem 15.8), there is a field extension E of F such that $a(x)$ has a root c_1 in E. So, $a(x) = (x - c_1)b(x)$, where $b(x) \in E[x]$. Since degree $b(x) <$ degree $a(x)$, by the inductive assumption, there is a field K that contains E and all the roots of $b(x)$. Let's call these roots $c_2, \ldots, c_n$.

Then $F(c_1, c_2, \ldots, c_n)$ is a splitting field of $a(x)$ over F. $\qquad \square$

11. Prove that the splitting fields for $x^2 - 2x - 2$ and $x^2 - 3$ over $\mathbb{Q}$ are the same.

Proof: The roots of $x^2 - 2x - 2$ are $\frac{2 \pm \sqrt{4+8}}{2} = \frac{2 \pm \sqrt{12}}{2} = \frac{2 \pm \sqrt{4 \cdot 3}}{2} = \frac{2 \pm 2\sqrt{3}}{2} = \frac{2}{2} \pm \frac{2\sqrt{3}}{2} = 1 \pm \sqrt{3}$. So, the splitting field for $x^2 - 2x - 2$ over $\mathbb{Q}$ is $\mathbb{Q}(1 + \sqrt{3}, 1 - \sqrt{3})$.

The roots of $x^2 - 3$ are $\pm\sqrt{3}$. So, the splitting field for $x^2 - 3$ over $\mathbb{Q}$ is $\mathbb{Q}(\sqrt{3})$ $(-\sqrt{3} \in \mathbb{Q}(\sqrt{3})$ because fields are closed under taking additive inverses).

We will now show that $\mathbb{Q}(1 + \sqrt{3}, 1 - \sqrt{3}) = \mathbb{Q}(\sqrt{3})$. Since $1 \in \mathbb{Q}$ and $\sqrt{3} \in \mathbb{Q}(\sqrt{3})$, we see that $1 + \sqrt{3}, 1 - \sqrt{3} \in \mathbb{Q}(\sqrt{3})$. So, $\mathbb{Q}(1 + \sqrt{3}, 1 - \sqrt{3}) \subseteq \mathbb{Q}(\sqrt{3})$.

Now, $\sqrt{3} = \frac{1}{2}\left((1 + \sqrt{3}) - (1 - \sqrt{3})\right) \in \mathbb{Q}(1 + \sqrt{3}, 1 - \sqrt{3})$. So, $\mathbb{Q}(\sqrt{3}) \subseteq \mathbb{Q}(1 + \sqrt{3}, 1 - \sqrt{3})$.

Since $\mathbb{Q}(1 + \sqrt{3}, 1 - \sqrt{3}) \subseteq \mathbb{Q}(\sqrt{3})$ and $\mathbb{Q}(\sqrt{3}) \subseteq \mathbb{Q}(1 + \sqrt{3}, 1 - \sqrt{3})$, we see that $\mathbb{Q}(1 + \sqrt{3}, 1 - \sqrt{3}) = \mathbb{Q}(\sqrt{3})$. $\qquad \square$

LEVEL 4

12. Let F be a field. Prove that every element of $F(c_1, c_2, \ldots, c_n)$ is a finite sum of terms of the form $kc_1^{j_1} c_2^{j_2} \cdots c_n^{j_n}$, where $k \in F$ and $j_1, j_2, \ldots, j_n \in \mathbb{N}$.

Proof: Let Y be the set of finite sums of terms of the form $kc_1^{j_1} c_2^{j_2} \cdots c_n^{j_n}$. We will prove by induction on $t \in \mathbb{Z}^+$ with $t \leq n$ that $F(c_1, c_2, \ldots, c_t) \subseteq Y$.

If $k \in F$, then clearly $k \in Y$. So, $F \subseteq Y$. If $x \in F(c_1)$, then $x = k_0 + k_1 c_1 + k_2 c_1^2 + \cdots + k_m c_1^m$. Each term in this expression has the form $kc_1^{j_1}$, and so, $x \in Y$.

Now assume that $t \in \mathbb{Z}^+$ with $t \leq n$ and every element of $F(c_1, c_2, \ldots, c_t)$ is a finite sum of terms of the form $kc_1^{j_1} c_2^{j_2} \cdots c_t^{j_t}$.

Let $x \in F(c_1, c_2, \ldots, c_{t+1}) = F(c_1, c_2, \ldots, c_t)(c_{t+1})$. Then $x = k_0 + k_1 c_{k+1} + k_2 c_{t+1}^2 + \cdots + k_m c_{t+1}^m$, where $k_0, k_1, \ldots, k_m \in F(c_1, c_2, \ldots, c_t)$. Then for each $i = 1, 2., \ldots m$, k_i is a sum of terms of the form $kc_1^{j_1} c_2^{j_2} \cdots c_t^{j_t}$. So, $k_i c_{t+1}^i$ is a sum of terms of the form $kc_1^{j_1} c_2^{j_2} \cdots c_t^{j_t} c_{t+1}^i$.

In particular, if $x \in F(c_1, c_2, \ldots, c_n)$, each term of x is a sum of terms of the form $kc_1^{j_1} c_2^{j_2} \cdots c_{n-1}^{j_{n-1}} c_n^{j_n}$. $\qquad \square$

13. Let F be a field of characteristic 0. We say that c is a multiple root of a polynomial $a(x) \in F[x]$ if $(x - c)^k$ is a factor of $a(x)$ for some $k \in \mathbb{Z}^+$ with $k > 1$. Let $p(x) \in F[x]$ be an irreducible polynomial. Use the derivative of $p(x)$ to prove that $p(x)$ does **not** have any multiple roots (see Problem 7 above for the definition of the derivative of $p(x)$).

Proof: Let $p(x) \in F[x]$ be irreducible with leading term $a_n x^n$ and suppose toward contradiction that c is a multiple root of $p(x)$, where c is in some extension E of F. So, in $E[x]$, we can factor $p(x)$ as $p(x) = (x - c)^2 q(x)$.

It follows from part (iii) of Problem 7 above that $p'(x) = (x - c)^2 q'(x) + 2(x - c)q(x)$. We see that $(x - c)$ is a factor of $p'(x)$, and so, c is a root of $p'(x)$. Also, since the leading term of $p(x)$ is $a_n x^n$, the leading term of $p'(x)$ is $na_n x^{n-1}$.

Let $r(x)$ be the minimal polynomial of c over F. Since c is a root of both $p(x)$ and $p'(x)$, each of $p(x)$ and $p'(x)$ is a multiple of $r(x)$. Since $p(x)$ is irreducible, $p(x)$ and $r(x)$ must be associates. So, $p(x)$ divides $p'(x)$. But $p'(x)$ has lower degree than $p(x)$, and so, $p'(x)$ must be 0. In particular, the leading coefficient of $p'(x)$ must be 0. So, $na_n = 0$. Since the characteristic of F is 0, we must have $a_n = 0$, contradicting our assumption that a_n is the leading coefficient of $p(x)$. $\qquad\square$

14. Prove that the algebraic closure of $\mathbb{Q}$ in $\mathbb{C}$ is **not** equal to $\mathbb{C}$ (see Problem 9 above for the definition of algebraic closure).

Proof: Let A be the algebraic closure of $\mathbb{Q}$ in $\mathbb{C}$. Since $\mathbb{C}$ is uncountable, it suffices to show that A is countable. For each $n \in \mathbb{Z}^+$, let P_n be the set of polynomials of degree n with coefficients in $\mathbb{Q}$. Define $f: P_n \to \mathbb{Q}^{n+1}$ by $f(a_0 + a_1 x + \cdots + a_n x^n) = (a_0, a_1, \ldots, a_n)$. Since f is clearly injective and $\mathbb{Q}^{n+1}$ is countable, P_n is countable. If we let P be the set of all polynomials with coefficients in $\mathbb{Q}$, then we have $P = \bigcup\{P_n \mid n \in \mathbb{Z}^+\}$. This is a countable union of countable sets. Therefore, P is countable. Now, let X be the set of finite subsets of $\mathbb{N}$. By Problem 19 from Problem Set 5, X is countable. So, $P \times X$ is countable. Now, define $g: A \to P \times X$ as follows. Given $c \in A$, let $p(x)$ be the minimal polynomial of c over $\mathbb{Q}$. Let $c_1, c_2, \ldots c_n$ be the roots of $p(x)$, where $p(x)$ is also the minimal polynomial of each of $c_1, c_2, \ldots, c_n$. Let $g(c_i) = (p(x), i)$. Then g is injective. So, A is countable. $\qquad\square$

15. A field that has no proper algebraic extension is said to be **algebraically closed**. Let F and E be fields with $F \leq E$ and let A be the algebraic closure of F in E (see Problem 9 above). Prove that A is algebraically closed.

Proof: Let B be an algebraic extension of A and let $c \in B$. Since c is algebraic over A, by part 2 of Example 15.12, $A(c)$ is an algebraic extension of A. Now, $[A(c):F] = [A(c):A][A:F]$. Since $[A(c):A]$ and $[A:F]$ are both finite, so is , $[A(c):F]$, and therefore, $A(c)$ is an algebraic extension of F. So, c is algebraic over F, and thus, $c \in A$. Since $c \in B$ was arbitrary, $B = A$. It follows that A has no proper algebraic extension, and so, A is algebraically closed. $\qquad\square$

LEVEL 5

16. Let F be a field of characteristic 0 and let E be a finite extension of F. Prove that there is $c \in E$

166

such that $E = F(c)$.

Proof: We first show that any iterated extension of length 2 is a simple extension. Specifically, we will show that if $E = F(a, b)$, then there is $c \in E$ such that $E = F(c)$. So, let $E = F(a, b)$, let $p(x)$ be the minimal polynomial of a over F, and let $q(x)$ be the minimal polynomial of b over F. Let K be an extension of F containing all the roots of both $p(x)$ and $q(x)$, say $a = a_1, a_2, \ldots, a_m, b = b_1, b_2, \ldots, b_n$. Let $k \in F$ with $k \neq 0$ and $k \neq \frac{a_i - a}{b - b_j}$ for each $1 < i \leq m$ and $1 < j \leq n$. Then for each $1 < i \leq m$ and $1 < j \leq n$, we have $k(b - b_j) \neq a_i - a$, or equivalently, $a + kb \neq a_i + kb_j$. Let $c = a + kb$. We will show that $F(a, b) = F(c)$.

Define $f(x) \in E[x]$ by $f(x) = p(c - kx)$. Then $f(b) = p(c - kb) = p(a + kb - kb) = p(a) = 0$. Also, for $j = 2, 3, \ldots, n, f(b_j) = p(c - kb_j) = p(a + kb - kb_j) \neq p(a_i)$ for any $i = 1, 2, \ldots, m$, and so, $f(b_j) \neq 0$. Therefore, b is the only root common to both $q(x)$ and $f(x)$.

We now show that $b \in F(c)$. To this end, let $r(x)$ be the minimal polynomial of b over $F(c)$ and assume toward contradiction that degree $r(x) > 1$. Since $q(x)$ and $f(x)$ have b as a root, they are both multiples of $r(x)$. Since degree $r(x) > 1$, $q(x)$ and $f(x)$ must have at least 2 roots in common. But b is the only common root of $q(x)$ and $f(x)$. This contradiction tells us that degree $r(x) = 1$, and so, $r(x) = x - b$. Therefore, $b \in F(c)$.

We now show that $a \in F(c)$. To see this, note that $c, b \in F(c)$, $a = c - kb$, and $F(c)$ is a closed under subtraction.

We can now use induction to prove that an iterated extension of any length is a simple extension.

By part 2 of Example 15.12, every finite extension is an iterated extension. It now follows that if E is a finite extension, then there is $c \in E$ such that $E = F(c)$. ◻

> 17. Let $E = \mathbb{Q}\left(\sqrt[3]{2}, \sqrt[5]{2}, \ldots, \sqrt[2n+1]{2}, \ldots\right)$. Prove that E is an infinite algebraic extension of $\mathbb{Q}$ that is not equal to the algebraic closure of $\mathbb{Q}$ in $\mathbb{C}$ (see Problem 9 above for the definition of algebraic closure).

Proof: Let $n \in \mathbb{Z}^+$. Since $\sqrt[2n+1]{2}$ is a root of $x^{2n+1} - 2 = 0$, $\sqrt[2n+1]{2}$ is algebraic over $\mathbb{Q}$. Since 2 divides -2, 2 does **not** divide 1, and $2^2 = 4$ does **not** divide -2, by Eisenstein's Irreducibility Theorem (see Problem 21 from Problem Set 14), $x^{2n+1} - 2$ is irreducible over $\mathbb{Q}$. So, $x^{2n+1} - 2$ is the minimal polynomial of $\sqrt[2n+1]{2}$ over 2, and therefore, $\left[\mathbb{Q}\left(\sqrt[2n+1]{2}\right), \mathbb{Q}\right] = 2n + 1$. Since $\mathbb{Q}\left(\sqrt[2n+1]{2}\right) \subseteq E$, we have $[E, \mathbb{Q}] \geq 2n + 1$. Since $n \in \mathbb{Z}^+$ was arbitrary, E is an infinite extension of $\mathbb{Q}$.

Let $c \in E$. Then $c \in \mathbb{Q}\left(\sqrt[3]{2}, \sqrt[5]{2}, \ldots, \sqrt[2n+1]{2}\right)$ for some $n \in \mathbb{Z}^+$. Since $\sqrt[3]{2}, \sqrt[5]{2}, \ldots, \sqrt[2n+1]{2}$ are all algebraic over $\mathbb{Q}$, it follows that $\mathbb{Q}\left(\sqrt[3]{2}, \sqrt[5]{2}, \ldots, \sqrt[2n+1]{2}\right)$ is an algebraic extension over $\mathbb{Q}$. Therefore, c is algebraic over $\mathbb{Q}$. Since $c \in E$ was arbitrary, E is an algebraic extension of $\mathbb{Q}$.

Now, $\sqrt{2}$ is in the algebraic closure of $\mathbb{Q}$ because it is a root of the polynomial $x^2 - 2$. Assume toward contradiction that $\sqrt{2} \in E$. Then $\sqrt{2} \in \mathbb{Q}\left(\sqrt[3]{2}, \sqrt[5]{2}, \ldots, \sqrt[2n+1]{2}\right)$ for some $n \in \mathbb{Z}^+$. We have that $\left[\mathbb{Q}\left(\sqrt[3]{2}, \sqrt[5]{2}, \ldots, \sqrt[2n+1]{2}\right):\mathbb{Q}\right]$ is odd because $\left[\mathbb{Q}\left(\sqrt[2k+1]{2}\right):\mathbb{Q}\right]$ is odd for each $k \in \mathbb{Z}^+$. Since

$\sqrt{2} \in \mathbb{Q}\left(\sqrt[3]{2}, \sqrt[5]{2}, \dots, \sqrt[2n+1]{2}\right)$, we have

$$\left[\mathbb{Q}\left(\sqrt[3]{2}, \sqrt[5]{2}, \dots, \sqrt[2n+1]{2}\right) : \mathbb{Q}\right] = \left[\mathbb{Q}\left(\sqrt[3]{2}, \sqrt[5]{2}, \dots, \sqrt[2n+1]{2}\right) : \mathbb{Q}(\sqrt{2})\right]\left[\mathbb{Q}(\sqrt{2}) : \mathbb{Q}\right]$$
$$= 2\left[\mathbb{Q}\left(\sqrt[3]{2}, \sqrt[5]{2}, \dots, \sqrt[2n+1]{2}\right) : \mathbb{Q}\right].$$

So, $\left[\mathbb{Q}\left(\sqrt[3]{2}, \sqrt[5]{2}, \dots, \sqrt[2n+1]{2}\right) : \mathbb{Q}\right]$ is even, a contradiction.

Therefore, $\sqrt{2} \notin E$, and so, E is not equal to the algebraic closure of $\mathbb{Q}$. $\qquad\square$

Problem Set 16

LEVEL 1

1. Let F and E be fields with $F \leq E$. Prove that $G(E/F)$ is a subgroup of $\text{Aut}(E)$.

Proof: Since $i_E: E \to E$ fixes F, $i_E \in G(E/F)$.

Let $f, g \in G(E/F)$. Then if $x \in F$, $(g \circ f)(x) = g\big(f(x)\big) = g(x) = x$. So, $g \circ f \in G(E/F)$.

Let $f \in G(E/F)$ and let $x \in F$. Then $f(x) = x$. So, $f^{-1}(x) = x$. Since $x \in F$ was arbitrary, f^{-1} fixes F. Therefore, $f^{-1} \in G(E/F)$. $\qquad\square$

2. Prove that if $f: \mathbb{Q} \to \mathbb{Q}$ is a field homomorphism, then f is the identity function.

Proof: Since f is a homomorphism, $f(0) = 0$ and $f(1) = 1$. We now prove by induction that for all $n \in \mathbb{N}$, $f(n) = n$. The base case of $k = 1$ was already done. Assuming that $f(k) = k$, we have that $f(k+1) = f(k) + f(1) = k + 1$. By the Principle of Mathematical Induction, for all $n \in \mathbb{N}$, $f(n) = n$.

Now, if $n \in \mathbb{Z}$ with $n < 0$, then $f(n) = f\big(-(-n)\big) = -f(-n) = -(-n) = n$.

Now, if $n \in \mathbb{Z}$, then $1 = f(1) = f\left(n \cdot \frac{1}{n}\right) = f(n)f\left(\frac{1}{n}\right) = nf\left(\frac{1}{n}\right)$. Thus, $f\left(\frac{1}{n}\right) = \frac{1}{n}$.

Finally, if $\frac{n}{m} \in \mathbb{Q}$, then $f\left(\frac{n}{m}\right) = f\left(n \cdot \frac{1}{m}\right) = f(n)f\left(\frac{1}{m}\right) = n\left(\frac{1}{m}\right) = \frac{n}{m}$. $\qquad\square$

LEVEL 2

3. Let F be a field, let E be the splitting field for a polynomial $a(x)$ over F, and let H be a subgroup of $G(E/F)$. Prove that $H_* = \{x \in E \mid f(x) = x \text{ for all } f \in H\}$ is an intermediate field of $a(x)$ between F and E.

Proof: Clearly $H_* \subseteq E$. Since every automorphism in H fixes F, $F \subseteq H_*$, and so, $H_* \neq \emptyset$. Let $x, y \in H_*$ and let $f \in H$. Then $f(x - y) = f(x) - f(y) = x - y$ and $f(xy) = f(x)f(y) = xy$. So, H_* is closed under subtraction and multiplication. Let $x \in H_* \setminus \{0\}$ (usage of the expression H_*^* might be confusing, so I avoid it here) and let $f \in H$. Then $f(x^{-1}) = \big(f(x)\big)^{-1} = x^{-1}$. So, H_* is closed under taking multiplicative inverses. Therefore, H_* is a subfield of E.

We already showed that $F \subseteq H_*$, and so, H_* is an intermediate field of $a(x)$ between F and E. $\qquad\square$

4. Let $F, E,$ and L be fields such that E and L are extensions of F and let $f: E \to L$ be an isomorphism that fixes F. Prove that $[E:F] = [L:F]$.

Proof: Let $\mathcal{B}$ be a basis for E over F and let $y \in L$. Since f is an isomorphism, there is $x \in E$ such that $f(x) = y$. Since $\mathcal{B}$ spans E, there are $c_1, c_2, \ldots, c_k \in F$ and $x_1, x_2, \ldots, x_k \in E$ such that

$$x = c_1 x_1 + c_2 x_2 + \cdots + c_k x_k.$$

So, $y = f(x) = f(c_1 x_1 + c_2 x_2 + \cdots + c_k x_k) = c_1 f(x_1) + c_2 f(x_2) + \cdots + c_k f(x_k)$. It follows that the set $\{f(z) \mid z \in \mathcal{B}\}$ spans L. So, $[L:F] \leq [E:F]$.

A symmetric argument shows that $[E:F] \leq [L:F]$. Therefore, $[E:F] = [L:F]$. $\qquad\square$

LEVEL 3

5. Let $F, E,$ and L be fields such that E and L are extensions of F and E is the splitting field for a polynomial $a(x)$ over F. Let $f: E \to L$ be an isomorphism that fixes F. Prove that $f \in G(E/F)$.

Proof: Let $c_1, c_2, \ldots, c_n$ be the roots of $a(x) = a_0 + a_1 x + \cdots + a_n x^n$ so that $E = F(c_1, c_2, \ldots, c_n)$. Since f fixes F, for each $x \in F$, $f(x) \in F \subseteq E$. For each $i = 1, 2, \ldots, n$, $f(c_i)$ is a root of $a(x)$. To see this, observe that $a\big(f(c_i)\big) = a_0 + a_1 f(c_i) + \cdots + a_n\big(f(c_i)\big)^n = f(a_0 + a_1 c_i + \cdots + a_n c_i^n) = f(0) = 0$. Since E contains all the roots of $a(x)$, for each $1, 2, \ldots, n$, $f(c_i) \in E$. By Problem 12 from Problem Set 15, every element of $E = F(c_1, c_2, \ldots, c_n)$ is a finite sum of terms of the form $k c_1^{j_1} c_2^{j_2} \cdots c_n^{j_n}$, where $k \in F$ and $j_1, j_2, \ldots, j_n \in \mathbb{N}$. It follows that for any $x \in E$, we have $f(x) \in E$. Since f is a bijection, $L = E$. Therefore, $f \in G(E/F)$. $\qquad\square$

6. Let E be the splitting field for a polynomial $a(x)$ over a field F of characteristic 0. Prove that $|G(E/F)| = [E:F]$. (This is Theorem 16.9.)

Proof: Since E is the splitting field for $a(x)$ over F, E is a finite extension of F. Suppose that $[E:F] = n$. By Problem 16 from Problem Set 15, there is $c \in E$ such that $E = F(c)$. Let $p(x)$ be the minimal polynomial of c over F. If d is any root of $p(x)$, then by Theorem 16.6, there is $f \in G(E/F)$ such that $f(c) = d$. By part 3 of Example 15.10, $p(x)$ has n roots. So, there are precisely n choices for d, and therefore, by Theorem 16.8, there are exactly n automorphisms in $G(E/F)$. $\qquad\square$

7. Let G be a group, let N be a normal subgroup of G, and let H be the commutator subgroup of G ($H = \langle xyx^{-1}y^{-1} \mid x, y \in G \rangle$). Prove that G/N is commutative if and only if $H \subseteq N$.

Proof: Assume that G/N is commutative and let $x, y \in G$. Since G/N is commutative, we have $xyN = (xN)(yN) = (yN)(xN) = yxN$. So, $xyx^{-1}y^{-1} = (xy)(yx)^{-1} \in N$. Since $x, y \in G$ were arbitrary, $H \subseteq N$.

Conversely, assume that $H \subseteq N$ and let $x, y \in G$. Then $xyx^{-1}y^{-1} \in N$. So, by Lemma 10.13, we have $xyN = (x^{-1}y^{-1})^{-1}N = (y^{-1})^{-1}(x^{-1})^{-1}N = yxN$. So, $(xN)(yN) = (yN)(xN)$. Since $x, y \in G$ were arbitrary, G/N is commutative. $\qquad\square$

8. Let F, K, L, E be fields of characteristic 0 such that K and L are extensions of F and E is a common extension of K and L with E the splitting field for some polynomial over F. Prove that any isomorphism $h: K \to L$ that fixes F can be extended to an element of $G(E/F)$. (This is Theorem 16.5.)

Proof: Since E is the splitting field for a polynomial over F, E is a finite extension of F. Since $[E:F] = [E:K][K:F]$, E must be a finite extension of K. By Problem 16 from Problem Set 15, there is $c \in E$ such that $E = K(c)$. If $c \in K$, let $d = h(c)$. Otherwise, let $d = c$. By Corollary 16.4, h can be extended to an isomorphism $f: K(c) \to L(d)$ such that f fixes F and $f(c) = d$. Since $K(c) = E$, we have an isomorphism $f: E \to L(d)$ that fixes F. By Problem 5 above, $f \in G(E/F)$. $\quad\square$

9. Let p be prime and let G be a p-group. Prove that G is solvable.

Proof: Since G is a p-group, there is $n \in \mathbb{Z}^+$ such that $|G| = p^n$. We now prove the result by induction on $n \in \mathbb{Z}^+$.

Base case ($k = 1$): In this case, $|G|$ is prime, and so, G is cyclic. Since every cyclic group is commutative, the result follows from part 1 of Example 16.13.

Inductive step: Suppose that any group of order p^j is solvable for each $j \in \mathbb{Z}^+$ with $j \leq k$. Let G be a p-group of order p^{k+1}.

Let $G_0 = \{e\}$. By Theorem 13.7, $Z(G) \neq \{e\}$. Let $G_1 = Z(G)$. Then $G_0 = \{e\} \lhd Z(G) = G_1$. We also have that $G_1/G_0 = Z(G)/\{e\} \cong Z(G)$, which is commutative.

Now, $G/Z(G)$ is either $\{e\}$ or has order p^j for some $j \leq k$. If $G/Z(G) = \{e\}$, then G is commutative, and once again, by part 1 of Example 16.13, G is solvable.

If $G/Z(G)$ has order p^j for some $j \leq k$, then by the inductive hypothesis, $G/Z(G)$ is solvable.

By Problem 22 in Problem Set 11, G is solvable. $\quad\square$

10. Let G and H be groups with G solvable and let $f: G \to H$ be a homomorphism. Prove that $f[G]$ is solvable.

Proof: Since G is solvable, there exist subgroups $G_0, G_1, \ldots, G_n$ such that $\{e\} = G_0 \lhd G_1 \lhd \cdots \lhd G_n = G$, where for each $i = 1, 2, \ldots, n$, the quotient G_i/G_{i-1} is commutative. By part 5 of Example 7.21, we have $\{e\} = f[G_0] \lhd f[G_1] \lhd \cdots \lhd f[G_n] = f[G]$.

Let $1 < i \leq n$. Since $G_{i-1} \lhd G_i$ and G_i/G_{i-1} is commutative, by Problem 7 above, G_{i-1} contains the commutator subgroup of G_i. In other words, if $x, y \in G_i$, then $xyx^{-1}y^{-1} \in G_{i-1}$. It follows that for all $x, y \in G_i$, $f(x)f(y)f(x)^{-1}f(y)^{-1} = f(xyx^{-1}y^{-1}) \in f[G_{i-1}]$. So, $f[G_{i-1}]$ contains the commutator subgroup of $f[G_i]$. Once again, by Problem 7 above, $f[G_i]/f[G_{i-1}]$ is commutative.

Therefore, $f[G]$ is solvable. $\quad\square$

11. Let F_1 and F_2 be fields, let $f: F_1 \to F_2$ be an isomorphism, and let $p(x) \in F_1[x]$ be irreducible. Furthermore, let c and d be roots of $p(x)$ and $g(p(x))$, respectively (where $g: F_1[x] \to F_2[x]$ is defined by $g(a_0 + a_1 x + \cdots + a_n x^n) = f(a_0) + f(a_1)x + \cdots + f(a_n)x^n$, c lies in an extension field of F_1, and d lies in an extension field of F_2). Prove that f can be extended to an isomorphism $h: F_1(c) \to F_2(d)$ such that $h(c) = d$. (This is Theorem 16.3.)

Proof: As suggested before the statement of the theorem, we define $h: F_1(c) \to F_2(d)$ by

$$h(a_0 + a_1 c + \cdots + a_n c^n) = f(a_0) + f(a_1)d + \cdots + f(a_n)d^n.$$

Let's check that h is an isomorphism from $F_1(c)$ to $F_1(d)$.

We must first check that h is well-defined. To see this, suppose that $a(c) = a_0 + a_1 c + \cdots + a_n c^n$ and $b(c) = b_0 + b_1 c + \cdots + b_n c^n$ are in $F_1(c)$ and $a(c) = b(c)$. Then $(a - b)(c) = a(c) - b(c) = 0$, and so, c is a root of the polynomial $(a - b)(x) \in F_1[x]$. Since $p(x)$ is irreducible and c is a root of $p(x)$, it follows that $(a - b)(x) = q(x)p(x) = (qp)(x)$ for some $q(x) \in F_1[x]$. Therefore, it follows that

$$h(a(x)) - h(b(x)) = h(a(x) - b(x)) = h((qp)(x)) = h(q(x))h(p(x)).$$

So,

$$f(a(c)) - f(b(c)) = g(a(d)) - g(b(d)) = h(a(d)) - h(b(d)) = h(q(d))h(p(d))$$
$$= g(q(d))g(p(d)) = f(q(c))f(p(c)) = f(q(c))f(0) = f(q(c)) \cdot 0 = 0.$$

Therefore, $f(a(c)) = f(b(c))$. Since $a(c), b(c) \in F_1(c)$ were arbitrary, h is well-defined.

To see that h is injective, suppose that $h(a_0 + a_1 c + \cdots + a_n c^n) = h(b_0 + b_1 c + \cdots + b_n c^n)$. Then we have $f(a_0) + f(a_1)d + \cdots + f(a_n)d^n = f(b_0) + f(b_1)d + \cdots + f(b_n)d^n$. It follows that

$$(f(a_0) - f(b_0)) + (f(a_1) - f(b_1))d + \cdots + (f(a_n) - f(b_n))d^n = 0.$$

So, $f(a_0) - f(b_0) = f(a_1) - f(b_1) = f(a_n) - f(b_n) = 0$, and thus, $f(a_0) = f(b_0)$, $f(a_1) = f(b_1)$, .., $f(a_n) = f(b_n)$. Since f is injective, $a_0 = b_0$, $a_1 = b_1$,..., $a_n = b_n$. Therefore,

$$a_0 + a_1 c + \cdots + a_n c^n = b_0 + b_1 c + \cdots + b_n c^n.$$

To see that h is surjective, let $b_0 + b_1 d + \cdots + b_n d^n \in F_2(d)$. Let $a_0, a_1, \ldots, a_n \in F_1$ with $f(a_0) = b_0$, $f(a_1) = b_1$,...,$f(a_n) = b_n$. Then $f(a_0 + a_1 c + \cdots + a_n c^n) = b_0 + b_1 d + \cdots + b_n d^n$.

Checking that h is a homomorphism is straightforward. □

12. Let F be a field of characteristic 0, let E be the splitting field for some polynomial $p(x)$ over F, let H be a subgroup of $G(E/F)$, and let $K = H_*$. Prove that $|H| = [E:K]$.

Proof: Let $H = \{f_1, f_2, \ldots, f_n\}$ so that $|H| = n$. By Problem 16 from Problem Set 15, there is $c \in E$ such that $E = K(c)$. Let $a(x) = (x - f_1(c))(x - f_2(c)) \cdots (x - f_n(c))$. Since the identity function is in H, there is i with $1 \le i \le n$ such that $f_i(c) = c$. Thus, c is a root of $a(x)$.

We now show that all coefficients of $a(x)$ are in K. By Theorem 16.2, each f_i can be extended to $h_i: E[x] \to E[x]$. Then we have

$$h_i\big(a(x)\big) = h_i\big[(x - f_1(c))(x - f_2(c)) \cdots (x - f_n(c))\big]$$
$$= h_i(x - f_1(c))h_i(x - f_2(c)) \cdots h_i(x - f_n(c))$$
$$= \big(x - (f_i \circ f_1)(c)\big)h_i\big(x - (f_i \circ f_2)(c)\big) \cdots h_i\big(x - (f_i \circ f_n)(c)\big).$$

Now, $f_i \circ f_1, f_i \circ f_2, \dots, f_i \circ f_n$ are n distinct elements of H. Since H has exactly n elements, $f_i \circ f_1, f_i \circ f_2, \dots, f_i \circ f_n$ is a complete list of all the elements of H. So, $h_i\big(a(x)\big) = a(x)$ (the factors of both polynomials are the same; they may appear in two different orders). So, h_i leaves the coefficients of $a(x)$ fixed, and so, every coefficient of $a(x)$ is in $H_* = K$.

It follows that $a(x) \in K[x]$. Therefore, $a(x)$ is a multiple of the minimal polynomial of c over K. Since the degree of the minimal polynomial of c over K is equal to $[E:K]$ (by part 2 of Example 15.12), we have that $|H| = n \geq [E:K]$.

By Problem 6 above, $[E:K] = |G(E/K)| \geq |\{h_1, h_2, \dots, h_n\}| = n = |H|$.

Since $|H| \geq [E:K]$ and $[E:K] \geq |H|$, we have $|H| = [E:K]$. $\qquad\qquad\square$

About the Author

Dr. Steve Warner, a New York native, earned his Ph.D. at Rutgers University in Pure Mathematics in May 2001. While a graduate student, Dr. Warner won the TA Teaching Excellence Award.

After Rutgers, Dr. Warner joined the Penn State Mathematics Department as an Assistant Professor and in September 2002, he returned to New York to accept an Assistant Professor position at Hofstra University. By September 2007, Dr. Warner had received tenure and was promoted to Associate Professor. He has taught undergraduate and graduate courses in Precalculus, Calculus, Linear Algebra, Differential Equations, Mathematical Logic, Set Theory, and Abstract Algebra.

From 2003 – 2008, Dr. Warner participated in a five-year NSF grant, "The MSTP Project," to study and improve mathematics and science curriculum in poorly performing junior high schools. He also published several articles in scholarly journals, specifically on Mathematical Logic.

Dr. Warner has nearly two decades of experience in general math tutoring and tutoring for standardized tests such as the SAT, ACT, GRE, GMAT, and AP Calculus exams. He has tutored students both individually and in group settings.

In February 2010 Dr. Warner released his first SAT prep book "The 32 Most Effective SAT Math Strategies," and in 2012 founded Get 800 Test Prep. Since then Dr. Warner has written books for the SAT, ACT, SAT Math Subject Tests, AP Calculus exams, and GRE. In 2018 Dr. Warner released his first pure math book called "Pure Mathematics for Beginners." Since then he has released several more books, each one addressing a specific subject in pure mathematics.

Dr. Steve Warner can be reached at

steve@SATPrepGet800.com

BOOKS BY DR. STEVE WARNER

 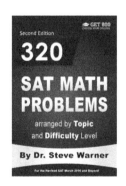  

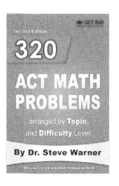 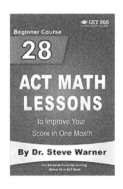 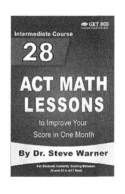 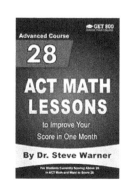

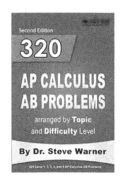
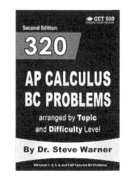

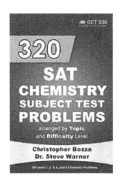

Made in the USA
Coppell, TX
22 August 2021